CLICHÉ DE COUVERTURE

Prof. de la carte des îles Seychelles établie par
W. F. FELLER & BROSSIER (1970).
(Cap. 841542-50 Fol. 32, n° 8).

CLICHE DE COUVERTURE

D'après la carte des Iles Seychelles établie par
M. LAFFITTE de BROSSIER (1777)
(Cliché B.N. doc Port 222 3P 9').

INVENTAIRE
DES ARCHIVES NATIONALES
DES SEYCHELLES

PEUPLES ET PAYS DE L'OCEAN INDIEN

COLLECTION DIRIGEE PAR J.L. MIEGE

INVENTAIRE DES ARCHIVES NATIONALES DES SEYCHELLES

par A.W.T. WEBB et H.J. MAC GAW

préface de C. WANQUET

ARCHIVES NATIONALES DES SEYCHELLES _ VICTORIA
CENTRE UNIVERSITAIRE DE LA REUNION _ SAINT DENIS

INSTITUT D'HISTOIRE DES PAYS D'OUTRE-MER
AIX EN PROVENCE

Avec l'inventaire des archives des Seychelles est publiée pour la première fois dans la collection Peuples et Pays de l'océan Indien, après différentes études, un instrument de travail. Il est inutile de souligner l'intérêt pour les chercheurs de l'inventaire de Webb et Mac Gaw. Désormais alterneront l'édition d'études -la prochaine sous presse étant consacrée aux Tamouls de Sri-Lanka par M. Lamballe- et celle d'outils de recherche.

Cette publication, qui souligne la coopération scientifique des Archives Nationales des Seychelles, du Centre Universitaire de Saint-Denis de la Réunion et de l'Institut d'Histoire des Pays d'Outre-Mer de l'Université de Provence, a également bénéficié de l'aide du G.R.E.C.O. 15 océan Indien, de l'A.C.O.I. et du G.I.S. 2.

Il m'est agréable de souligner ce concours d'efforts et d'en remercier très chaleureusement tous les responsables.

J.L. MIEGE

PREFACE

Pendant longtemps quelque peu oubliées au coeur de l'Océan Indien, les Seychelles sont aujourd'hui célèbres dans le monde entier pour la variété et la splendeur de leurs paysages. Leur histoire également a éveillé et éveille de nombreuses curiosités. Depuis la publication par A.A. Fauvel, en 1909, de documents inédits de la période antérieure à 1810, jusqu'à la parution prochaine d'un manuel de synthèse destiné à l'enseignement secondaire et réalisé par J.M. Filliot, maître de recherches à l'O.R.S.T.O.M., la liste des travaux qui lui ont été consacrés serait longue. Sans prétendre l'établir de façon exhaustive, on peut rappeler les ouvrages de Bradley, Webb, du P. Dayer, ou, plus récemment de G. Lionnet ou R. Touboul. Des articles souvent fort précieux, dus, par exemples, à J. Moine, P. Eymonet, M. Ly Tio Fane, A. Toussaint ..., parus surtout dans le très intéressant Journal of Seychelles Society, complètent ou précisent ces travaux d'ensemble.

Il reste cependant, dans l'histoire des Seychelles, diverses zones d'ombres à explorer ou, tout au moins, de nombreux sujets à approfondir. Par sa richesse même, cet inventaire en témoigne.

Ses auteurs ont été les véritables créateurs du dépôt d'archives nationales séchelloises dont l'existence est tout récente puisqu'elle remonte à 1961 seulement.

Le capitaine A.W.T. Webb était un officier retraité de l'Armée de l'Inde et des Services Politiques de Bombay. Il fut par la suite Surintendant du Recensement à Rajaputna, Responsable des Réfugiés, Secrétaire adjoint du Gouvernement de l'Inde, et, enfin, Premier secrétaire au Haut Commissariat Britannique en Inde. Il fut nommé Commissaire du Recensement aux Seychelles en décembre 1959, puis Responsable de l'Information en mars 1961, et Archiviste en juillet 1961. Il occupa ce dernier poste jusqu'en juillet 1968 et créa également le noyau du musée des Seychelles. Il mourut en 1968, à l'âge de 78 ans.

M. H.J. Mac Gaw fut nommé Assistant Archiviste en 1964.
En 1968, au moment de la retrait du capitaine Webb, il fut promu
Archiviste et Conservateur du Musée. Lors de la réorganisation,
en 1979, de la Section du Musée des Archives, il fut nommé Directeur des Archives Nationales et du Musée National de la République
des Seychelles.

Les archives dont l'inventaire est ici publié pour la première
fois in extenso, s'échelonnent sur plus de deux siècles, de 1772
à 1979. Leur richesse, dans l'ensemble considérable, est cependant
inégale. Les documents de l'époque française sont en effet relati-
vement peu nombreux, surtout en comparaison des fonds importants
qui existent à Paris, à Port Louis et même à Saint-Denis. En
revanche les sources britanniques postérieures à 1810 s'avèrent
abondantes et offrent de multiples informations sur la vie et
les problèmes de l'archipel aux XIXe et XXe siècles.

Les questions d'ordre institutionnel ou politique sont vraisembla-
blement celles qui reviennent le plus fréquemment dans l'ensemble
des documents. On peut ainsi suivre les transformations des struc-
tures administratives ou judiciaires intérieures et leurs répercus-
sions au niveau des rapports, parfois conflictuels, qui s'établissent
entre les habitants et les autorités locales. Il est surtout intéressant
de voir l'évolution des relations entre l'archipel et l'île Maurice,
entre l'archipel et Londres, qui va dans le sens d'une affirmation
de plus en plus nette de la spécificité séchelloise jusqu'à l'indépen-
dance finale. De nombreux documents mettent également en valeur
la diversité de l'activité agricole des Seychelles et leur rôle non
négligeable d'entrepôt ou d'escale dans le domaine maritime,
par exemple pour le commerce servile ou la pêche à la baleine.
Problèmes sanitaires, délinquance, débats judiciaires, activité
des missions ou des écoles ... tous les multiples aspects de la
vie sociale des îles apparaissent également en filigrane dans les
documents inventoriés. Les sources concernant le peuplement
de l'archipel, témoignant de son originalité et de son extrême
diversité, méritent une mention spéciale ; leur abondance et leur
richesse devraient retenir l'attention d'un spécialiste de démogra-
phie historique. Un intéressant ensemble d'articles et d'ouvrages
imprimés complète heureusement les sources manuscrites qui
viennent tout récemment d'être encore enrichies par un don important, réalisé par l'O.R.S.T.O.M., de photocopies de documents
glanés, lors de ses recherches, par J.-M. Filliot dans différents
dépôts d'archives.

L'histoire des Seychelles m'a toujours personnellement intéressé.
J'ai consacré une étude à leur premier peuplement et espère mener
à bien un travail d'ensemble sur la période française. Aussi est-
ce avec un réel plaisir que j'ai travaillé à la publication de cet
inventaire et joué un rôle de coordinateur entre les divers individus

et organismes dont la collaboration l'a rendu possible. La parution de cet osuvrage n'a en effet pu se faire que grâce à un concours de bonnes volontés. L'initiative de la publication est venue du gouvernement séchellois et le manuscrit m'a été confié par M. Guy Lionnet, conseiller culturel auprès du Ministère de l'Education et de l'Information, dont la connaissance de l'archipel est sans doute sans égal. Le Centre Universitaire de la Réunion - en particulier son Laboratoire d'Histoire de l'Océan Indien - a encouragé et financé l'édition. Mais celle-ci n'aurait pas été possible sans l'appui décisif de l'Institut d'Histoire des Pays d'Outre-Mer d'Aix-en-Provence et de son Directeur, le Professeur Jean-Louis MIEGE. Ma gratitude va également à l'Association des Chercheurs de l'Océan Indien qui a contribué au financement de l'impression de l'ouvrage.

Ce livre aura pleinement atteint son objectif s'il représente un encouragement à de nouvelles recherches sur l'histoire des Seychelles et un instrument utile à leur réalisation.

Claude **WANQUET**
Professeur au Centre Universitaire
de la Réunion.

LES ARCHIVES NATIONALES DES SEYCHELLES

La première référence aux archives des Seychelles se trouve dans l'Acte de Capitulation signé par le Commandant français des Seychelles, le Chevalier Jean-Baptiste Quéau de Quinssy, et le commandant de Marine Britannique, le Capitaine Henry Newcome, du H.M.S. **Orpheus**, le 17 mai 1794. L'article en question prévoit que les archives des Seychelles seront conservées.

Ce n'est cependant qu'en 1961, qu'un Département des Archives a été créé aux Seychelles. Entre-temps les documents d'archives qui se trouvaient aux Seychelles avaient subi l'injure de près de deux siècles d'indifférence, sinon de négligence. Le Département des archives fut constitué en Archives Nationales par un loi adoptée par le Conseil Législatif des Seychelles le 7 novembre 1964.

Les historiens qui ont étudié l'histoire des Seychelles avant 1961 ont donc eu à se référer principalement aux documents conservés à Paris, au Port Louis de l'Ile Maurice et à Londres.

Le premier Archiviste des Seychelles fut nommé en 1961 et un dépôt temporaire fut constitué en attendant la création d'un dépôt central. Tous les documents d'archives qui furent alors retrouvés, ainsi que les dossiers administratifs, furent acheminés vers le dépôt temporaire avant d'être conservés au dépôt central. Au moins la moitié des volumes de documents reliés ont dû être reliés de nouveau et plusieurs milliers de dossiers furent examinés aux fins de conservation.

La tâche d'indexer ces dossiers a été très ardue, du fait qu'aucune indexation n'avait été entreprise auparavant.

Au dépôt central les documents d'archives sont conservés dans des classeurs en métal. L'accès à ces documents est facilité à partir du catalogue et index par sujet.

Comme prévu par l'Ordonnance n°7 de 1964, tous les documents datant de plus de 30 ans sont accessibles au public.

Les Archives Nationales des Seychelles sont classées suivant l'ordre de présentation des documents de l'ouvrage.

M. Henri J. **Mc. GAW**
Directeur des Archives Nationales
des Seychelles

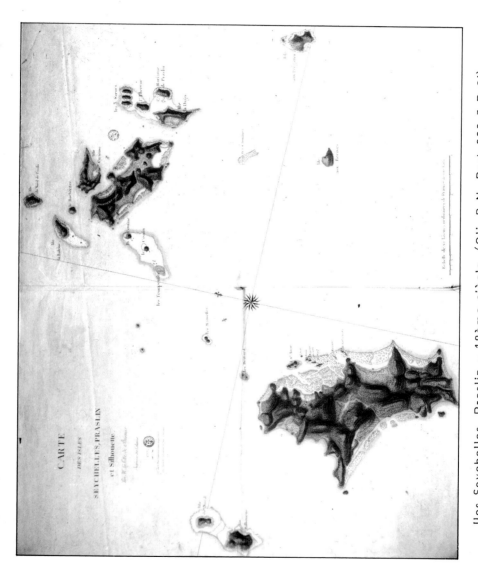

Iles Seychelles, Praslin – 18ème siècle. (Cli. B.N. Port 222 3 P 9').

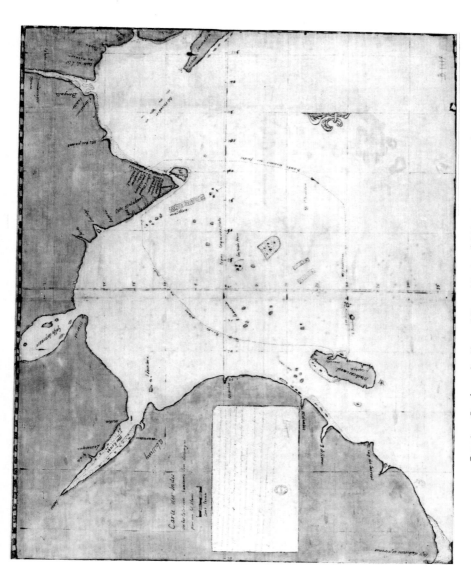

Carte Océan Indien 18e siècle (Cli. B.N. D 320).

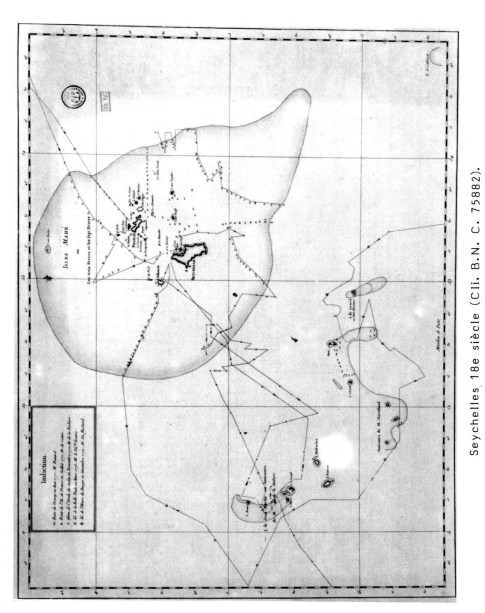

Seychelles, 18e siècle (Cli. B.N. C. 75882).

DOCUMENTS OFFICIELS DE LA PERIODE FRANCAISE

(JUSQU'EN 1810)

- CLASS A -

OFFICIAL RECORDS OF FRENCH PERIOD OF ADMINISTRATION

The reason why in 1961, except for a few copies, no archives for the
French period of administration could be traced here is to be found
in B/29 page 108 and B/5 page 39. They had been transferred to the
Mauritius Archives in 1829. In 1963, however, the Government of Mauritius
agreed to return many of them, and a list of documents received will be
found in office file SA/CA/1/20 page 24. These together with certain
photostat copies and a copy of Mr. Fauvel's volume of documents relating
to Seychelles provide a reasonably complete cover of Seychelles history
prior to 1810.

C L A S S   A

Date	Head	N° of Volumes	Code N°
	ETABLISSEMENT DE LA PREMIERE PAROISSE ET DU PREMIER CIMETIERE AUX SEYCHELLES. Décembre, 1771	1	A/1
	MINUTES NOTARIALES		
	Bataille, T 1787	1	A/2.1
	Dumont, L.H.G. 1806-1822	2	A/2.2 & A/2.3
	Dargent, J.B.R. 1818-1842	6	A/2.4 to A/2.9
	Lefebure de Marcy, A 1820-1833	5	A/2.10 to A/2.14
	Joineau, P 1831-1835	2	A/2.15 & A/2.16
	Slade, J.H. 1837-1840	1	A/2.17
	Savy, H.C. 1840-1844	1	A/2.18
	Jorre de Saint Jorre, A.D. .. 1844-1870	3	A/2.19 to A/2.21
	Loizeau, T.A. 1848-1870	1	A/2.22
	Jouanis, J-B.N. 1870-1874	1	A/2.23
	Duchesne, L.A. 1871	1	A/2.24
	ORIGINAL FRENCH TEXT OF A/3.		
	PORTFOLIO OF MANUSCRIPTS	A/3	
1772 (29 avril)	Précis des observations et opérations faites sur l'Isle Seychelles depuis le 1er novembre 1771 jusqu'au 15 février 1772 et sur l'Isle Praslin depuis le 22 février jusqu'au 3 mars 1772 par M. Gillot L'ainé que le Gouvernement de l'Isle de France voulut bien charger de cette mission le 16 octobre 1771	A/3.1	
1784 (1er décembre)	Relation du voyage du St. Anacleto Gomez natif de la ville de Porto en Portugal propriétaire d'un tonie sur lequel il s'embarqua à Tranquebar pour se rendre à Trinquemalay avec une quantité de passagers qui, comme lui, après avoir été réduits aux plus cruelles extrémistés de la faim et de la soif pendant une traversée de près de 50 jours sont venus se perdre sur l'Isle du Nord à six lieues de l'Isle Seychelles....................	A/3.2	

Date	Head	N° of Volumes	Code N°
1786	Précis de l'affaire que le Sr. Quienet veut susciter à M. Gillot commandant à Seychelles.........................		A/3.3
1786 (5 novembre)	Décisions provisoires et préparatoires à l'Ordonnance qui sera rendue pour l'Administration des Isles Seychelles..		A/3.4
1787 (1er avril	Lettre de T. Bataille aux administrateurs en chef des îles de France et de Bourbon concernant certains procès-verbaux d'arpentage, états d'observations et plans remis par lui à Mr. de Malavois et (2) les instructions données à sa femme chargée pendant son absence de la tutelle des mineurs Bataille...............................		A/3.5
1787	Observations de Bataille sur la nature du sol des terrains arpentés à Seychelles depuis le 14 mai 1787		A/3.6
1791 (6 août)	Lettre de Gautier et Yvon à Dupuy, Intendant des Iles de France et de Bourbon, sollicitant pour les îles Seychelles les secours de l'Ile de France		A/3.7
1792 (19 août)	Travail sur les concessions aux Iles Seychelles par Malartic et Dupuy..		A/3.8
1792 (12 novembre)	Lettre de Malavois à Dupuy, intendant des établissements français, relative à l'acquisition de vingt jeunes esclaves propres aux travaux du génie.....		A/3.9
1793 (20 août)	Affranchissement du nommé Bagatelle par J.B. Quienet. 2 annexes : 1) Une copie certifiée d'une requête en date du 24.7.1793 du citoyen Quienet habitant des Seychelles, au Commandant et agent civil Enouf. 2) Une copie certifiée d'un certificat dressé par Hangard, D'Offay de Beuze, et Quienet en date du 17.8.1793.........................		A/3.10

Date	Head	N° of Volumes	Code N°
1793 (5 décembre)	Arrêté de J.B. Queau de Quinssy, commandant militaire et agent civil à Seychelles, relatif à la sûreté publique et aux précautions indispensables pour la défense de la colonie....		A/3.11
1794	Lettre de J.B. Queau de Quinssy au Président de l'Assemblée Coloniale de l'Ile de France relatant la capitulation de Seychelles aux Anglais et les événements qui suivirent Les annexes sont au nombre de 7 : (1) Copie certifiée du procès-verbal relatant les événements conduisant à la capitulation de Seychelles dressé par les habitants de Seychelles (16.5.1794). (2) Copie certifiée de la sommation du capitaine de Sa Majesté Britannique Henery Newcombe au commandant des Seychelles de rendre l'île Mahé et ses dépendances (16 mai 1794). (3) Copie certifiée du discours de Quinssy aux habitants de Seychelles (1794) (4) Copie certifiée de la Capitulation de Seychelles (17 mai 1794) (5) Copie certifiée d'une note détaillant divers articles pris par les Anglais des magasins de Mahé et envoyés à bord de la Princesse Royale et du Valliant (24 mai 1794) (6) Copie certifiée de la lettre circulaire adressée par Queau de Quinssy le 2.6.1794 aux habitants de Seychelles les informant du départ de la division anglaise et les engageant à se réunir en Assemblée générale le 5 juin suivant. (7) Copie certifiée de propositions faites à l'Assemblée des habitants de Seychelles par le Commandant Quinssy le 5.6.1794		A/3.12

Date	Head	N° of Volumes	Code N°
1800 (28 août)	Titre de concession provisoire d'un terrain accordée à F. Savy par Queau de Quinssy, commandant militaire et agent civil aux îles Seychelles (10 fructidor An VIII)		A/3.13
1801 (31 janvier)	Rapport sur les pièces relatives à l'arpentage des terrains FFGG à l'île Mahé envoyé par Lislet Geoffroy aux Administrateurs Généraux (11 pluvoisan IX)...................................		A/3.14
1804 (22 mars)	Lettre de J.B. Queau de Quinssy commandant aux îles Seychelles, à l'administrateur civil aux dites îles, lui demandant l'estimation de trois esclaves (1er germinal An XII)............		A/3.15
1804 (22 mars)	Réponse de J. Bigaignon, administrateur civil aux îles Seychelles au commandant des dites îles, relative à l'estimation de la valeur de divers esclaves (1er germinal An XII)		A/3.16
1804 (2 avril)	Requête présentée par Laurent Derville, aide de camp, capitaine au 16e régiment de Cavalerie, ci-devant Royal Bourgogne, un des citoyens français mis en surveillance à Mahé, à Léger, préfet colonial des établissements français à l'Est du cap de Bonne Espérance, réclamant la décision de ce dernier au sujet de ses droits civils en vue de son mariage avec une habitante de Seychelles (12 germinal An XII)		A/3.17
1804 (14 avril)	Requête présentée par Lablache au commandant et à l'administrateur civil des îles Seychelles demandant la place d'archiviste des îles Seychelles (24 germinal An XII)		A/3.18
1805 (15 décembre)	Lettre de Quinssy, commandant et administrateur civil aux îles Seychelles à Léger, préfet colonial des établissements français à l'île de France, concernant le sieur Hangard, l'approvisionnement des magasins de Seychelles,		

Date	Head	Nº of Volumes	Code Nº
	le prochain envoi de cocos de mer et la conduite de Dumont, notaire		A/3.19
1805 (30 décembre)	Lettre du Sieur Hangard, habitant à Mahé, a Masse père, habitant de l'Ile de France, lui demandant de faire des démarches pour le renvoi de ses esclaves naufragés aux frais de l'administration		A/3.20
1806 (24 avril)	Déclaration signée Blin, Mondon, Lacour, Hodoul ainé et Hangar, relative a l'estimation de la pirogue La Mille Pattes appartenant au sieur Hangard et perdue au service de la division du contre-amiral Linois pendant sa relâche aux îles Seychelles (4 floréal An XIV).		A/3.21
1806 (19 septembre)	Acte de décès à Mahé du sieur Fragniaux, officier débarqué malade du corsaire L'Emilien, capitaine Peyre..........		A/5.22
1806 (20 novembre	Arrêté des administrateurs de l'Ile de France concernant l'Ile Sainte Anne, l'Ile aux Cerfs et l'Ile Curieuse qui sont déclarées inconcédables et réservées à l'usage des vaisseaux de l'Etat et de ceux du commerce		A/3.23
1806 (20 novembre)	Arrêté des administrateurs de l'Ile de France relatif aux concessions de terrains à accorder aux personnes mises en surveillance aux Iles Seychelles		A/3.24
1807 (10 mars)	Requête présentée par Michel Boulay, ancien menuisier au service de l'Etat aux administrateurs de l'Ile de France demandant le paiement de sa pension...		A/3.25
1807 (8 août)	Lettre de Le Roy à Léger, préfet colonial, lui annonçant l'envoi des paquets par le brick l'Adèle et l'arrivée d'immigrants venus de l'Ile Bonaparte		A/3.26
1808-1810	Travail des concessions des îles		

Date	Head	N° of Volumes	Code N°
	Seychelles adressé à Messieurs le Général de Caen, capitaine général et Léger, préfet colonial des établissements français à l'Est du Cap de Bonne Espérance, par Monsieur de Quinssy, commandant aux îles Seychelles		A/3.27
1809 (14 avril)	Rapport du Directeur des Ponts et Chaussées aux Administrateurs Généraux sur un travail qui leur a été envoyé le 1er novembre 1808 relatif aux concessions à accorder à l'Ile de la Digue, archipel des Seychelles........		A/3.28
1809 (29 décembre)	Requête présentée par Renaud, gardien des magasins à Mahé à Monsieur Quinssy commandant des îles Seychelles, et à Monsieur Le Roy, commissaire comptable, demandant à être payé de ses salaires en vieux fer		A/3.29
1808	Accord autorisant l'établissement d'esclaves par Louis Granada des Seychelles approuvée par le Général Decaen		A/3.30
	Seychelles Population Census - 1807 ...		A/4
	Portfolio of Photostat Copies of certain early documents concerning Seychelles		A/5
	Unpublished documents of the history of the Seychelles Islands anterior to 1810, by A.A. Fauvel		A/6
	Portfolio (With printed list) of ancient maps of Seychelles archipelago collected by A.A. Fauvel		A/7
	Metal cylinder containing photostat copies of : (1) "Plan des Isles Seychelles" According to Abbe Rochon in 1742. (2) Plan by Bataille of Existing Habitations in 1787 and		

Date	Head	N° of Volumes	Code N°
	(3) Plan of Mahe showing all Grants of Land made up to 1789		A/8
	Instrument of sovereignty Drawn up by Captain Corneille Nicolas Morphey on taking possession of the Seychelles archipelago, in the name of the king of France and of the french east India Company, on 1st november 1756		A/9
	List of maps and plans of the Seychelles archipelago collected by A.A. Fauvel		A/10
	Instruction du plan de la Côte d'Afrique faites en 1806 et 1807, et expédition ordonné par M. Queau de Quinssy pour prendre possession des Amirantes au nom du Gouvernement français. Dressé par Constant Dupont..		A/11

CORRESPONDANCE OFFICIELLE DE L'ADMINISTRATION BRITANNIQUE

(A PARTIR DE 1811)

- CLASS B -

OFFICIAL CORRESPONDENCE BOOKS FOR PERIOD OF BRITISH ADMINISTRATION

AFTER 1811

This class consists of bound volumes of manuscripts dating from 1822 and covering a number of subjects. The following are notes concerning the various sections.

Volumes B/1 to B/28 (B/14 & B/16 renumbered B/72A & B/72B) consist of inward letters from the Government of Mauritius to Seychelles. The earliest three volumes are missing as well as volumes for the years 1849 to 1877.

Volumes B/29 to B/50 consist of outward letters to the Government of Mauritius and, in a few cases, to the Secretary of State. Volumes for the years 1830 to 1834, 1836 to 1848 and 1856 to 1870 are missing.

In a report made in 1881 for the information of the Secretary of State (B/38 page 369) it is admitted that these volumes were without indicies, and that no record of despatch or receipt of letters had been maintained. A promise was made, however, to "institute a proper system or registering letters, of jacketting, docketting and filing them". At a considerably later date it appears that these volumes were rebound, and in a few instances indicies of important letters added. Indicies or important letter for all these volumes have now been compiled, and copies are printed below for easy reference.

Volume B/52 to B/65 are the Correspondence Books of the Legal Adviser for the years 1898 to 1902, giving his opinion on matters referred to him as Legal Adviser by the Administration. Indicies of important matters only have been added, and copies of these have also been printed below for ready reference.

Volumes B/66 to B/71 contain the minutes of the Board of Civil Commissioners, which under the tulelage of Mauritius administered Seychelles from 1811 to 1888.

Volumes B/72 to B/80 are bound volumes of local correspondence, but contain little of general interest, through certain letter might prove of interest to individual inhabitants.

Volume B/81 consists of correspondence with the Crown Agents between 1889 and 1895. Of interest are the banking services performed by Government for private individuals before establishment of banks in the Colony.

Volumes B/82 and B/83 are office records of the Inspector of Education, and include Primary Education Examination results, which might be of considerable interest to research workers.

Volume B/84 provides information concerning compensation paid to slave owners in Seychelles when slavery was abolished.

Volume B/85 is a most interesting register of Africans liberated by the British Navy from Arab dhows en route to the slave market at Zanzibar.

Volume B/86 is a Medical register of "Certificates of competency to midwife" and of certificates to doctors applying for permission to practice in Seychelles.

Volume B/87 records the proceeding of the Prison Board between 1892 and 1900.

Volumes B/88 to B/91 are Oath Books signed by certain high officials on appointment.

C L A S S B

INWARD LETTERS B/1 to B/28   VOL - B/1.

Date	Subject Matter	Page
2.3.1822	Mauritius to Madge. The return of Harrison enables the Governor to give his instructions as to the points raised by you. The Petition of the inhabitants that an armed force be sent for the security of the settlement is granted. 17 gendarmes are being sent. There are 3 already in Seychelles. The whole force will be under Harrison. Barracks to be built The question of intoxicating drink in Seychelles is under consideration. An usher must be appointed.	5
2.5.1822	de Quinssy to Suzor, Charge de la Police. Illegible. Evidently a dispute.	7
8.5.1822	Suzor to Madge. Complains of being obstructed, by Q., in carrying out his duties.	9
28.8.1822	de Quinssy to Madge. Lavoquer, Juge Suppleant, has gone without handing over Registers of Civil Status and papers of Commisariat Civil. He says you told him to. Also you named a second Suppleant without consulting me. What is your authority for this ?	14
27.1.1823	Treasurer, Mauritius, to Harrison Recognises difficulty of collecting taxes since people will only pay in kind.	1
8.5.1823	de Quinssy to Madge Encloses copies of two letters he has sent to Lavoquer without reply "ce qui est une insubordination indecente" (Lavoquer had insulted de Quinssy in public).	5
9.5.1823	Mauritius to Madge. H.M.S. "Espiegle" to be sent to Seychelles to	

Date	Subject Matter	Page
	prevent attempts to receive illicit traffic in slaves.	12.A
15.5.1823	de Quinssy to Madge.	
	These letters set out in detail de Quinssy argument that he is responsible for controlling the "suppleant" who acts as Commissaire Civil, and Madge has no authority. The fundamental law is the arreté of 23 septembre 1806, and this is not affected by the Proclamation of 3rd Nov. 1817.	6 & 7
23.6.1823	Mauritius to Madge.	
	Every vessel coming to Mauritius from Seychelles carries numbers of blacks. There seems no doubt that the traffic in slaves is carried on through the medium of those islands. The laws must be strictly attended to. In particular the laws as to the admission of strangers in to the Seychelles.	12
21.12.1824	Mauritius to Madge.	
	The owner of a negress killed by a "marroon detachement" is not entitled to compensation.	24
16.3.1825	de Quinssy to Madge.	
	I was established in this colony in 1806 as Commandant and Juge de Tribunal. 18.3.1812 appointed Juge de Paix by Farquhar at Ps. 60 p.m. + Ps. 15 for office expenses. In 1813 this payment ceased to be paid till 1817. It was confirmed by S of S despatch 25.3.1820.	8
		VOL. - B/2.
23.3.1827	Cardew certifies that the majority of slaves are well treated and well fed by their owners. There are exceptions but they are few.	7
1.8.1826	Circular from Mauritius to Commandant and Commissaire Civil des Quartiers. Contrary to law the slaves on some "habitations" are made to work on Sundays. This can be no longer tolerated. It is an "abus criant".	

Date	Subject Matter	Page
	"You are surrounded by your friends and relations and must persuade the habitants to cease the practice in their own interest". On other days the slaves should not start work more than half an hour before sunrise or finish more than a quarter of an hour after sunset. Their food and clothing must be seen to. The law is laid down in an Ordinance of 1767. Ration is two pounds of maize per day or an equivalent quantity of rice, manioc, haricots and patates. There must be an annual issue of clothing. Not more than 30 coups de fouet without authority.	24
8.8.1826	Mauritius to Harrison. Madge is to proceed to Mauritius handing over his duties to Harrison.	26
31.8.1826	Mauritius to Madge. Copy of Governor's Minute. Mude to be Superintendent of the Matricule at Mauritius. Harrison to be Govt. Agent receiving the full pay of £ 600 a year. To continue to act as Collector of Taxes and Chief of Police. Allowances £ 24 p.m. E. Cardew (writer in the Civil Service) to be Sub-Agent and charged with the registration of slaves at £ 400 p.a. Mr. Knowles (in charge of slave Registration) to return to Mauritius.	27
6.10.1826	Mauritius to Cardew. You are to report on the appearance and treatment of the slaves in Seychelles.	37
5.12.1826	Mauritius to Harrison. The Governor is the only person who can grant licences to move slaves from one island to another. The practice followed by Madge of granting these licences must cease.	41.A.
8.12.1826	Mauritius to Harrison. The Governor is seriously displeased that Madge did not report to him a correspondence which he had with the Captain of H.M.S. "Samarang" relative to movement of slaves in Seychelles. Such matters relating to the slave population should always be reported.	44

Date	Subject Matter	Page
3.1.1827	Slave Registry. Mauritius to Cardew. Detailed instructions for "recensement" of slaves.	2
26.2.1827	Mauritius to members of the "Tribunal Special". Subject : Trial of one Lindor, sentenced to penal servitude for life for armed theft and murder of a slave belonging to Mme. Jorre de St. Jorre. The irregularities of the trial must not occur again. 1st. The Juge de Paix sat. The law of 12.3.1810 provides that the Tribunal shall consist of the Commandant, Premier Supplant and 4 Notables. 2 nd. No mention of any law under which the sentence was passed. 3 rd. Lindor was never confronted with one Grand Joseph, a marron, who was alleged by him to be the culprit. 4 th. No certified copy of proceedings was sent to Chief Judge.	6 6
15.3.1827	Mauritius to Harrison. Permission granted to Charles de Quincy and his two sisters to transfer 80 slaves to Mauritius.	9
10.5.1827	Mauritius to Cardew Approval of appointment of one Jouanis as clerk in the Slave Registration Dept :	20
	VOL. B/3.	
9.2.1827	Mauritius to Harrison. Request for a return of vessels arrived and left Mahe 1815-1826.	5
11.5.1827	Mauritius to Harrison Question about a slave owned by Madge. In the year 1816 Madge seized a brig called the "Marie Louise" owned by Sausse and d'Alborede with 48 slaves which had been landed on Praslin. Sausse recaptured the ship and escaped with 11 slaves. In 1818 the brig and slaves were condemned by the Admiralty Court at Mauritius. At subsequent sale Madge bought 4 slaves. N.B. Discussion about this affair went on till 1829.	21

Date	Subject Matter	Page
4.7.1827	Mauritius to Harrison. Slaves may be embarked in whalers to assist the crew.	38
20.7.1827	Mauritius to Harrison Brook (of the "Chantier") may act as ship Surveyor when necessary	43
28.7.1827	Mauritius to Harrison. The slaves manning small boats should have their certificates with them to render the work of the Navy easier	49
3.8.1827	Mauritius to Harrison. Permission for 79 slaves belonging to Madge to go to Mauritius.	51
4.10.1827	? to Cardew Interesting list of slaves showing "caste" or country of origin	70
27.11.1827	Mauritius to Harrison. A detatchement of the 82nd Regt. of 1 Lieutenant, 1 Sergeant, 2 Corporals, 24 Privates, under Lt. Latham are to proceed to Mahe	81
30.11.1827	Mauritius to Harrison. Military to be lodged in Gendarmerie Barrack. The force of Gendarmes to be reduced to a Brigadier and 4 men. Lt. Latham has instructions to assist Civil power but this should only be used on urgent occasions.	83
		VOL. B/4.
25.7.1828	Mauritius to Harrison. The act of piracy by the "Espoir" was supposed to have been committed about 1817 on the persons of the master and crew of a Portuguese vessel near Isle aux Arbres.The "Espoir" has been seized for slave trading.	46

Date	Subject Matter	Page
26.7.1828	Mauritius to Harrison. Harrison's action in refusing permission to Mr. Michaud to take two domestic slaves to Mauritius approved as on a previous occasion Michaud had sold a domestic slave in Mauritius.	48
30.7.1828	Mauritius to Harrison. There was never any definite grant of Daros although Young, his widow, and subsequently Lefevre have occupied it. Lefevre may have the use of the coco palms he has planted until a definite grant is made.	54
6.8.1828	Mauritius to Harrison. It has been ascertained that the "Victor" commanded by Dubois Dunillac called at Daros and threatened to take water by force if it were refused. Further the Captain and Mate spent 4 days on the island as guests of M. Lefevre. It is believed the "Victor" was freighted with slaves. Further "La Petite Clementine" a supposed slaver has been repaired at Seychelles. No vessels which have any objects on board indicative of their being engaged in Slave Trading should be allowed to repair or refit in Seychelles.	57
30.8.1828	Mauritius to Dowland. Note that foreigners only reside on sufferance and are prohibited from purchasing any property without permission of Government.	65
11.9.1828	Mauritius to Harrison. Encloses petition of Quincy family asking for leave to enclose their mother's grave. Petition states that their mother died in 1809 and was buried on the Mont Pavillon near the Bourg de Mahe. Signed :- Queau de Quinssy S. Quinssy Marcy nee Quinssy Lefebure Marcy.	67
2.12.1828	Mauritius to Harrison. Encloses copy of letter to M. de Bongars. It is contrary to the wish of the Government to grant permission to reside in the Seychelles to persons not owing allegiance to His Majesty.	79

Date	Subject Matter	Page
6.12.1828	Mauritius to Harrison. With reference to the carrying off of the slaves from Providence, Captain Thornton was blameable and is responsible to M. Mangiot.	82
		VOL. B/5.
12.2.1829	Mauritius to Harrison. Whaler "Asp" of London wrecked on Madge Rocks near St. Ann Island.	3
13.2.1829	Mauritius to Harrison. Re : the mud boats being built by Crook and Nage at Seychelles for service in Mauritius.	5
21.5.1829	Mauritius to Harrison. With regard to exhumations, the time after burial must depend on the circumstances of each case. The C.M.O. states that the burial ground of the blacks at Fort Blanc has been used three times over in five years without the slightest inconvenience or deleterious effects.	20
3.6.1829	Mauritius to Harrison. Mme.Vve. Morel Duboil may remove some blacks from Denis Island.	27
11.6.1829	Police, Mauritius to Harrison. Certain members of the crew of the "Jeune Laure" have remained at Seychelles (they include Comarmond and Hermith). This is contrary to the rule that no persons shall proceed to live in Seychelles without the previous consent of the Govt.	37
11.6.1829	Dowland to Harrison. When I came here I understood it would only be for about a year. I have been expecting the arrival of a successor but I do not see that the termination of my unhappy sojourn here is fixed nor that I have any prospect of leaving shortly a country where almost everything is uncongenial to my mind and feelings and unpropitious to my future utility and welfare.	38

Date	Subject Matter	Page
11.6.1829	Mauritius to Harrison. A number of documents in the archives at Seychelles should be sent to Mauritius, e.g. Capitulation of 1794. Original concessions. Two reports on the concessions dated 1792 and 1808.	39
21.7.1829	Mauritius to Harrison. Dowland can not return to Mauritius until after the Biennial Recensement.	45
29.9.1829	Mauritius to Harrison. Devillaine granted the jouissance of Ile Plate.	60
27.10.1829	Mauritius to Harrison. The money which the captain of the "Coquette" paid as compensation for taking two slaves from Providence has been received. It exceeds M. Margiot's most sanguine expectations.	64
19.11.1829	Mauritius to Harrison. Hodoul granted permission to erect a "Marine Establishment" about 300 ft square in the harbour.	72
4.12.1829	Mauritius to Harrison. The Governor of Bombay requires a quantity of the best Seychelles cotton seed as the Bourbon cotton has very much degenerated. You are to collect a quantity of the very best description of cotton seed and forward it.	79
	Census, Biennial. ==================	
11.11.1829	Various letters relating to : Harrison to Dowland, Sub - Agent & Asst. Registrar of Slaves. Re : charter of schooner to visit outlying islands.	69
14.11.1829	Mauritius to Dowland. Re : hire of blacks.	70
17.11.1829	Chief Secretary. Mauritius to Salter, Acting Registrar of Slaves, Mauritius.	

Date	Subject Matter	Page
	Relating to questions asked by Seychelles about amendments to last census returns.	71
21.11.1829	Salter, Mauritius, to Dowland, Seychelles. Regarding supply of forms being sent. Several pages raising queries re : census, and answers thereto. These begin after the two pages which follow n° 75.	74
21.11.1829	Mauritius to Dowland. Instructions re : census.	76
28.11.1829	Salter, Act. Reg. of Slaves, Mauritius to Dowland. Instructions re : census.	78
		VOL. B/6.
20.2.1831	Mauritius to Harrison Four to five hundred dollars authorised for additional Pavillion in premises of Prison Establishment.	15
21.2.1831	Mauritius to Harrison Matter of export of sugar from Seychelles to India has been referred to Collector of Customs, and directions will be sent.	17
28.2.1831	Mauritius to Harrison. Subject as above.	24
28.5.1831	Mauritius to Harrison. Re : ship "Carnatic" Sending enclosures of copy letter from Bengal Govt. and one to them from Cruttenden, Mc Killop & Co.	38
23.6.1831	Mauritius to Harrison.. Uniforms for Gendarmes will be sent at early opportunity.	52
	An extract from H.E's minute n° 71 of 1831 bearing on proposed changes in administration	56

Date	Subject Matter	Page
28.7.1831	Extract of a Despatch from Lord Goderich dated Downing Street 28.7.1831. re : proposed changes in administration.	57/8
14.9.1831	Minute 47/1831 Relates to Mr. Elliott, from office of Registrar of Slaves, Mauritius proceeding to Seychelles for the certification of certain biennial returns which do not agree with the original of 1826.	N° number. Page before 72
16.10.1930 + query	Mauritius to Harrison. Endorsed duplicate. Re : advances by Govt. in connection with ship "Carnatic".	82
3.11.1831	Elliott to Harrison. He reports finding at Ile des Roches, a Capt. Thompson and 3 men of the "Duke of Kent" of Mauritius wrecked off Providence Island, from whence they had proceeded in a whaleboat, leaving 4 men at Alphonse island.	85
10.11.1831	Humfrey, Lt. 29th Regt. to Harrison. Asking for "the necessary" in the Police Yard to be repaired.	88
13.2.1830	Dowland, Asst. Reg. of Slaves to Harrison. Reporting on conditions found at various islands.	8
14.5.1830	Minute n° 15, 1830. John Ormsby, Chief Clerk, Port Louis, to be Sub-Agent and Asst. Reg. of Slaves, Seychelles. Islands to be visited on passage in H.M.S. "Jaseur" ; and those to be visited by Dowland (being relieved) on return voyage.	after 26
13.7.1830	Mauritius to Harrison. The landing at Seychelles of 2 horses from Brig "Sans Pareil" (brought cargo of rice) which Captain took on board in India for own use, approved by Governor.	42
16.7.1830	Civil Engineer, Port Louis, to Harrison.	

Date	Subject Matter	Page
	Fire engine and 6 leather buckets shipped in British Brig "L'Etoile" for Seychelles.	43
17.8.1830	Mauritius to Harrison. Secretary of State has asked for certificate of death of Robert Guillaume Antoine Delabarre, a French subject "déporté à Mahé in 1801", where he died during 1806.	52
28.8.1830	Mauritius to Harrison. The petition that Proclamation of Nov. 1817 be modified to allow exports (at same duties as levied at Mauritius) to all ports, particularly to India, must await result of Secretary of State communicating with Board of Trade.	53
20.9.1830	Mauritius to Harrison. Acknowledges letter of 25.7.1830 reporting the discovery on Aldabra Island of 12 to 1500 muskets, and advises Harrison that they have been taken possession of by H.M.S. "Jaseur".	58
28.9.1830	Mauritius to Harrison. Enclosing copy of report, made by Surgeon of H.M.S. "Jaseur", on state of Lepers on Curieuse Island, dated 24.7.1830. Report follows letter.	60
		VOL. B/7.
3.1.1832	Mauritius to Harrison. The Governor will not grant permission to Mr. Devillaine to import free labourers from India.	1
12.1.1832	Mauritius to Harrison. Grant of Ile Platte to Mellon and La Porte refused.	5
26.1.1832	Mauritius to Harrison. Circular. The revised establishment fixed by the Secretary of State must on no account be exceeded. Every economy must be employed as the allowance for some offices is quite inadequate.	11

Date	Subject Matter	Page
21.2.1832	Mauritius to Harrison.	
	Extract of Report of Commissioners of Enquiry (on the subject of emancipating the slaves) No grants of land should be made in the Dependencies of Mauritius except subject to a rigid condition that the land will be forfeited if slaves are employed on it.	14
	It may be expected that slave trading vessels will call at the outlying islands. "Regisseurs" should report the arrival of all vessels and protest if they take provisions by force as happened in a recent case.	14
10.3.1832	Mauritius to Harrison.	
	Rations of Govt. slaves to be :- 1 1/2 lbs. Rice 2 lbs Wood. 5 ozs Salt meat. 1/4 oz salt. Per diem. 12 ozs Tobacco p.m.	16
13.6.1832	Mauritius to Harrison.	
	Mr. Mc Donald, a medical man, permitted to reside and practice his profession in Seychelles.	29
13.6.1832	Mauritius to Harrison.	
	Lepers on Curieuse to be supplied with coconuts at price of eight dollars per 1 000.	30
4.8.1832	Mauritius to Harrison.	
	Comarmond granted petition to employ a certain number of slaves to fish for turtle on the islands west of Madagascar.	42
24.8.1832	Harrison to Mauritius. Mauritius approves.	
	"For two months I have had two gendarmes. There are no volunteers from the local inhabitants so I have had to engage anyone I could find". Has enlisted two discharged sailors. Joseph Thomas a man of great bodily strength (which is essential when dealing with drunken sailors), but who had been discharged for insolence to his officers ; and one Dell, whose appearance is in his favour, it is doubtful, however, if he will behave himself for 14 dollars a month.	43

Date	Subject Matter	Page
29.8.1832	Mauritius to Harrison. Mr. Arthur Wilson appointed to be Sub Agent, Asst. Registrar and Protector of slaves, relieving Mr. Ormsby.	46
20.9.1832	Mauritius to Harrison. Rev. Mr. Morton appointed by Secretary of State, Resident Clergyman of the Church of England at Seychelles. Arrived Mauritius from Calcutta. To have use of Govt. House for his services until a chapel can be built.	51
29.10.1832	A report by Harrison on certain slaves which had been condemned by Govt. All unfit to earn their own living except one "Castor". He had been a leader of the maroons, but after living 3 or 4 years in the woods, gave himself up, and has since been employed in capturing runaway blacks with great success, for which he has acquired a sort of celebrity.	47
29.9.1832	Mauritius to Harrison. Encloses the opinion of King's Proctor. Under no circumstances can children be sent to Daros even though their parents can legally be sent. The law on the subject is inflexibly rigid, although this involves seperation of families. He is really sorry to come to this conclusion	55
7.12.1832	Mauritius to Harrison. With reference to your representation as to the inadequancy of the police force, you may arrange with the O.C. Troops to employ soldiers without arms on police duty from time to time.	61
12.12.1832	Mauritius to Harrison. With reference to Monvoisin's request to bring 14 domestic slaves with his family to Mauritius the number is at first sight startling. However, in view of the size of his family and the custom of child slaves being employed in the service of the children of the family, the request is granted.	64

Date	Subject Matter	Page
		VOL. B/8.
7.1.1833	Mauritius to Harrison. Until a chapel can be erected at the expense of the inhabitants your office should be used for divine worship if possible.	1
18.1.1833	Mauritius to Harrison. Mr. Caffard may not import soda free from Pondicherry for manufacturing soap. There is no objection to his exporting soap direct to the Cape and New Holland (Australia).	3
29.1.1833	Dugand, Mahe, to Harrison. A slave belonging to Monvoisin has been sentenced to 30 lashes, 5 days, in the stocks, for an injury done to Dugand. Monvoisin will not give him up. There is no Ministère Public to execute the judgement. Therefore the law is treated with contempt. He prays that a Ministere Public "adhoc" be appointed.	6
30.1.1833	Fressange, Juge de Paix, to Harrison. It is impossible for me to appoint a Ministere Public "Ad hoc". Only the Procureur General can do so.	7
20.2.1833	Capt. Toosey to Harrison. The whaler "Greenwich" (of which he is Master) has been lost on Denis Island. Will put all salvage in Harrison's charge as "Lloyds Agent".	9
28.2.1833	Toosey to Harrison. Regrets mistake about Lloyds Agent. Wishes to employ Mr. Savy as Agent. Crew behaving disgracefully and refuse to assist in salvage work as were not allowed liquor.	10
13.6.1833	Mauritius to Harrison. Devillaine to be appointed Officer of Police and Ministere Public. This will get over the difficulties of enforcing judgement.	25
17.6.1833	Mauritius to Harrison. With reference to Hodoul's request to take 25	

Date	Subject Matter	Page
	Blacks to Desroches to grow cotton, you should report on the state of the island, water supply etc., and whether the blacks wish to go.	28
18.6.1833	Mauritius to Harrison. Approves of appointment of "Castor" as a Commandeur in the police. J. Thompson is dead.	30
21.6.1833	Mauritius to Harrison. Collect about 10 bags of the best cotton seed and send to Bombay. Cotton growing at Bourbon has almost ceased.	32
4.7.1833	Mauritius to Harrison. Devillaine has done nothing to develop Ile Platte. If he will not do so, a grant should be made to F. Melon.	35
16.8.1833	Marcy, Mahe, to Harrison. Resigning his position as Notary.	37
29.8.1833	Mauritius to Harrison. In view of the death of Ray, Medical Supt. of Curieuse, in July, an endeavour will be made to find a successor at Mauritius, but this is improbable.	38
17.10.1833	Capt. Skey to Harrison. Reports wreck of whaler "Harriet" on Land Cay near Poivre. (Only a very little of letter is legible).	42
26.11.1833	Mauritius to Harrison. Approves of appointment of Boswood, late Surgeon of the "Harriet", to be Medical Supt. at Curieuse. The Govt, will give assistance to Boswood to establish a hospital for seamen and poor blacks.	48
3.12.1833	Mauritius to Harrison. Permission to a young Englishman, Butler, to establish himself in Seychelles. Also a Frenchman, Duchesne, who has married a daughter of one of the oldest and most respectable inhabitants.	50

Date	Subject Matter	Page
16.12.1833	Mauritius to Harrison. The Governor will pay no attention to the petition of one Babet Loiseau to be relieved from the penalty to which she had been condemned under the Slave Laws. Further, the "calumnious attacks upon the local authorities, and the indecorous language in which they are couched, would if legally prosecuted submit her to severe punishment" <u>Memorandum from Protector of Slaves.</u> The character of the Loiseau family for illtratment of slaves is proverbial. Apart from the offence, the subject matter of the petition, her son Adolphe was convicted in 1831, and the petitioner was reprimanded, for cruel and inhuman treatment. One son Adolphe was fined £ 100 and 3 months imprisonment. In the present case, Babet was convicted of unlawfully flogging three negresses and fined £ 30, and her two sons, Desire and Domzille, 3 months imprisonment for further illegal floggings.	58
		<u>VOL. B/9.</u>
5.5.1834	Mauritius to Harrison. Encloses two copies of Act for the abolition of Slavery in British Colonies. Also 20 copies of a French translation to be delivered to the principal Slave Proprietors.	8
8.5.1834	Fressange to Wilson. Forwards depositions taken in the case against Celestian Savy for burning the house of Mme. Vve. Debray Payet and murdering his female slave "Virgine".	9
21.5.1834	Mauritius to Harrison. Amede Savy appointed as Chief of Police vice Devillaine (3 months leave of absence on health grounds).	12
26.5.1834	Mauritius to Harrison. Approves his proceeding Mauritius for a few months on health grounds.	16
2.6.1834	Mauritius to Wilson, Sub Agent.	

Date	Subject Matter	Page
	Approves measures taken to arrest Celestine Savy who has escaped from prison. With regard to letter sent Capt. of French ship "Astrolabe", the language of threats or dictation should not be used in these cases.	
7.6.1834	Chief of Police, Mauritius to Colonial Secretary. C. Savy has probably gone to India in the "Astrolabe" which left Seychelles for India.	21
26.6.1834	From Commissioners of Compensation to Harrison (in Mauritius). You and Mr. Ormsby should proceed with your enquiries as to the value of slaves in Seychelles The depositions can be taken in French.	29
15.7.1834	Resolution of Colonial Commissioners of Compensation. Wilson to put himself in touch with Fressange and Harrison, Devillaine and Ormsby or any of them who are in Seychelles, to enquire into all sales of slaves from the year 1826 in order to ascertain value.	34
28.8.1834	Colonial Secretary to D'Offay and Wilson. Cannot pay attention to D'Offay's letter of 1.4.34 as Amede Savy has already been appointed acting Police Officer in place of Devillaine resigned. If this had not been already done D'Offay's application would be considered favourably, as he has performed public service gratuitously. Note by Harrison. "Devillaine must have been in possession of D'Offay's letter, but did not transmit it till he had sent in his resignation from Bourbon.	37/38
5.9.1834	D'Argent appointed Notary in place of his father.	39
5.9.1834	Mauritius to Harrison. 184 acres may be granted to Ferdinand Savy in "Jouissance" at Praslin at a rent to be fixed.	40
24.9.1834	Petition from Mr. Charles Savy to Governor. Mauritius. His daughter, Mme.Comarmond, with her 6 children, and Mme Amedee Savy live at his principal residence, St. Anne Island. On Sunday	

Date	Subject Matter	Page
	13.7.34 about noon while they were all at their meal some 30 sailors from the whalers "Zephyr" and "Harpooner" came into the house. The family, terrified ran upstairs, and their cries attracted H. Savy, L. Adam, and two faithful blacks. They tried to resist the sailors but one black was stunned and all the others injured. Then the sailors broke everything they could find but did not succeed in forcing their way upstairs. They next armed themselves with batons and went beating and chasing the inoffensive slaves. At last, on the approach of help, they retreated. When prosecuted they were only sentenced to a few days in prison and a small fine. The petitioner is very annoyed at this. The Govt. Agent bows before the power which these horders of half-savage sailors, the scum of the canaille of great cities, execices. The troops and the six poor and weak Gendarmes are helpless. This state of affairs cannot continue. Comment by Harrison, on leave at Mauritius :- "It is improper to criticise the acting Govt. Agent. No more could be done by the Seychelles Court. Sailors belonging to whaling ships are more difficult to handle than other crews, and the justice of the Peace should be granted greater powers".	42
24.9.1834	The masters of the "Zephyr" and "Harpooner" have complained of the inconvenience resulting from the unrestricted sale and barter of spirits at St. Anne which appears to be encouraged by the Proprietor and his family. The law as to the sale of spirits must be strictly enforced.	44
	VOL. B/10.	
6.1.1835	Mauritius to Harrison. Encloses Ordinance N° 11 of 1834 giving effect to the abolition of the Slavery Trade. Wilson appointed Special Justice for the purpose.	1
8.1.1835	Commissioners of Compensation, Port Louis, to Harrison. A petition from Seychelles praying that the interests of the slave owners with regard to compensation shall not be seperated from those of Mauritius will be forwarded to England. The Commissioners of Compensation do not agree with the petition.	2

Date	Subject Matter	Page
17.1.1835	Dr. Robertson to Harrison. Arrived at Curieuse. Will take steps to segregate the lepers and prevent strangers coming. The present dresser unable to act owing to the state of his feet.	5
6.2.1835	Mauritius to Harrison. The Governor's Proclamation and Address to the Blacks to be read and explained "in the most impressive manner possible" to the apprentices of the several habitations.	7
11.6.1835	Mauritius to Harrison. Approves the appointment of four appraisers at Seychelles to value ex-slave.	21
24.6.1835	Mauritius to Harrison. Apprentices, who while they were slaves, marooned, can now only be ordered corporal punishment by the Special Justice, not by the Officer of Police.	26
22.8.1835	Mauritius to Harrison. In the view of the Procureur General the Court at Seychelles has no power to try a leper for attempted murder. In view of the objections to sending him to Mauritius disciplinary measures should be taken at Seychelles.	47
19.9.1835	Lists of stores and clothing shipped in schooner "Etoile" ex : Mauritius, for the Leper Establishment at Curieuse.	Follows 50 (2 pages not numbered).
24.9.1835	Mauritius to Harrison. Encloses letter from U.S. Consul together with letter and Memorial from Capt. Cross, referring to the episode of the whaler "Thames" in Curieuse sound, and the cruel manner in which he had been treated. The Memorial sets out :- In May 1834 he arrived in the whaler "Amanda" at Praslin. The ship was leaky and was abandoned. He agreed with Dunn, master of the ship "Thames" to take himself and his oil to England. Shortly before leaving, a dinner on shore. Capt.	

Date	Subject Matter	Page
	Dunn and Chief Officer Day of the "Thames" present, together with Mellon of La Digue. Quarrel arose between Mellon and Day, when Mellon drew knife. Dunn seperated them but certain seamen put a rope round Mellon's neck and dragged him to the door. Cross rescued him and Mellon returned to table. Next day he was friendly.	
	On 18 th Nov., 5 days later, "Thames" was putting to sea and fired a gun as usual. An armed pinnace was then sighted and came alongside. Lieut. Creagh and 15 soldiers boarded, together with an usher who served a summons from the Judge, Fressanges, calling on Dunn and Cross to appear before him to answer for assault on Mellon. They accordingly went on shore and Dunn was interrogated by the Judge. Cross remained outside. They were then surrounded by the troops with fixed bayonets and two policemen and Dr. Robertson with drawn sabres. Robertson uttered "outrageous threats" and made to stab Cross then Creagh restrained him. This was due to malignancy on R's part as a result of previous misunderstandings. No food was supplied to Dunn and Cross at Praslin. The Judge dined with all the witnesses for the prosecution under a large tree. They were finally brought to Mahe in the company of slaves and negroes. The Judge interrogated them privately and without making a definite charge against them. They were not allowed knives, forks, or razors. After some days in prison they were discharged without any formal aquittal. Meanwhile the "Thames" had been brought to Mahe manned by the military and under the command of a Brigadier of Police who had previously been responsible for casting away the "Greenwich".	51
30.9.1835	Mauritius to Harrison.	
	Approves of the Canteen near the Barracks being closed.	55
23.12.1835	Mauritius to Harrison.	
	A small gun with ammunition is being sent in order that an evening signal may be fired to warn the apprentices in the town to retire.	71
		VOL. B/11.
7.1.1836	To Mauritius from certain seamen of the Barque "Warrens" at Praslin.	
	Complaint of ill-usage by Capt. and Officers.	

Date	Subject Matter	Page
	Threats with loaded firearms and cutlasses "Considering our lives in danger we have asked the captain to take the ship to Mahe for you to settle our affair but he said "Damn Governor Harrison. I will not go to see him, let him come to me. Write and be damned"... We cannot bring him to reconciliation. He is generally intoxicated". They have refused duty and rations have been stopped.	2
9.1.1836	To Harrison from Dr. Stuart, Health Officer. Many cases of sickness in the special prison for apprentices. A hospital should be formed.	3
13.1.1836	Mauritius to Harrison. With regard to the 10 gun Brig, "Saky", belonging to the Iman of Muskat wrecked on Providence on a voyage to Zanzibar, the Iman's Agent at Mauritius will pay all expenses.	4
13.1.1836	Governor of Bourbon to Harrison. The Naval Corvette "L'Isere" and the Brig "Colibri" are being sent to Seychelles to be repaired.	5
12.2.1836	Fressanges, J.P., to Harrison. Dupuy, 1st. Suppleant to the Court, is always ill. Another should be named. It is almost impossible to get any Notable to act. The Court should be reorganized as the Suppleants have no knowledge of law.	9
9.3.1836	Fressanges, J.P., to Harrison. Names P. Joineau, former Notary, as 1st. Suppleant, vice Dupuy, as desired by D'Offay, 2nd Suppleant. Benezet to be Greffier.	13
17.3.1836	Robertson to Harrison. Capt. Howard of "Harponner" has requested Mr. Forbes to take the ship to Mahe as he has been wounded in two places by Gontier of Praslin. His hand will have to be amputated.	18
21.3.1836	Dr. Stuart to Harrison. Tenders his resignation as Health Officer as it occasions too much exposure to the sun and wind.	20

Date	Subject Matter	Page
19.5.1836	Mauritius to Harrison Acknowledges letter reporting that Captain of a Whale ship has been severely wounded by an arrack seller at Praslin. Approves a Committee being appointed to consider Regulations governing the sale of arrack. Regrets that it has not been set up before.	26
19.5.1836	Mauritius to Harrison. It is found that such bad effects to military discipline result from having a detachment of soldiers at such a distance that it is to be withdrawn. 8 or 10 well-behaved policemen will be sent to Seychelles.	29
25.5.1836	Police Department, Mauritius to Harrison. Advises despatch in "Constance" of uniforms and material for Gendarmes and Special Guards.	30
25.5.1836	Police Dept. Mauritius to Harrison. 8 Police Guards of good character being sent in "Constance". 4 of them are English. One 1st. class guard at £ 4. p.m. and 6d. a day in lieu of rations. Seven 2nd class guards at £ 3 p.m. and 6d. a day.	31
10.6.1836	Mauritius to Harrison. Dr. Pottier appointed Health Officer.	38
17.8.1836	Dr. Robertson, Curieuse, to Harrison. The New Bedford whaler "Ansley Gibbs" called at Praslin with smallpox on board. Also an Embassy from the Sultan of Johanna to Mauritius. The ship will not stay. The Embassy has been put on shore on Curieuse in quarantine.	49
30.8.1836	Mauritius to Harrison. Enquiries have been made by a family resident at Lisle as to the fate of one Ferdinand de la Porte, a music master, who left France for Mauritius at end of 1792. It is understood that there is a La Porte now resident in Seychelles. Please report.	50
8.9.1836	Lieutenant Armstrong, Comdg. detachment 99 th	

Date	Subject Matter	Page
	Regt. to Harrison.	
	The sails and ropes of the "Constance" appear inefficient. Requests a survey.	
	Survey Report by Officers of H.M.S. "Pelican" report sails and ropes totally unfit for service.	57
9.9.1836	C.O., H.M.S. "Pelican" to Harrison.	
	Refuses to take Johanna Ambassadors as he is not aware whether their arrival would be agreeable to the Government of Mauritius.	
	Attached. Draft letter from Harrison to Mauritius stating that in view of the service in which the "Pelican" had been employed, no doubt the Captain was acquainted with the views of the Government. He would therefore retain Embassy.	61
17.10.1836	Mauritius to Harrison.	
	The Johanna Ambassadors to be sent by the first fitting opportunity.	66
21.10.1836	Harrison to Robertson on Curieuse.	
	The Ambassadors may go bye the "Etoile" at their own expense.	68
6.12.1836	Governor of Bourbon, to Harrison.	
	The Kings Corvette "Prévoyante" is coming to Seychelles for overhaul and refit.	79
24.12.1836	Mauritius to Harrison.	
	The Johanna Ambassadors have safely arrived. Harrison's conduct approved.	84
24.12.1836	Mauritius to Harrison.	
	Dr. Bernard is being sent to be Health Officer, vice Pottier.	89
		VOL. B/12.
4.4.1837	This book is for the years 1837 and 1838. Each year is paged separately.	
	From Commandant French Corvette "Prévoyante" to Harrison.	
	Requests that part of the prison be set aside for	

Date	Subject Matter	Page
	his sailors who may require confinement during the refit of the ship.	8('37)
9.6.1837	From Fressange to Harrison. Suggests Dantoine as 2nd Suppleant. D'Offay to be 1st. Suppleant vice Joineau resigned.	26('37)
22.6.1837	From Dr. Bernard to C.M.O., Mauritius. It is urgently necessary to send good vaccine. Most of the population is unvaccinated, and in spite of rigid quarantine there is constant risk of infection. He also wants a hospital and a boat.	31('37)
24.6.1837	One La Blache accuses Fressanges, Joineau and Dantoine of corruption.	32('37)
29.6.1837	Mauritius to Harrison. With reference to a petition from various inhabitants of Seychelles protesting against the "jouissance" of Aldabra being given to Huteau as it prevents their collecting "tortues de terre", a great resource for Seychelles, the Governor states that they must not land on Aldabra but may fish off its coasts.	36('37)
18.10.1837	Mauritius to Harrison. Mr. Nezet who has married in Seychelles is not to be permitted to reside there. In future no aliens should be permitted to marry in Seychelles unless they have persmission to reside.	57('37)
18.11.1837	Police, Mauritius to Harrison. It is impossible to get a Brigadier or any respectable guards to volunteer for Seychelles.	65('37)
21.11.1837	The Governor has refused to permit 7 persons who tried to stir up an insurrection in Bourbon to be exiled to Seychelles.	66('37)
2.12.1837	D'Offay to Governor. As he has served 12 years as suppleant to the Tribunal requests that he may be allowed a salary.	68('37)

Date	Subject Matter	Page
6.12.1837	Mauritius to Wilson, as Govt. Agent. Oath of allegiance to Her Majesty to be taken by all persons employed in any public capacity Private persons only when it is considered desirable.	69('37)
22.01.1838	Mauritius to Wilson. Clement has been appointed Special Justice.	5('38)
22.01.1838	Mauritius to Wilson. Nezet granted permission to reside owing to respectability of family he has married into. His conduct otherwise has been unsatisfactory.	6('38)
31.01.1838	Mauritius to Wilson. Requests information as to a seaman named Whitehead or Martain, otherwise "Bill" or "Old Bunk" formerly in whaler "Greenwich". Keast, now a Gendarme, formerly 2 nd Mate of "Greenwich" reports that he knew Martin, called by the Captain, "Bill", and by the men "Bill in Bunk", as he was always ill either from venereal or the effects of wounds received at the battle of Navarino. He is still at Mahé and known by the same names.	11('38)
6.02.1838	Michaud to Wilson. Complains that though he is the oldest merchant and shopkeeper here he has only been granted a second class licence. The Police report that in Michaud's absence his wife sells exessive quantities of drink to the blacks.	12('38)
5.04.1838	Dr. Bathcort sets up as a private medical practioner.	21('38)
28.04.1838	Ed. Lefevre to Governor. Owing to the impossibility of getting labour to work his sugar estate he requests permission to import 100 Indians from India.	23('38)
3.05.1838	Petition to the Governor praying that Fressanges be removed owing to his unfairness and favouritism. Signed by 44 persons.	25('38)

Date	Subject Matter	Page
4.6.1838	Ile Plate to be retained as Quarantine Station.	30('38)
6.6.1838	Mauritius to Govt. Agent. Governor sanctions provision of sabres and light muskets for use of Police, but to be kept in a place of security under supervision.	32('38)
30.11.1838	Fressange report both Suppleants of the Court, D'Antoine and D'Offay are dead, and no one can be found to take their place.	65('38)
7.12.1838	A military detachment will be sent to Mahé in answer to a petition of the inhabitants. The Governor expects that in consequence the inhabitants will bear the cost of repairing the quarters for the troops. Five or six men may be added to the Police Force.	67('38)
		VOL. B/13.
30.03.1839	Letters received from Mauritius. 1839 Clement appointed Stipendiary Magistrate before whom all labourers for more than a month must be engaged.	6
22.05.1839	To Mylius. Approves of expenditure in connection with the Special Justice visiting the islands. "A highly desirable object". Encloses a circular letter announcing that apprentices are absolutely and entirely free.	
22.05.1839	Governor expresses gratification that 1 st. Feb. the day of liberation passed off in a manner creditable to the population.	10
31.05.1839	To Mylius. Acknowledges receipt of his general report and suggestion for improvement on the Seychelles Islands. The tone of the Report "conveys the impression of Seychelles being considered a seperate colony, and dependant at present upon Mauritius only because it is too poor to provide	

Date	Subject Matter	Page
	for itself". It is not a separate Colony. Regrets the total want of Religious Institutions and the lamentably degraded state of religious and moral feeling. If the inhabitants will build churches, the Govt. will advance money. The state of the burial ground is not creditable to the island, and argues a lamentable deficiency of feeling. Convicts can not be sent from Mauritius for road building. Not possible to have a Civil Hospital at Mahe, and Dispensaries at Praslin, La Digue, Silhouette. Impossible to import 1200 Indians. Generally the inhabitants must help themselves if they want the benefit of religion, education and roads, as no assistance from Mauritius can be expected.	9
17.06.1839	List of stores shipped in Schooner "Anais" for Leper establishment on Curieuse Island.	17
9.07.1839	To Mylius. A. Savy's resignation as Police Officer has been accepted. All vacancies should be filled locally if possible, as suitable Mauritian will not go to Seychelles.	22
20.09.1839	To Mylius. Clement may be pardoned for his breach of Quarantine regulations. There have been disputes with the military. The detachment is being recalled.	38
20.09.1839	The Governor can not help expressing surprise and regret at seeing so little harmony among the four public officers at Seychelles, and so much evidence of personal animosity among them as is shown by the correspondence.	38
21.09.1839	To Mylius. Your duties and rights as Civil Commissioner and Government Agent, are similar to your predecessors and not more extensive. Authority to build a market for which Mauritius will advance money, but not other assistance can be expected.	43
21.09.1839	To Mylius. With regard to the dispute with Clement there is evidently much personal feeling to the prejudice	

Date	Subject Matter	Page
	of the service. The parties must put an end to it. The Civil Commissioner is an executive officer and should not interfere with the Stipendiary Magistrates Judicial work. The Stipendiary Magistrate is a sedentary officer and need not visit estates as the Special Justice used to.	44
23.9.1839	To Mylius. With regard to request for £ 700 to meet expenditure former experience shows that £ 300 is sufficient.	49
23.9.1839	To Clement. The Magistrate must live near the town of Mahe.	50 and next page no number.
24.9.1839	Governor observes Mylius describes himself as Chief of the Administration and Civil Commandant, and refers to Seychelles as a Colony. This is not correct.	52
19.10.1839	To Mylius. No field pieces can be supplied for firing salutes.	62
7.10.1839	To Mylius. The Seychelles can never become the seat of an extensive legal commerce, so there is no use appointing a separate customs establishment there.	63
25.10.1839	To Mylius. Satisfaction expressed at the favourable report on the working of the free labour system.	71
13.11.1839	To Mylius. Does not appear that complaint against Clement of having set up a Police Court is justified.	78
28.11.1829	Police Office, Mauritius to Mylius. A fire engine has been shipped in the "Prevoyante" for Seychelles.	98

Date	Subject Matter	Page
13.12.1839	To Mylius. It might be as well for the Stipendiary Magistrate to sit in the various islands, but there is not enough work for a second Magistrate, and the Executive Officer should never assume judicial functions.	105
17.12.1839	To Mylius. Tranquility and order must be maintained during the New Year celebrations. The only legal holiday is New Year's Day, but it is possible that "The old usage" may be followed. The masters should be agreed on the holidays to be given.	3
11.02.1840	To Mylius. Proposed reorganization of Police Force on more efficient footing approved except that pay of Police Officer cannot be increased beyond £ 10 a month. Total strength : 1 Police Officer, 1 Brigadier, 2 Under Brigadiers, 5 1st. Class, 8 2 nd Class, 6 3rd Class.	10
28.05.1840	To Mylius. Approved that one Mamin should publish a Gazette or Journal at Mahe, although "His Excellency entertains considerable doubts of the advantage of a free press, where there are no means of punishing its licentiousness".	17
30.05.1840	To Mylius. All your accounts are in arrear. Pay of Departments in arrear will be stopped if they are not promptly rendered.	19
3.07.1840	To Mylius. Macintyre appointed Brigadier of Police.	27
1.07.1840	To Mylius, from Police Dept., Mauritius. Advises re : Clothing for police (including 2 yards of gold lace for Brigadier's uniform) being shipped in "Mouche".	28
8.10.1840	To Mylius. Approves of the suggestion to name the village	

Date	Subject Matter	Page
	of Mahe Port Victoria - also his suggestion as to names of streets.	85
20.10.1840	To Mylius.	
	It has been reported to Governor that the Brig "Lady Wilmot Harton" has been taken up by a Denis La Poussiere to go to Madagascar in search of labourers to be employed cutting timber, on Silhouette island. Mylius to inquire into circumstances and report fully.	87
31.10.1840	To a Mr. Galenne of Bourbon.	
	No objections to his going to Seychelles for his health. He may bring servants, but they will become free on arrival, and at liberty to serve any master they choose.	91
9.11.1840	To Mylius	
	The request of D'Argent and La Poussière to introduce 100 Malgache labourers cannot be acceded to.	99
12.11.1840	To Mylius.	
	Encloses petition from Amedee Savy, late Police Officer. Petition states that for 5 years he acted as Police Officer but had to pay all office expenses, boat hire etc..., and he claims to be reimbursed these sums.	100
28.11.1840	To Mylius.	
	It is not possible at present to send a party of Indian convicts to work on the road you propose making to South Mahe.	112
		VOL. B/17.
4.12.1840	To M. La Poussière.	
	You cannot be allowed to import 50 Malgache natives into Silhouette.	12
10.12.1840	To Mylius.	
	You cannot be allowed the sum of £ 130 (sic) which he paid for passage from Mauritius to Seychelles.	16

Date	Subject Matter	Page
12.12.1840	To Mylius. Aldabra may be under control of Mahe, it is worked from there.	17
20.04.1841	To Mylius. His Excellency cannot nominate Mr. Lablache to act as a "Suppleant" to Fressanges, J.P., unless the differences which formerly existed between them have left no recollection which would hinder them in acting in cordial co-operation.	27
2.04.1841	To Mylius. (with accompanying letter, 29.3.1841, from Custom House to Mylius). No proper customs accounts have been received and he has not accounted for £.73 received from Wilson on taking over.	34
31.05.1841	To Mylius, with reference to a letter sent by him direct. The Secretary of State cannot enter into any discussion with you except through the Governor of Mauritius.	41
11.02.1841	Circular. All official correspondence to be in English in future.	43
15.04.1841	To Mylius. You have no power to close Billiard Rooms on Sundays and Religious Holidays.	44
15.04.1841	To Mylius. Particulars of amount of £ 1.13s. which it is proposed to surcharge him.	54
26.10.1841	To Mylius. Mr. Fondamiére may be granted leave to establish an hotel at a reduced licence duty of £ 20 p.a. Reference to Proclamation of the 4 th November 1817 concerning taxes which may be levied in Seychelles.	73
27.10.1841	To Mylius. Report what taxes can be fairly levied in	

Date	Subject Matter	Page

Seychelles.
Endorsed on back :-
Capitation (from 10 to 60) at 2/- on 2500 persons.

Chantier	£ 20	
Huissier	£ 8	
Commissaire Priseur	£ 5	
Licences 1st. Cl. say	10 a £ 6each	
" 2nd. " "	6 a £ 3 "	
Hawkers	5 a £ 2 "	
Notaries	2 a £ 8 "	
Fishermen	12 a £ 1 "	

(not to affect private fishing)
"Cantine"   £140
Arrack   £ 20

                    TOTAL   £959   78

13.10.1841 To Mylius.
Tax Rolls for 1838 have not been received.   79

10.10.1841 To Mylius.

With reference to an Audit query with regard to office sent, His Excellency "anxiously hopes you will dismiss from your mind any ungenerous suspicious against the Auditor General". The A.G. states that Mylius complains "that numerous humiliations have been heaped on him". He should know better as he was formerly Assistant in this Department.   91

31.12.1841 To Mylius.

Correspondence regarding the loss of the ship "Tyger" of Liverpool wrecked on Astove in 1836. It has been alleged that part of her cargo was stolen and concealed on Aldabra and Providence. Mr. Spurrs, the Chief Mate is still at Seychelles.   2

22.12.1841 To Mylius.

It is impossible to check your Customs Accounts.   3

31.12.1841 To Mylius.

The Society for the Propagation of the Gospel is willing to renew the grant of £ 100 p.a. for a clergyman at Seychelles and will try to find a suitable person. Assistance for a church is under consideration.   4

Date	Subject Matter	Page
31.12.1841	To Mylius. To report on petition of Fressanges. Petition. F. states he has been Juge de Paix since 1828, and as an old man with a family to support £ 276 is not enough, especially as he has only one Suppleant, has to pay his office expenses and also the hire of a house for his Court. Procureur General reports that F. is an old and recommendable servant, and his salary is insufficient, but cannot understand why he has to pay expenses, etc...	5
28.04.1842	To Mylius. Requests explanation of Dr. Cathcart's letter. Cathcart's letter enclosed. Since 1838 has practiced as a Medical Practitioner at Seychelles. Has frequently performed duty for Government, at Mylius request. Mylius refuses to pay, and has insulted him.	9
9.05.1842	To Mylius. Felicité having reverted to Crown, the petition of Mylius to be granted the concession of it has been forwarded to S of S for favourable consideration.	13
11.05.1842	To Mylius. Forwards letter from Collector of Customs and requests him to afford his best attention to that branch of the Public Service. (Enclosed letter states that the Seychelles Customs Accounts are so inaccurate that no one can understand or check them).	17
31.08.1842	To Mylius. It is reported that the Caret turtle at Aldabra are being exterminated by the lessee. This must be put a stop to.	42
1.09.1842	To Mylius. You may take possession of Felicité pending decision of Secretary of State as to your petition.	43
26.09.1842	To Mylius. Vve.Michaud may retain the "Jouissance" of Glorieuse held by her husband.	47

Date	Subject Matter	Page
23.09.1842	To Mylius. The paper "Le Seychellois" published by Mamin need only pay stamp duty at the rate of 1/2d a sheet not 3d.	50
29.09.1842	To Mylius and Clement. Re : correspondence between them forwarded by Clement. "I have been directed to express to you His Honor's disappointment and regret at seeing the time of Public Officers occupied in discussions of such trivial importance".	52
18.03.1843	To Mylius. H.E. having considered your suggestions as to taxes, considers that they should not be adopted before being submitted to the "Notables". A meeting of the principal inhabitants should therefore be held.	16('43)
1.05.1843	To Mylius. The Secretary of State directs that all Crown Lands must be disposed of by public sale, and therefore you cannot have free concession of Felicité.	19('43)
11.09.1843	To Mylius. An Ordinance No. 13 of 1840 is to be put into force at Seychelles, the jurisdiction of the J.P. will be much extended. He is to receive a salary of not less than £ 300 a year. The Stipendiary Magistrate to act as Suppleant and Assistant Judge.	200('43)
23.09.1843	To Mylius. With reference to the petition of the inhabitants dated June 1842, the S of S cannot sanction the admission of Indian Labourers to Seychelles. They are only allowed into Mauritius because they are under special supervision by an Officer appointed by the Indian Government.	30('43)
1.12.1843	To Mylius. Deal with statements in petition of Leflecher, French subject who had been refused leave to reside in Seychelles.	

Date	Subject Matter	Page
	Petition. Leflecher states : He arrived in Seychelles in 1840 after a shipwreck, and desired to marry a Creole. Mylius sent him to Mauritius to ask permission, which was refused. He was allowed to go to Mahe to settle his affairs within 14 days. As he could not find a security, Mylius threatened to put him in prison. He then left for Pondicherry but returned to get married. Mylius allowed him to get married but insisted on he, his wife and her family leaving the Colony. He then got married and went to Bourbon with his wife and her mother. He claims that the property of his mother-in-law is now abandoned, owing to the arbitrary acts of the British Government. Mylius notes on back "It is singular that Flecher called on me before he left to thank me for all my kindness and particularly for facilitating his marriage to Miss. Hoareau".	5 (of 1844 number).
30.11.1843	To Mylius. The inhabitants of Silhouette may be authorised to destroy dogs without a master.	7 (of 1844).
10.02.1844	To Mylius. Approved to hire a building as church and school for the Rev. Delafontaine who arrived in September '43.	18
21.09.1844	Petition of Raymond Hodoul that the "Jouissance" of a portion of the Barachois for a "careenage" granted to his father in 1829 may be renewed to him.	47
19.10.1844	To Mylius. £ 3 a month may be allowed to resident clergyman for chapel and school rent on his transferring them to his own premises, by which a saving will be effected.	60
31.10.1844	To Mylius. The Seychelles are such a burden on the revenue of Mauritius that no allowance can be made to you as Collector of Customs.	62

Date	Subject Matter	Page
		VOL. B/19.
	Letters from the Customs Department of Mauritius, between 1819 and 1832.	
		VOL. B/20.
28.11.1844	To Mylius. He cannot have "Jouissance" of Felicité Island. Secretary of State says such grants injurious to Public interest. Occupancy of all such islands to be put up annually to Public Auction and disposed of to highest bidder.	3
16.12.1844	To Mylius. Mr. R. D'Argent's petition to establish sugar mill and distillery on Frigate Island not agreed to.	6
26.12.1844	To Mylius. Capt. Cauvin may collect, and import into Mauritius, but without any exclusive privilege, guano from Isle aux Recifes, and Isle aux Vaches.	13
31.12.1844	Petition from a Mr. Auguste Souys (?) for concession of some land at Praslin cannot be granted. (Precluded by regulations of Secretary of State).	18
24.01.1845	Petition from Messrs. Audibert and Mouline to collect guano from Ile aux Recifs, Banc d'Africanis and Ile Platte, granted (no exclusive privilege).	22
19.06.1845	The Governor does not deem it advisable that a military detachment be sent to Seychelles.	34
19.06.1845	Gazettes were sent by "Briton", which vessel is feared may be lost, not having yet reached Seychelles.	37
17.09.1845	The petition from a number of inhabitants that a tax on labour be established, returned by Colonial Secretary, to Civil Commissioner for opinion and report.	53

Date	Subject Matter	Page
19.11.1845	James Mc Intyre, Police Brigadier, to be 2nd Officer of Police, provisionally.	64
20.11.1845	No monoply re : guano can be sanctioned.	66
29.10.1845	Delafontaine, Civil Chaplain, Mahe to Colonial Secretary. While willing to conduct occasional services in the prison for the prisoner, he contends that because of its much delapidated state and unsuitability otherwise, it is no place in which to hold Public worship.	69
8.07.1846	The report that adjacent islands visited and perfect good order found to exist among the emancipated population has been read with much satisfaction.	2 (of'46).
24.06.1846	Refers to a letter of 10 th January under the circumstances stated therein, H.E. approves of Civil Commissioner not giving effect to appointment of James Mc Intyre as Provisional Second Officer of Police	8 (of'46).
26.09.1846	Letters from Colonial Secretary to Civil Commissioner and to Stipendiary Magistrate. Regarding dissensions between Govt. Officials at Seychelles. H.E. expects tolerance and amicable relations to prevail-for the good of the service-so that there may be harmony and he spared disagreeable duty of inquiring into disputes and reporting them to H.M. Government.	31 (of'46).
10.11.1846	The petition of Madame Huteau re : a continuation of the "Jouissance" of Aldabra, granted to her late husband, cannot be complied with.	39 (of'46).
16.11.1846	10 copies of proclamation for giving effect to the Ordinances encouraging vaccination against smallpox, and 4 copies of each of the Ordinances.	43 (of'46)
7.11.1846	Colonial Secretary sends copies of correspondence between the Police Officer (Mr. Lablache) and the Clergyman at Seychelles. H.E. wishes enquiry made and report furnished. H.E. states letters demons-	

Date	Subject Matter	Page
	trate very clearly the unsatisfactory feeling between them, and recommends better understanding and kindlier disposition.	45 of 846
10.11.1846	Encloses letter from Collector of Customs regarding very unsatisfactory state in which Customs accounts have been transmitted although previous communications on the matter have been sent.	47 of '46
16.11.1846	Long letter (filling 16 pages) from Procureur and Advocate General to the Colonial Secretary concerning marriage regulations.	
		VOL. B/21.
17.05.1847	Expresses dissatisfaction that because of dilatoriness by several Heads of Depts. The Blue Book returns are in arrear. They are to be told the above, and any future irregularities will result in their salaries being stopped by the Pay Office.	7
2.06.1847	Approves of Mr. Jones having temporary charge of Lepers on Curieuse (Dr. Robertson having died) until a proper medical person can be sent from Mauritius. Mr. Ford (recommanded by C.M.O.) to visit at stated periods, with the meantime.	18
29.06.1847	Advises that Mr. W. Laidlaw is to be M.O. in charge of Lepers at Curieuse.	25
31.08.1847	Acknowledges draft for £ 105. 12. subscribed by inhabitants of Seychelles for relief of distressed Irish and Scotch. The Governor very pleased at liberal response.	34
14.09.1847	Additional subscription for above fund amounting to £ 25. 10. acknowledged.	38
24.09.1847	Inhabitants of Seychelles cannot be called upon to pay Immigration Tax, as none of the laws re: such Tax have been made applicable to Seychelles, and moreover the inhabitants are not allowed the advantage of Indian immigration.	47

Date	Subject Matter	Page
24.09.1847	To the Rev. Delafontaine. Approves of an extra £ 1 a month be allowed for renting a more suitable building for use as place of public worship and school.	50
30.10.1847	Request to be relieved from collecting the Customs cannot be agreed to. Recommendations of the Commissioners of Eastern Inquiry have been only partially carried out. Regarding reported increase of smuggling, the Police to be instructed to keep a vigilant look-out.	54
24.12.1847	Fire engine and instructions will be sent at first opportunity.	3 (of '48)
3.03.1848	At request of the Governor of Bourbon, a Monsieur Gendron, resident there since 1805, may proceed to Seychelles, where a daughter is married to Mr. F. Mellon, Shipmaster.	9 (of '48)
11.04.1848	Colonial Postmaster, Mauritius to Col. Secy. In Consequence of "Culpable negligence" by the Agent of the "Henry Voltigeur", a bag of mail for Seychelles was not shipped. A report, by the "Ship Clerk" of the P.O., of the circumstances, to the Colonial Postmaster, accompanies.	12 (of '48)
3.06.1848	Fressanges, Juge de Paix, is ill, and Clement, the Asst. doing duty in his stead, is holding his office at his residence in the country, which is irregular. He must remove it to Victoria.	19 (of '48)
28.06.1848	Encloses copy of letter from Colonial Secretary, to Stipendiary Magistrate Clement. Owing to paucity of cases brought before the S.M. other arrangements for the duties of S.M. may be made, and he should await H.E.'s decision.	24 (of '48)
31.08.1848	Advises Fressanges, Juge de Paix, that S.M. Clement has been instructed to turn over all records of his office to him, and proceed to Mauritius. Fressanges to hear and decide any complaints in the relation of master and servant, until other arrangements can be made.	28 (of '48)

Date	Subject Matter	Page
19.09.1848	Regarding recommendation that premises known as the Establishment Delorie be purchased (because of ruinous state of the Prison) for use as Prison, Court, and Customs, H.E. cannot-in view of absence of all information as to terms on which purchase could be made-form an opinion as to propriety of the idea. In the meantime, he authorizes hiring them.	33(of'48)
21.09.1848	Application having been made by the Council of Govt. of Mauritius to be relieved from the expense of the Seychelles, to which permission to trade direct with other countries has been granted, the Secretary of State has intimated that such relief cannot be granted, and Mauritius must continue charged with expenses of Seychelles public establishments. It becomes urgent that measures should be taken to reduce expenditure, and to ascertain the extent to which the Islands can contribute to cost of administration. Full report to be made.	35(of'48)
13.12.1848	Appointment of Mr. J.P. Stevenson to be Supt. of Quarantine at Flat Island (without salary) because of depredations by crews of whaling vessels, approved.	51(of'48).
		VOL. B/22.
2.02.1878	Long letter relative to various phases of the proposed leasing of Felicité Island to Mr. E. Serret.	15
19.02.1878	Approves Rev. Mr. Chancellor doing the duties of Port Victoria Chaplaincy during absence on leave of Rev. Mr. Bichard, and of his drawing half that gentleman's salary at expiration of his 3 months leave on full pay.	25
27.02.1878	The petition of a Mr. J.B. Le Gentel to be allowed to practise dental surgery in Seychelles is not granted (No reason given).	37
27.02.1878	Requests that the lease (of about 50 acres at Capucin, Mahe, referred to in Colonial Secretary's letter A. 413 of 25.2.1878) be sent Mauritius for the signature of the Board of Commissioners of the Church of England as soon as	

Date	Subject Matter	Page
	the modifications required have been made to it	39
28.02.1878	Re : application of Rev. Ignace, Prefet Apostolique, Seychelles, that mission of Franciscan Fathers may hold property. This will be considered after he has conformed to conditions of Ordinance 22 of 1874.	41
1.03.1878	Relates to complaint by Dr. Brooks, medical Officer, Mahe, against Mr. Leipsic, Chief Officer of Police. Matter dealt with by Executive Council which came to conclusion that Leipsic opened an official letter not addressed to him, and that in his report and explanations he has not been as truthful as he should have been, and therefore rendered himself liable to punishment. Salary as Inspector of Liberated Africans (Rs. 1000 p.a.) to be reduced to Rs.500 for 1 year from receipt of order at Seychelles.	56
29.03.1878	Acknowledges accounts for Qr. ending 31st Dec. 1877 in connection with Political prisoners.	91
24.04.1878	Expresses Governor's pleasure that more communication with Mahe by steamer is anticipated. He recognises that Civil Commissioner has mainly contributed to this by breaking up coal wharf monopoly which so long oppressed Port Victoria.	100
		VOL. B/23.
11.03.1881	The Hon. Henry Cockburn Stewart, Acting Receiver General, to act as Chief Civil Commissioners until a successor to the late Capt. Blunt be appointed by Secretary of State for the Colonies.	2
22.03.1881	Forwards extract from Minutes of Executive Council on the subject of certain proposed changes in the administration and constitution of the Seychelles. Requests observations and report thereon.	41
	Printed copy of Secretary of State's despatch of 14 th December, 1880 relative to affairs in Seychelles.	49

Date	Subject Matter	Page
24.08.1880	Copy of very long letter from Governor of Mauritius to the Secretary of State.	52
18.03.1881	Very long letter from Chief Judge, Mauritius to Lieut. Governor. Comments upon proposed modifications and administration of Seychelles.	79
16.04.1881	The articles applied for on behalf of ex-Sultan of Perak (Political Prisoner) cannot be obtained in Mauritius, and requisition has been sent to Colonial Secretary of Straits Settlements.	146
10.05.1881	Statement of disburements at Seychelles on account of exhumation and transport of the body of the mother of Datuh of Perak.	148
18.04.1881	Suggestion by Agent of Messageries Maritimes Co., regarding establishment of a light on Denis Island, is under consideration.	188
9.05.1881	Mr. G. Hollier Griffith appointed by Governor subject to a probation of 3 months-to succeed Mr. Leipsic as Chief of Police, Inspector of Liberated Africans, and Inspector of Nuisances on the retirement of that Officer.	202
10.05.1881	Sends copy of letter from Colonial Secretary of the Straits Settlements reporting Mr.Strugnell's return to Mahe to resume his duties as Interpreter with the Political Prisoners.	225
11.05.1881	Encloses prison dietary scale asked for.	236
11.05.1881	The idea that Dr. Lepper, M.O., should be allowed to attend private cases and receive fees without affecting claim to pension, is approved. He is to understand that concession is a favour likely to be withdrawn at any time without entitling him to any compensation.	240
17.05.1881	Forwards a Minute by H.E. dated 16 th May 1881 concerning condition of liberated Africans and other labourers in Seychelles as indicated by report of 15th July last, by Mr. Leipsic, Inspector of Immigrants. (Report had only lately reached	

Date	Subject Matter	Page
	the Government). A full and prompt inquiry necessary. Mr. J. Ackroyd, Police and Stipendiary Magistrate, being sent to assist in this. (Mr. Leipsic's report, of a number of printed pages, follows Governor's minute).	272
22.11.1881	Secretary of State to Lt. Govt. of Mauritius, Mr. A.C.S. Barkly is to be Chief Civil Commissioner of the Seychelles. Leaves Marseilles early January, 1882.	338
11.06.1881	Authorises payment of Rs.700 to Census Superintendents and Enumerators.	362
14.06.1881	Long letter on subject of Seychelles finances. Accompanied by long report from Audit Office.	380
4.10.1881	Not advisable to raise a loan, but if funds are required for any purpose, such as the making of roads, the amount should be borrowed from Government balance of Mauritius.	9
4.10.1881	Relates to danger of introduction of coffee plants and seeds from Ceylon, and sends copy of report from Director of Gardens and Forests.	30
4.10.1881	Valcain Angdowokau, charged with murder to the tried in Mauritius. Passages to be secured for witnesses as listed which include Dr. Lepper, (M.O.), and G. Griffiths (Chief Officer of Police)	38
4.10.1881	Forwards 6 printed copies of Mr. J.H. Ackroyd's report on conditions of liberated Africans (sent separately).	48
29.10.1881	The application of ex-Sultan of Perak for permission to spend 2 or 3 months in Mauritius has been forwarded to Secretary of State for consideration.	68
31.10.1931	Approves of steps taken regarding cocoanut disease. Copy of the letter, and insects received with it, have been forwarded to Ceylon for comment.	85
24.11.1881	Advises that the memorial addressed to H.M. the	

Date	Subject Matter	Page
	Queen by ex-Sultan of Perak has been forwarded to Secretary of State for the Colonies.	129
29.11.1881	Relates to 6 copies of Ordinance No. 29 of 1881 (sent separately) concerning establishment of a Savings Bank at Victoria. Copy of Ordinance follows letter in book.	187
23.12.1881	Advises that Secretary of State has fixed the amount of pension for Dr. J.H. Brooks, late G.M.O. at £ 204. 11. 6. per annum, as from 1st. Jan.1881.	241
26.12.1881	Forwards copy of letter from Secretary to the Govt. of India to Colonial Secretary, Mauritius, relative to report by Mr. H. Cockburn Stewart and Mr. Horne on the agriculture resources of Seychelles and which have been furnished to several newspapers.	247
26.12.1881	The hope is expressed by His Excellency that the Seychelles Govt. will always be fully alive to importance of preserving the Coco-de-mer palm. Sends copy of letter from Royal Gardens, Kew, dated 1.11.1881.	295
26.12.1881	Acknowledges Mr. H. Cockburn Stewart's letter 216 of 29 th Oct, with Mr. A. Hodoul's report on co-conut disease. Forwards copy of remarks (on the report) by Director of Gardens and Forests. Documents will be sent to Sir Joseph Hooker, Kew.	317
27.12.1881	The Annual Report on Crown Lands for year 1880 asked for in July 1881 has not reached Mauritius. Several pages of "Precis showing the action taken here regarding Seychelles Crown Lands Report for 1880" follow.	334
		VOL. B/25.
18.01.1882	The making of a survey of Mahe, and the temporary appointment of a Custodian of Forests, approved.	13
18.01.1882	The accompanying reports from Mr. Thistleton Dyer and Mr. Mc Lachlan on coconut disease are to be printed.	16

Date	Subject Matter	Page
18.01.1882	Forwards Secretary of State's Letter, 18.11.1881, re : Primary Education in Seychelles, and asking certain information. Inspector of Schools to report.	30
19.01.1882	Mr. William Hoad to be Medical Officer for Praslin	37
6.02.1882	Encloses copy of despatch from Secretary of State for Colonies which states he cannot sanction ex-Sultan of Perak making a visit to Mauritius, as Ordinance 7 of 1877 only provides for detention in one of the Dependencies of Mauritius, and not in Mauritius itself. (See further on this in item 17.3.82).	138
10.02.1882	Forwards very long letter dated 11.10.81 from J.H. Ackroyd on subject of regulating Civil and Criminal procedure of District Court of Seychelles and another from Mr. E. de Lapeyre.	142
14.02.1882	Sends copy of letter from Colonial Secretary Straits Settlements relating to ex-Sultan of Perak wanting allowance increased.	331
20.02.1882	Enquires as to action taken by Seychelles Govt. re : establishing a Government School. Also requests report on (1) general state of aided Schools. (2) Establishment of a Govt. School. (3) Teaching of English in aided schools.	365
9.03.1882	Sends copy of letter from Secretary of State for the Colonies saying that H.M. The Queen is unable to grant petition of deposed Sultan of Perak that he be restored to his former position.	402
17.03.1882	Forwards copy despatch from Secretary of State for Colonies, 26.1.1882. He had decided, in view of further good conduct of ex-Sultan of Perak, to allow him to visit Mauritius and the Ordinance governing his detention will be amended to permit this.	429
18.03.1882	Encloses copy of a report by Conservator of Mortgages relating to what Crown Lands there may be on Silhouette Island, and mentioning difficulties as to old records being wanting.	442

Date	Subject Matter	Page
		VOL.B/26.
12.04.1882	Send copies of some more documents re : Silhouette and other islands, found in Archives Office. (Fills many pages).	1
17.04.1882	Forwards copy of despatch from Secretary of State for Colonies, enclosing extract from correspondence from Royal Botanical Gardens, Kew, re : cocoanut disease.	137
17.04.1882	Sends copy of report by Procureur General on subject of marriages between Liberated Africans.	147
17.04.1882	Sends copies of letters from Secretary of State for Colonies, and Royal Gardens, Kew, regarding preservation of coco-de-mer palm.	160
3.06.1882	Encloses copy of despatch from Secretary of State for Colonies 27.4.1882 which says ex-Sultan of Perak should be allowed to live permanently in Mauritius if he wants to.	275
13.06.1882	Sends copy of long letter from Director of Royal Gardens at Peradeniya Ceylon, on disease of cocoanut palms in Seychelles.	328
8.07.1882	Relates to subject of Crown Lands in Silhouette including copy of report from Govt. Surveyor.	372
8.07.1882	Sends letter from Director of Woods and Forests, Mauritius, to Colonial Secretary re : supplying coco-de-mer seeds to Botanical Gardens, Ceylon.	382
24.07.1882	Acting District Judge sends to Secretary, Board of Civil Commissioners, a copy of Regulation No.1 of 1882 which consolidates and amends Regulations affecting larcenies of cocoanuts etc...	406
8.07.1882	Advises arrival of ex-Sultan of Perak at Port Louis on 22 nd ultimo.	423

Date	Subject Matter	Page
		VOL. B/27.
10.10.1883	Dr. Chastellier appointed to go to Seychelles to investigate nature of disease described as "Varicella" by Chief Civil Commissioner.	15
3.11.1883	Comments upon suggestions made with a view to reducing expenditure on administration.	57
	Outbreak of Disease in Seychelles. A great number of printed pages of Resolution of General Board of Heath at Mauritius, correspondence from and to Mahe, Petitions from Committee of some residents of Mahe to Chief Civil Commissioner, evidence of various Medical Officers etc, etc. Disease was at first reported as Varicella (chicken-pox). Dr. E. Chastellier, sent from Mauritius to investigate, writing on 28 th Oct. 1883 from Victoria (where been 4 days), says "I have seen 40 or 50 of the cases prevailing here ; that it is simply proposterous to state that the disease is Varicella ; that I have not the slightest hesitation in saying that it is Variola vera (small pox)".	83
5.11.1883	Sends on letter from Secretary of State, one from Dr. J.H. Brooks, and one from Colonial Office to him. Dr. Brooks is asking that decision his pension cannot be paid in England because he is in Seychelles be altered.	201
17.04.1883	Report on Agriculture by the Warden of North and South Mahe and Silhouette, for 1882.	219
3.12.1883	Acknowledges Annual Report on condition of Liberated Africans.	261
29.07.1885	This book begins 29.7.1885. N° 27 finished 31.12.1883. Approves of lease for 5 years to the Victoria Cricket Club of a portion of land in centre of town.	23
31.07.1885	Forwards copy of Regulations for the mark system in force in prisons of Mauritius, and requests consideration of possibility of adoption at Seychelles.	89

Date	Subject Matter	Page
4.08.1885	Permission granted that ex-sultan of Perak may go to Mauritius by mail steamer (if not under Quarantine) instead of in a sailing vessel.	133
28.08.1885	Decision as to leasing islands "Des Neuf" "African Bank", "King Rose" and "L'Etoile" to L. Baillon for Rs. 150 p.a. is left to Board of Civil Commissioners.	152
25.09.1885	Re : above matter. Notes that Board has approved but Governor not inclined to lease without further information, which he hopes to obtain when visits Seychelles. To remain in abeyance.	244
23.10.1885	Governor approves of the land formerly held by Cricket Club being resumed by Govt. for a public square. Does not sanction it being named after him. Suggests it would be appropriate to call it after General Gordon.	300
19.12.1885	Advises that Secretary of State for Colonies requires Inspector of Schools, in future to make his report for each year, before the end of March in succeeding year.	435
21.12.1885	Forwards report from Supt. of Public Works on condition of Denis Island lighthouse erected 1883.	449
28.11.1827	Harrison to Collector of Customs, Mauritius. Forwards copy of Deposition by Captain and Officers of Schooner "Sydonie" lost on reefs of Alphonse Island ; also certificate of Registry.	4
17.12.1827	Harrison to Acting Chief Secretary, Mauritius. Detachment of H.M's 82nd Regt. arrived. Building which formerly served Gendarmes as Barracks to be used for troops. Under existing regulations, he cannot undertake that enough funds will be available to provide Lt. Latham with all he will need for paying his men.	4
24.04.1828	Harrison to H.E's Private Secretary, Mauritius. Long letter (based on information received from Master of British Brig "Courier") concerning	

Date	Subject Matter	Page
	French schooner which arrived at Daros and asked permission of proprietor to take water. Papers shown by Master indicated vessel on passage Bombay/Bourbon. No one visited her so no idea of what cargo she might have had. It is suggested enquiries to Bourbon would clear up whether any grounds for suspicion or not.	31
15.04.1828	Harrison to Mauritius. Sends particulars re : proprietors who have left within last four years, number of slaves taken, land held, etc...	35
12.06.1828	Harrison to Mauritius. Acknowledges letter re : appointment of G.A. Fressanges as Justice of the Peace, Seychelles.	41
26.06.1828	Harrison to Mauritius. If it should be H.E's wish to have lepers collected on some insulated (sic) spot, he (Harrison) suggests Ile Plate, not yet conceded by Govt.	46
2.07.1828	Harrison to Mauritius. Robert Craig, Gendarme, having had repeated warnings about unsatisfactory conduct, has had to be discharged. Last offence : drunk on duty and allowed prisoners to get drunk also.	50
26.08.1828	Harrison to the Private Secretary to H.E., Mauritius. A very lenghty letter about the suspected nefarious ideas believed to be in the mind of a Greek named Chiefalo who arrived at Seychelles 13.6.1828 in "Carnatic", Shipton, Master and Owner. It appears the Greek wants to purchase a vessel (with Shipton's funds) to be armed as a Greek privateer. Letter sent as warning in case "Carnatic" turns up there.	71
24.10.1828	Harrison to Barry, Chief Secretary to Govt. Acknowledges letters with copy of petition from de Quincy family asking permission to enclose a piece of land where mother buried. Sanctioned provided Harrison sees no material objection. He says the place is near flagstaff but enclosure	

Date	Subject Matter	Page
	could be made without detriment or inconvenience.	95
21.10.1828	Harrison to Private Secretary to H.E. the Governor. Relative to coco de mer preservation on Praslin and Curieuse. Recommends Govt. trying to regain latter for the purpose, also as place for sick crews in quarantine to recuperate, and for a leper Colony.	98
7.01.1829	Harrison to Chief Secretary. Mauritius. Reporting loss of whaler "Asp", Rennick, Master, on Madge Rocks, 17.12.1828. All hands got away in the boats.	100
1.02.1829	Harrison to Chief Secretary. Mauritius. Refers to a letter of 17.6.1828 in which it appears H.E. imagines he (Harrison) has duplicates of all grants of lands either definitive or provisional. As he cannot obtain from Archives all the information asked for, he sends copy of inventory left by Late Govt. Agent.	108
1.03.1829	Harrison to Chief Secretary, Mauritius. Relative to the mud boats being built at Seychelles for Mauritius.	114
6.06.1829	Harrison to Chief Secretary. Mauritius. Long letter following up earlier correspondence re : proposed leper settlement on Curieuse.	147
25.07.1829	Harrison to Master of Whaler "Timor". It is not proper for vessels to communicate with any inhabited islands of the Archipelago, if they can avoid it, until crews and ships papers have been seen at Mahe. When he puts to sea from present anchorage, he is to proceed to Mahe.	178
19.08.1829	Harrison to Chief Secretary. Mauritius. This letter refers to Curieuse as being now the property of Government.	185
29.08.1829	Harrison to Chief Secretary. Mauritius. Re : the building of huts and hospital at Curieuse.	189

Date	Subject Matter	Page
13.09.1829	Harrison to George Forbes (appears to be Forbes). A very long letter relating to his appointment as Overseer of the Leper Settlement. (Difficult to read because of deletions, additions, and writing on other pages showing through).	192
26.09.1829	Harrison to Chief Secretary. Mauritius. Forwards petition from some of the inhabitants requesting a fire-engine and a large bell be sent.	210
		VOL. B/30.
	To be found between letters of 26 th and 27 th March 1835. Copy of document "Avis aux Propriétaires d'Apprentis (ci-devant Esclaves)" (Translated into French from a copy in English forwarded from Mauritius).	21
16.04.1835	Harrison to Colonial Secretary. Mauritius. Jean Edouard Emile, second commandeur of Police, £ 1 a month, from 1st. January.	34
9.06.1835	Harrison to Dr. Robertson, Medical Supt, Curieuse, Instruction re : construction of a prison.	75
8.07.1835	Harrison to Secretary to the Asst. Commissioners of Compensation. Long letter relative to work of the Appraisers on the outlying islands.	103
20.06.1835	Robertson, Curieuse, to Harrison. Reports attack by a man with a small axe on a woman with whom he had previously lived. She had left because of his violent temper. Also reports prison will be built by two persons from Praslin for Thirty dollars.	116
20.07.1835	Harrison to Colonial Secretary, Mauritius. The O.C. Troops considers the two canteen are too near the Barracks. H. assembled a Committee. Decided that could not order removal without owners consent (at all times difficult to obtain) "I prevailed upon the person who had purchased the	

Date	Subject Matter	Page
	privilege in Nov. last, for two hundred and eleven dollars, to abandon it, on paying to Govt. one half of the amount, and this enabled me to make arrangements which will prove satisfactory, I trust, to all parties". The class of persons most troublesome are men from whalers.	122
8.09.1835	Harrison to Colonial Secretary, Mauritius. Dr. Cordonan intends going to Mauritius. H. recommends Dr. Stuart, in medical charge of detachment, as successor. For 60 dollars a month he will take over Dr. C's duties, and also take medical charge of all Govt. prisoners (medicines to be supplied by Govt), and of the Special Guards to be appointed.	138
5.08.1835	Table estimating Slave values for compensation.	150
24.09.1835	Harrison to Colonial Secretary, Mauritius. Refers to request (from Mauritius) that deserters from ships be shipped from Seychelles instead of sent to Mauritius. Points out lack of opportunities because of few ships calling.	157
3.11.1835	Harrison to Colonial Secretary, Mauritius. Reporting conditions at Curieuse on his visit.	190
26.10.1835	Harrison to Colonial Secretary, Mauritius. Re : apprentices having to be sent to Mauritius, for trial because of existing lax. Could it be modified to allow the Justice of the Peace to judge Apprentices for all offences not of a very atrocious nature ?	194
8.11.1835	Harrison to Colonial Secretary, Mauritius. Requests Leathern hose for fire-engine. Present one useless.	211
10.02.1836	Harrison to Colonial Secretary, Mauritius. Long letter about Arab Brig of War "Saky" which went aground at Providence.	253

Date	Subject Matter	Page
10.04.1836	Harrison to Colonial Secretary, Mauritius. Relates to arrangements made re : opening a Hospital for Apprentices.	310
10.04.1836	Harrison to Colonial Secretary, Mauritius. Dr. Stuart resigns as Health Officer. Dr. Pottiers takes over.	312
24.06.1836	Harrison to Colonial Secretary, Mauritius. Advices that Mr. Brewster, Surgeon of English whaler "Harpooner" proceeds to Mauritius in that vessel as a prisoner. Note. There is no explanations why. There is a reference to Mr. B. in letter 7.5.1836.	335
		VOL. B/31.
10.01.1849 5.49	Mylius to Colonial Secretary. Acknowledges letter enclosing copy of memorial to H.E. from persons interested in religious welfare of Seychelles, and asks M's. Comment, He points out that he wrote 29.5.1840 and 18.10.1848 about the need for clergymen.	2
27.01.1849 8.49	Mylius to Colonial Secretary. He would like to retire, for health reasons.	3
5.02.1849 11.49	Mylius to Colonial Secretary. Long letter regarding Judicial Branch of the Service, and appointment of Fressanges as Stipendiary Magistrate "although he is totally altogether ignorant of the English language".	4
26.02.1849 23.49	Mylius to Colonial Secretary. Relates to difficulties caused by conduct of Rev. F.G. de Lafontaine, and requests he be ordered to drop the title of Civic Chaplain for Seychelles "which he obtained under incorrect representations".	11
17.03.1849 33.49	Mylius to Colonial Secretary. Long letter concerning his proposal and plans for economic and efficient establishment, not being	

Date	Subject Matter	Page
	approved ; and as requested - submitting others	13
9.04.1849 39.49	Mylius to Colonial Secretary. On the matter of aliens wishing to buy property.	15
12.04.1849	Mylius to Colonial Secretary. Re : state of bridge needing survey report.	16
13.07.1849	Mylius to J.B. de St. Perne, Registrar Peace Court. Requesting Official copy of sentence pronounced by Judge Fressanges in the matter of the Crown v the Rev. F.G. de Lafontaine, A. d'Antoine and others for a violation of the Quarantine laws.	27
28.10.1849	Mylius to Rev. De Lafontaine. The matter of piano imported in a foreign vessel contrary to Customs laws has been submitted to the Home Govt. by Mauritius. Pending decision, H.E. says piano may be delivered provided Delafontaine enters into a penalty (here follows a word illegible) for £ 20 and gives security to abide the decision.	36
31.10.1849 132.49	Mylius to Colonial Secretary. Sending correspondence between him and Delafontaine.	37
5.11.1849 137.49	Mylius to Colonial Secretary. Forwards memorial from principal inhabitants on their needing "a minister of their church and per-suasion". M. recommends petition.	38
11.02.1850 12.50	Mylius to A. Loizeau. He has been authorized by H.E. to deliver piano imported by Rev. Delafontaine on condition of his (Loizeau) entering into a penalty with two sureties to abide by decision of H.M. Customs.	43
25.05.1850	Mylius to Colonial Secretary. 7 1/2 page letter dealing with Customs matters in connection with illegalities by German Brig "Africa" (including the above-mentioned piano).	48
9.03.1850 32.50.	Mylius to Colonial Secretary.	

Date	Subject Matter	Page
	Advises that his reply to the complaints and mis-representations of Rev. Delafontaine will be forwarded by H.M.S. "Orestes", and requests that his letter of 30.8. may not be acted upon until the general reply reaches Govt.	59
8.04.1850 51.50.	Mylius to Colonial Secretary. Lafontaine, in one of his returns for Govt. Blue Book, refers to himself as Civic Chaplain, about which Mylius protests - as before.	66
9.04.1850 52.50	Mylius to Colonial Secretary. Replies to letter about idea for building a Protestant Church. He refers to a letter he wrote 29.9.1847. Feels sure £ 600 would suffice. Pays a warm tribute to religious and educational work of Mr. and Mrs George Clarke.	66
13.04.1850 55.50.	Mylius to Colonial Secretary. Because of continual unsatisfactory health (reported in November 1848) he leaves for Mauritius in Brig "Deborah". Dependencies will be in charge of Wm Ford ; customs in that of Mr. Germain.	69
16.05.1850 67.50.	Ford to Insp. of Distilleries. To investigate report that sale of cane juice and colon openly and illegally goes on.	73
31.05.1850 72.50.	Ford to Colonial Secretary. Everything at present going satisfactorily except always in the Judicial Dept. (On which aspect he writes at some length).	75
7.06.1850 77.50.	Ford to Colonial Secretary. Reports on "usual extraordinary, outrageous and unjust proceeding ...... sometimes disregarding the law itself" of Judicial Judge (Fressanges).	77
26.06.1850 83.50.	Ford to Fressanges. Long letter remonstrating him for his behaviour in official capacity.	80
5.07.1850 90.50.	Ford to Colonial Secretary.	

Date	Subject Matter	Page
	Very long letter (4 pages) about Judicial affairs and Fressanges conduct of them.	83
27.07.1850 1.50.	R.W. Keate (new Civil Commissioner) to Colonial Secretary. Reporting that he arrived on morning of the 26 th, to take over duty.	91
5.08.1850 7.50.	Keate to Rev. F.G. Delafontaine. Requesting report as required by Governor-on state of religious (Protestant and Roman Catholic); also on education.	93
6.08.1850 8.50.	Keate to J.M. Collie. Requesting report as required by Governor- on state of education.	93
6.08.1850 9.50.	Keate to E. Lefevre. As above.	94
7.08.1850 10.50.	Keate to Demoiselles D'Offay. As above.	94
21.08.1850 14.50.	Keate to C. Lablache and 5 others asking them to form a committee to report on state of Govt. House, also the old Police and Prison buildings ; and those at present hired for Court House, Police, Prisons, and Govt. Office.	95
29.08.1850 18.50.	Keate to Colonial Secretary. Long letter on the state of religion, Reference made to recent visit of Bishop Colombo.	96
3.09.1850 21.50.	Keate to Colonial Secretary. Long letter relative to condition of various Govt. buildings, and forwarding reports and estimates. Reference made to a site suitable for erection of church.	104
5.09.1850 22.50.	Keate to Colonial Secretary. On the matter of importing labour to prevent lands falling out of cultivation. Mr. A. Loizeau wants to	

Date	Subject Matter	Page
	have 30 men and 30 women from Madagascar, Keate recommends, provided certain conditions are undertaken.	108
6.09.1850 24.50.	Keate to Colonial Secretary. Relative to Port Matters - arrival of vessels, boarding, pilotage etc...	109
6.09.1850 25.50.	Keate to A. Loizeau and 11 others. Requesting they form a Committee to report on monetary circulation ; amount of capital, how employed, sources from which drawn, etc...	110
16.09.1850 34.50.	Keate to A. Loizeau and others. Asking them to form a Committee to report on labour situation in general, and opinion on question of introducing Immigrant Labour. '	113
18.09.1850 37.50.	Keate to Colonial Secretary. Sends copy of petition, Sept, 1847, by Rev. Delafontaine, wanting to be naturalized.	114
23.09.1850	Keate to Colonial Secretary. Long letter - reporting as desired - on the administration of justice, and the conduct, character and capabilities of Juge de Paix.	115
15.10.1850 50.50.	Keate to Lablache - Police Officer. The Police force - excepting that part required for other purposes - to attend divine service on Sunday morning.	123
15.10.1850 51.50.	Keate to Delafontaine. Advises him about Police attending Church service.	123
29.10.1850 67.50.	Keate to Colonial Secretary. A very long report (29 paragraphs) on general conditions of Seychelles, based upon what he has seen and upon data gathered. It has not been possible (because of pressure of work) to visit all the more important islands (which he had hoped to do). The inhabitants still look upon the Abolition of Slavery as the sole cause of present distress ; this is an attempt to cast the whole blame upon others. Prior to that mea-	

Date	Subject Matter	Page
	sure a great diminution in exports had already taken place. He concludes his detailed account by saying "I am induced to believe that the future prospects of these long neglected islands are not unpromising, and that hopes may be fairly entertained that the state of decay into which they are fallen is not such as to dealy all exertions which may be made for their improvement".	128
22.11.1850 71.50.	Keate to Colonial Secretary. Difficulties arising in disputes between Masters of Merchant ships and their crews because no measures have been provided for executing the Merchant Seamen's Act.	141
29.11.1850 78.50.	Keate to Lablache and others. Requesting they choose a Committee to deal with the question of the neglected state of the streets.	144
2.12.1850 80.50.	Keate to Colonial Secretary. Regarding dispute between Mylius and Delafontaine over piano imported by latter (contrary to laws of Customs according to former). D. has entered into a Bond, and piano has been delivered to him.	144
30.11.1850 79.50.	Keate to Colonial Secretary. Relates to the circumstances in which the market was established.	145
5.01.1851 1.51. 2.51.	Keate to F. Savy, Jr. and A. D'Antoine. Letter of appointment as Pilot, to each.	149
10.01.1851 4.51.	Keate to A. Loizeau. Petition of 8.1.1849, to import labour from Madagascar granted subject to complying with conditions.	150
10.01.1851	Keate to Madame Hodoul. Concession "en jouissance" granted late husband in 1828 for "Ilot Hodoul", continued for her and daughter, subject to conditions.	150
4.03.1851 33.51.	Keate to Rev. Leon des Avanchers.	

Date	Subject Matter	Page
	Latter has arrived and wishes to reside as a priest of the Church of Rome. The matter does not rest with Keate but with Governor of Mauritius, ship in which petitioner is a passenger is bound there, and he must address request to Governor on arrival.	157
8.03.1851 36.51.	Keate to Rev. Leon des Avanchers. Replies to letter of 7th and says that as he has come not merely to reside as a stranger, but to perform certain official functions, permission, for temporary leave of residence cannot be granted without previously communicating with Governor. Keate will report matter by same ship.	159
13.03.1851 37.51.	Keate to several petitioners. Regrets cannot give permission to Rev. Avanchers to remain until return of first vessel despatched to Mauritius. As ship in which he is passenger is going there he can put in his request on arrival for a temporary or more prolonged residence in Islands. Every facility has been granted for him to perform the functions of his office during ship's stay here.	159
18.03.1851 44.51.	Keate to Rev. Leon des Avanchers. Acknowledges a letter he has sent to Police Officer on receiving passport. Keate points out he is not being expelled from an English Colony, as the Seychelles are a dependancy of Mauritius ; and he hopes he will consider it his duty to continue voyage to Mauritius without further discussion.	162
18.03.1851 46.51.	Keate to Rev. Leon des Avanchers. Replies to letter of this date written by des Avanchers on getting Keate's of 18th. Keate cannot grant his request re : proceeding in the "Trois Frères" (instead of "Josephine Loizeau" in which he arrived) because the "Trois Frères" is not due to leave until during May.	163
19.03.1851 47.51.	Keate to Colonial Secretary. Full report regarding Rev. Leon des Avanchers stay in Mahe, with copies of various letters. keate thinks any R.C. priest sent to Seychelles "should be a fully educated regular parish priest, a man of mature age, and not a monk or a propagandist",	

Date	Subject Matter	Page
	and that it is of the greatest importance he should be a British subject.	163
20.03.1851 51.51	Keate to Loizeau and others. Their petition to the Governor (re : providing a R.C. priest) is being forwarded.	165
24.04.1851 64.51.	Keate to Mathiot (?) Premises hired from his for church and school have been flooded because of delay in carrying out work begun many weeks back.	169
24.04/1851 67.51.	Keate to Colonial Secretary. Suggests - for reasons given - closing of Leper establishment on Curieuse. A general hospital at Port Victoria is much needed....................	170
23.05.1851 80.51.	Keate to Lablache, Police Officer. Stating proceedings for Queen's Birthday.	176
28.05.1851 86.51.	Keate to Colonial Secretary. A very long letter concerning general conditions, sent after longer experience. (Follows up one of 29 th October, 1850, n° 67/50).	179
5.07.1851 103.51.	Keate to Cazol and others. Refers to petition for R.C. priest. The Governor wants information how it is proposed to meet the expense and the extent to which inhabitants could provide the means.	188
12.08.1851 120.51.	Keate to Cazol and others. He has not had reply to letter of 5.7.1851.	194
20.08.1851 125.51.	Keate to Colonial Secretary. Further observations on the matter of a R.C. priest	195
25.08.1851 126.51.	Keate to Cazol and others. Asks whether anything in the nature of preaching took place yesterday in building hired as a temporary chapel. No objection if used simply for rea-	

Date	Subject Matter	Page
	ding prayers, but he cannot sanction extempore discourses or addresses.	196
26.08.1851 129.51.	Keate to Colonial Secretary. Refers to bad state of some Govt. buildings. Also to Leper establishment matters, and need for a general hospital in Victoria.	200
3.11.1851 162.51.	Keate to Cazol and others. Refers to letter of 25.08.1851. It has come to his notice that rule is not being adhered to. He requests that on all occasions when building is to be used, a notice should be sent to Police Office.	212
3.11.1851 163.51.	Keate to Revd. Delafontaine, Dr. Ford, and several others. Asking them to meet at his office at 12 on 5 th to form a committee in connection with starting an adult school.	213
8.11.1851 164.51.	Keate to Lablache, Police Officer. Referring to his report that Mr. Charles Jouanis has asked for a guard at the R.C. Chapel because of intruders behaving in an unseemly manner at doors and windows. Keate cannot spare a man to be there always, but a guard on his occasional visits will warn off trouble makers.	213
8.11.1851 166.51.	Keate to C. Jouanis, F. Savy, and others. More on the subject of use of building as R.C. Chapel.	214
17.11.1851 169.51.	Keate to Mathiot (?) Says that it was M's intention many months ago to lay iron pipes on premises hired for church and school. Rainy season approaching ; narrow and shallow channel is closed up. Urgent that he fulfils his intentions.	215
19.11.1851 171.51.	Keate to Mathiot. Replies to M's letter saying lease expired 10 th. Asks him to call re : fresh arrangements K. proposes to make.	216

Date	Subject Matter	Page
20.11.1851 172.51.	Keate to Colonial Secretary. Requests that the £ 4 a month paid to Rev. Delafontaine for hire of premises be paid to K. in future. Lease has expired, and D. wishes new arrangements. K. is hiring in own name.	216
23.02.1852	Keate to President of Census Commission. Forwards Census returns, and comments upon some relative matters.	225
3.03.1852 23.52	Keate to Colonial Secretary. Forwards petition on subject of steam communication between Seychelles and Mauritius.	227
30.03.1852 36.52.	Long letter on various aspects and problems of administration.	320
22.05.1852 68.52.	Keate to Police Officer. Arrangements for observing Queen's Birthday.	242
16.06.1852 94.52.	Keate to Colonial Secretary. A long letter relative to various aspects of the question of possibility of estimating values of houses and land.	250
1.07.1852 105.52.	Keate to Colonial Secretary. A long letter on several matters ; Establishment of local boards ; House and Land Tax ; Schools ; Roads.	257
12.07.1852 111.52.	Keate to Colonial Secretary. Reports arrival of Mr. Charles M. Campbell, to be District Magistrate.	263
13.07.1852 112.52.	Keate to Colonial Secretary. Suggested ideas for Poor Relief Finance.	263
16.07.1852 113.52.	Keate to Colonial Secretary. Relative to Police affairs.	266

Date	Subject Matter	Page
19.07.1852 119.52.	Keate to Rev. Delafontaine, Civil Chaplain. The Governor has approved of his being naturalized.	269
27.07.1852 128.52.	Keate to Messrs. Albert, d'Argent, and others. Requesting a Committee be formed to make a report on cotton growing.	271
19.08.1852 136.52.	Keate to Colonial Secretary. Forwards report, supplied by a Committee, on Cotton.	275
20.09.1852 151.52.	Keate to Colonial Secretary. On the matter of proposed scheme to build a Church.	278
22.09.1852 153.52	Keate to Colonial Secretary. Drunkenness and disorderly conduct due to wide manufacture of fermented drinks from sugarcane, pineapples, cocoanuts. Tax of not less than £ 2 on every mill or machine so used, suggested.	280
24.09.1852 155.52.	Keate to Colonial Secretary. Rev. Delafontaine requests a year's leave because of his heath. K. hopes substitute will be sent ; highly desirable to have one.	281
6.10.1852 169.52.	Keate to Colonial Secretary. Relative to various Govt. buildings, and work required.	285
4.11.1852 182.52.	Keate to A. Germain and other. Asks for report of value of piece of Govt. land between the Chantier and the property of Mr. Clement.	290
30.11.1852 194.52.	Keate to Rev. Delafontaine. Governor hopes that if D's health allows, he will delay leaving until successor available - which will be the case if expected increase to the Clerical establishment of Mauritius be sanctioned.	294
4.12.1852 198.52.	Keate to Colonial Secretary.	

Date	Subject Matter	Page
	Forwards letter from Delafontaine who is willing to wait. K. suggests that when substitute available, D. be given an appointment in Mauritius.	298
14.12.1852 204.52.	Mr. Ricketts, Keate's successor (pro. tem.) to Colonial Secretary.	
	He arrived on 4th inst. Letter indicates he is only here temporarily. K. leaves in schooner "Reliance", bound Mauritius, leaving probably to-morrow.	301
2.02.1853 1.53.	Acting Civil Commissioner to Colonial Sec.	
	Forwards duplicate Register of Marriages for 1852 ; Statement of Baptisms, and of number of children attending Schools.	302
3.02.1853 4.53.	Acting Civil Commissioner to Colonial Sec.	
	Encloses observations from Mr. Joineau on draft of ordinance for relief of poor, taxes now in force, and way proposed to pay for R.C. clergyman.	303
5.04.1853	Acting Civil Commissioner to Col. Sec.	
	Reporting he has had to suspend Mr. Campbell from his duties as Asst. Magistrate, and enclosing documents.	316
29.03.1853	The A.C.C. to Campbell.	
	Advising him he must suspend him.	319
30.03.1853	A.C.C. to Campbell.	
	No objection to his going to Mauritius when it suits him but he should, with as little delay as possible turn over all papers documents, monies, etc.. to Mr. A. St.Jorre, his successor.	320
	There are only a few letters during April, none in May, and only one in June.	
7.07.1853 1.53.	G.T. Wade, new Civil Commissioner, to Col. Sec.	
	Reports his arrival to take over from the Acting Civil Commissioner, Mr. Ricketts.	328
8.07.1853 7.53.	Wade to Colonial Secretary.	

Date	Subject Matter	Page
	Forwards a memorial from Mr. Loizeau (in prison for statements made in public last December).	330
19.07.1853 13.53.	Wade to Delafontaine. He may give religious books for use of prisoners and others connected with the Police.	332
	The August and September letters in some cases can only be read in part, and in others are practically entirely illegible - the ink having run so much.	
8.10.1853 74.53.	Wade to Colonial Secretary. Relative to Police affairs.	355
20.10.1853 83.53.	Wade to Colonial Secretary. Forwards letter from Mr. Petit, contractor for repairs at Govt. House.	360
12.12.1853 105.53.	Wade to Telfair, District Magistrate. To call a meeting of the Prison Committee, and inform them that Government has granted £ 510 for putting the Police premises in repair.	366
24.12.1853 111.53.	Wade to Colonial Secretary. Reports that on 26th Ult. a boat was upset while attempting to land at La Digue and 12 persons were drowned, including a Police Guard.	368
28.12.1853 118.53.	Wade to Telfair, District Magistrate, Messrs. Cayol, Jouanis and Savy, have been asked to report upon condition of furniture of the District Court.	370
19.01.1854 14.54.	Wade to Colonial Secretary. Sending offers received for sale of Felicite and Isle aux Recife.	375
27.01.1854 18.54.	Wade to Prison Committee. On the subject of more and better use being made of prisoners' labour.	377
28.03.1854 28.54	Wade to Colonial Secretary.	

Date	Subject Matter	Page
	Dr. Ford has opened a Dispensary in the building formerly used as Civil Commissioner's Office.	380
6.04.1854 45.54.	Wade to Colonial Secretary. Observations upon various matters about which he was asked to report. Very difficult to follow, ink having run.	387
12.04.1854 53.54.	Wade to Colonial Secretary. Sending petition from Directors of Seychelles (next word not clear) Company. W. says "It is the first time such an institution ever existed in this Archipelago", and hopes H.E. will assist the Co., to the utmost. The word might be "Union". There follow a good many pages of which it is very difficult to make out much with accuracy, Ink has run, and writing on other pages shows through.	394 394
16.06.1854 92.54.	Wade to Colonial Secretary. A notorious character called "Etienne" who deserted from a ship some years ago and has ever since been living a lawless life, has, after being nearly murdered by one of his comrade some months ago, given himself up to the Police, in almost a dying state from the wounds he has received. He has recevered, and been tried by the District Magistrate. Case referred to Assize Court at Port Louis. He, a constable, and 5 witnesses going in "Sir George Anderson". Passage payable to Master on arrival - £ 3 each. Here follow several pages little of which can be read with any accuracy.	407
Undated. Follows one of. 14.10.1854 9.	W. Ford, Acting C.C., to T. Macpherson, Insp. of Police. Concerning necessary reduction of the Force.	424
18.10.1854	Ford, Acting C.C., to several residents (Named). There is no intention at present time to institute a House and Land Tax.	426
28.10.1854	Ford, Acting C.C., to Messrs. Payet, Dubignon and l'Esperance. Petition received from Father Jeremie for building	

Date	Subject Matter	Page
	of a R.C. Chapel at Anse Volbert at Praslin, will be sent to Mauritius.	429
30.10.1854 27.	Ford, Acting C.C. to Colonial Secretary. Forwards petition mentioned above. Says how much it is to be deplored that a respectable R.C. clergyman, and a British subject, under the orders of the R.C. Bishop of Port Louis, had not been sent here, instead of the foreign fanatical Capuchin Friars ; sent out from Italy by the Pope of Rome, and who are in no way responsible to the Episcopal Sec. in Mauritius.	429
1.11.1854 35.	Ford, Acting C.C. to Colonial Secretary. Police Force has been reduced, in accordance with instructions.	431
1.12.1854 46.	Ford, Acting C.C. to Colonial Secretary. On extremely delapidated state of Prison, Police and Court House. Buildings leak in streams when wet. Magistrate says will have to sit under umbrella ; clerk in difficulties to keep documents dry ; prisoners asking to be set at liberty until suitable place to confine them.	435
10.12.1854 48.	Ford Acting C.C. to Colonial Secretary. Reports Capt. Wade, C.C. as having this day returned from Mauritius, and resumed duty.	436
13.12.1854 130.	Wade, C.C. to Colonial Secretary. Reports arrived on 10th and resumed duty.	437
18.12.1854 133.	Wade to Colonial Secretary. Another Capuchin friar arrived sent expressly from Rome. The fourth in twelve months.	438
18.12.1854 134.	Wade to Colonial Secretary. Advises Mr. Telfair, Resident Magistrate, wishes to leave Seychelles. His petition forwarded.	438
21.12.1854 135	Wade to Colonial Secretary. Suggests W. Ford (Med. Off.), J. Macpherson (Insp. of Police), and J. Collie, to compose Local	

Date	Subject Matter	Page
	Board of Health.	
	Here follow many pages some of which are only readable in part, and others illegible (as before).	438
23.07.1855 89.55.	Wade to Colonial Secretary. French schooner "Aubis" put in for repairs having met with heavy weather.	468
24.07.1855 90.55.	Wade to Colonial Secretary. Acknowledges letter 9.6.1855 enclosing copy of one from Secretary of State approving proposed changes in Medical establishment, and discontinuing Leper Station on Curieuse.	469
30.07.1855 94.55.	Wade to Telfair, District Magistrate. Mr. Griffiths has arrived to relieve him.	470
6.08.1855 105.55.	Wade to Petitioners at L'Anse aux Pins. Petition to enlarge R.C. Chapel, and to call a Public meeting to form a "Conseil de Fabrique", approved by Governor.	475
23.08.1855 110.55.	Wade to Ford, Govt. M.O. He may go to Mauritius to procure a Medical Practitioner to succeed him. If unsuccessful, to be back in two months.	476
24.08.1855 113.55.	Wade to Colonial Secretary. The Rev. Mr. (? Dr.) Fallet arrived 27th July, and assumed duty as Colonial Chaplain on 1st August.	477
11.09.1855 119.55.	Wade to Colonial Secretary. Acknowledges letter of 31st July with copies of two despatches., received from Secretary of State relative to residence of alien R.C. priests. H. E's instructions will be attended to. Wade refers to having reported return of Rev. Leon des Avanchers and of having spoken about his bad conduct, to Bishop of St. Denis, when here on way to Europe, which resulted in an order from Rome for his recall, and he has accordingly taken his departure. The two friars sent by Bishop Collier give no trouble.	479

Date	Subject Matter	Page
2.10.1855 131.55.	Wade to Rev. Dr. Fallet. Relates to the Parochial Schools which he is asked to superintend.	464
8.10.1855 133.55.	Wade to Colonial Secretary. Refers to various Ordinances and comments thereon.	465
18.10.1855 145.55.	Wade to Colonial Secretary. Sends report made by Police Inspector Macpherson about parties in illegal occupation of Government Lands in Praslin.	472
7.11.1855 151.55.	Wade to Colonial Secretary. On the subject of repairs to Police Building, and sending copy of contract. (Part of letter rather difficult to make out).	474
8.11.1855 155.55.	Wade to Colonial Secretary. Forwards letter from Père Jeremie relative to introducing Sisters of Charity to establish a Hospital.	478
28.12.1855 171.55.	Wade to Colonial Secretary. Forwards petition from Senior R.C. Priest to Secretary of State soliciting that a salary be granted to him from Colonial Treasury. Wade reports that R.C. population have contributed largely towards their Church in acquiring possession of property on which it stands, have considerably enlarged it, and have built a comfortable dwelling for their clergymen.	484
8.03.1871	Franklyn, Civil Commissioner, to Colonial Secretary. He has been obliged to appoint a matron, urgently required because of crowded state of female prison, at £ 2 a month.	VOL. B/32. 7
9.03.1871	Franklyn, to Colonial Secretary. He has had a letter dated 19.1.1871 from Dr. Kirk, acting Political Agent and H.M. Consul at Zanzibar saying that George Gardener, British subject, long	

Date	Subject Matter	Page
	domiciled at Seychelles was murdered on 18th December 1870 by the Chief Mate of an Arab vessel in which he was 2nd Mate. Accused and chief witness been sent to Marseilles that Authorities may decide whether case can be tried in France or sent to Reunion. Franklyn has received papers and effets of deceased, and advised family living on Praslin.	13
17.03.1871	Fanklyn to President of Prison Committee. Supt. of Works instructed to enlarge the goal.	24
20.03.1871	Franklyn to Underwood. Appoints him Enumerator of section No. 1 of Mahe re : the census. Similar letters to others follow.	25
27.03.1871	Franklyn to Colonial Secretary. Prison labour is used on roads.	30
4.04.1871	Fanklyn to Colonial Secretary. Reporting proceedings of Prison Committee.	45
6.04.1871	Franklyn to Colonial Secretary. The Inspector General, Colonel O'Brien, landed on his way to England, examined Police Station, said in his opinion it required rebuilding, and he would recommend it to Govt. of Mauritius.	51
6.04.1871	Franklyn to Colonial Secretary. On subject of Quay dues, landing of cargoes, and the construction of new pier now going on.	60
13.04.1871	Franklyn to Colonial Secretary. A passage for a lunatic to go to Mauritius has at last been obtained.	69
27.04.1871	Franklyn to Colonial Secretary. On the matter of Crown Lands.	80
3.05.1871	Franklyn to Colonial Secretary. Reference to Quarantine regulations, and the Guardian of Long Island.	85

Date	Subject Matter	Page
5.05.1871	Franklyn to Census Commissioner, Mauritius. Forwards the tabulated statement.	91
5.05.1871	Franklyn to M. Duperrel. His tender to rent Isle Recifes from 14 th inst. to 14th May 1872 at £ 40 per annum, accepted.	93
15.05.1871	Franklyn to Colonial Secretary. Pays tribute to the Brothers in charge of college "Notre Dame du Sacré Coeur", and the Sisters managing orphanage and school.	96
26.05.1871	Franklyn to Surveyor General. Sends sketch of doors and windows to be made at Mauritius for new Customs House.	110
3.07.1871	Franklyn to Colonial Secretary. Reporting circumstances of suspension of Mr. E. Lefevre, Clerk of Customs and Internal Revenue Dept.	120
10.07.1871	Franklyn to Rev. Père Ignace. Govt. has granted £ 20. 18st to College of Notre Dame du Sacré Coeur, and same sum to school of the Sisters, provided equivalent amounts have been contributed from private sources.	121
17.07.1871	Franklyn to Sir Arthur Gordon, Governor, Mauritius. Relative to draft Ordinance to amend laws concerning Quarantine.	139
30.09.1871	Franklyn to E. Domenjod. The latter to be Consular Agent for France.	184
18.10.1871	Franklyn to Colonial Secretary. Acknowledges receipt of Mr. Descroizille's letter and box of cocoons.	204
18.10.1871.	Franklyn to Colonial Secretary. H.M.S. "Columbine" arrived 5 th with 206 libera-	

Date	Subject Matter	Page
	ted African Slaves, landed on Long Island next day 135 have already been alloted to Proprietors and other respectable persons.	207
20.10.1871	Franklyn to Colonial Secretary. Forwards minutes of Prison Committee.	212
	VOL. B/33.	
17.11.1871	Franklyn to Colonial Secretary. 2.000 fresh cocoanuts and 20 cocos de mer shipped to Mauritius for planting.	9
4.12.1871	Franklyn to V. Alvarez, Mahe. Permission to put up a circus roofed with leaves on a piece of ground in town, in which lights would be kept "turning" (burning, surely) at night, cannot be granted.	19
15.12.1871	Franklyn to Colonial Secretary. Scheme to improve the system of collecting road tax.	25
15.12.1871	Franklyn to Colonial Secretary. Owing to number of prisoners in goal it is still necessary to lodge some of them in the Hospital at night.	28
12.01.1872	Franklyn to Colonial Secretary. Robberies much more frequent, and of greater audacity. Sentry placed at Govt. House (because of safe containing Public Funds being there).	41
23.01.1872	Franklyn to Colonial Secretary. The German steamer "Africa", chartered by Capt. Tucker, R.N., of HMS. "Columbine" arrived on 4th bringing 158 liberated Africans, captured by that vessel.	54
23.01.1872	Franklyn to Colonial Secretary. Recommending the great desirability that Mahe be made a free Warehousing port, like Mauritius.	55

Date	Subject Matter	Page
9.02.1872	Franklyn to Colonial Secretary. Because of increasing trade and the number of vessels using port, Harbour Regulations have become an urgent necessity. He suggests that Proclamation of 24th March 1860 be extended to Mahe, in an altered form, and states the changes appropriate.	74
9.02.1872	Franklyn to Colonial Secretary. Concerning new road being made from "Les Mamelles" across the island to "Barbaron".	
29.02.1872	Franklyn to J.D. Revera, Victoria. Grants a license, gratuitous for first year, to open a Pharmacy.	99
8.03.1872	Franklyn to Colonial Secretary. Requests another mule, and harness, for public works.	110
9.03.1872	Franklyn to Colonial Secretary. Forwarding plan for additions to the Hospital and requests sanction of commencement.	124
9.03.1872	Franklyn to Colonial Secretary. Enclosing estimates for alterations to Prison.	125
		VOL. B/34.
23.07.1873 214.	Franklyn to F. Cheyron. Recognising him as Consular Agent for France.	4
28.07.1873 217.	Franklyn to Colonial Secretary. Comments upon matters raised by Dr. Brooks in the document from him which is enclosed.	7
30.07.1873 218.	Franklyn to J.D. Revera. Recognising him as Consul for Italy.	10
11.08.1873 234.	Franklyn to the Governor. Concerning two persons committeed by District	

Date	Subject Matter	Page
	Judge to stand trial for infanticide ; and the difficulties and expense of these cases which have to go to Mauritius.	27
2.09.1873 248.	Franklyn to Dr. Brooks. Protesting about his delays in answering letters.	47
19.09.1873 260.	Franklyn to Admiral Cumming, C.B. Concerns scheme, on the basis of which sick men from H.M. Ships could be admitted to Hospital.	57
3.10.1873 278.	Franklyn to Govt. Med. Officer (Dr. Brooks). As he has not paid £ 29.6. Quay Dues on Coal, Directions given to deduct from his salary.	71
15.10.1873 285.	Franklyn to J.J. Prentis Esq., Consul for the United States at Seychelles. Recognising Mr. Richard Myles Brown as acting American Consul.	78
13.11.1873 313.	Franklyn to G.M.O., Dr. Brooks. Regarding scheme proposed for treatment of sick from H.M. Ships.	105
14.04.1873 315.	Franklyn to H.C.Langlois. Regarding idea of proposed turtle pond.	108
19.11.1873 319.	Franklyn to Rev. Père The Prefet Apostolique. Notes he has applied for aid from Govt. The Inspector of Schools will be visiting shortly.	112
1.12.1873 331.	Franklyn to G.M.O., Dr. Brooks. The lease of Curieuse granted to Dr. Mc. Gregor, who will assume charge, as Supt. of the Leper Asylum on 1st. Jan. 1874.	124
9.12.1873 338.	Franklyn to Colonial Secretary. The Lithographic Press and printing materials have been landed.	131
8.01.1874 378.18.	Franklyn to the Governor.	

Date	Subject Matter	Page
	Applies, as advised by his medical attendant, for 3 months leave to go to Bourbon.	172
30.01.1874 45.	Memo by Franklyn. The Sergeant Major of Police is directed that diligent enquiry made by Police as to the spread of measles, and report to G.M.O.	201
4.02.1874 51.	Franklyn to Colonial Secretary. Reports several cases of measles having appeared.	206
6.02.1874 58.	Franklyn to Colonial Secretary. Reports wreck of British steamer "Doh" on Alphonse Island. Crew brought Mahe by French Naval Ship.	213
27.02.1874 81.	Franklyn to Governor. A lengthy report on many diverse matters.	236
18.03.1873 91.	Franklyn to Governor. He has had letter from Admiral Cumming accepting terms proposed for medical treatment of R.N. Personnel. Asks for direction as to accommodation for Commissioned Officers. Suitable houses being scarce, he has secured one lately occupied by U.S. Consul on 3 months lease, with option of extension.	254
18.03.1873 92.	Franklyn to Governor. Follows up letter of 8.01.1874, and requests an extension of leave, not exceeding 3 months on half pay. Has to go to England to have an operation.	255
4.04.1874 107.	Havelock, Acting C.C.C. to Colonial Secretary. Reporting death, at Govt. House of W.H. Franklyn, C.C.C. on 3rd inst., after a prolonged illness.	266
16.04.1874 116.	Havelock to Inspector of Liberated Africans. He is to begin visiting the estates and localities, and report under the several heads mentioned.	273
21.04.1874 124.	Havelock to Colonial Secretary. Returns correspondence about lease of Ilet Hodoul to Dr. Brooks and requests lease be drawn up.	280

Date	Subject Matter	Page
-27.04.1874 146.	Havelock to the Governor. Acknowledges letter 2nd April enclosing copy of Royal Order in Council amending and enlarging Order of 22nd April 1872, and H.E's Proclamation fixing 1st. May as date for provisions of new order to come into force.	297
29.04.1874 156.	Havelock to the Governor. Concerning proposed scheme to buy, for £ 200, a piece of land about 4 acres and a quarter, for a new Cemetery.	303
1.05.1874 165.	Havelock to the Governor. Relates to accommodation of sick Commissioned Naval Officers.	310
6.05.1874 176.	Havelock to Dr. Brooks. On the subject of sick R.N. personnel.	318
29.05.1874 188.	Havelock to Governor. Acknowledges letter 18.04.1874 authorizing Board of Civil Commissioners to vote L 100 **for** passages to England of widow and daughter of late Chief Civil Commissioner. Because a 1st. class passage to Marseilles costs £ 75, Board voted L 150 subject to approval.	326
2.06.1874 192.	Havelock to The Earl of Carnarvon. Sending, for Board of Trade, certified copies of depositions of Master, Officers and portion of crew of ship "Merrie Monarch", wrecked 17th April on one of the Cosmoledo Islands. Copies being sent Governor, Mauritius.	329
6.06.1874 205.	Havelock to Colonial Secretary. Schooner "Vistula" arrived 18th May, bringing the ship's company of British vessel "Merrie Monarch" wrecked Cosmoledo Islands on passage Calcutta to New York with jute. An account of the circumstances is given.	337
12.06.1874 210.	Havelock to Dr. Brooks. Acknowledges letter of 11th that two cases of the contagious disease, varicella, had come to his	

Date	Subject Matter	Page
	notice.	341
		VOL. B/35.
1.04.1876 96.	C.S. Salmon, Chief Commissioner, to Colonial Secretary. Long letter on how the Public Cash Accounts are kept.	8
25.04.1876 112.	Salmon to The Governor. Quarantine matters (arising because of some cases of chicken-pox).	22
29.04.1876 132.	Salmon to Colonial Secretary. About Medical Affairs, and Dr. Brooks.	39
29.04.1876 139.	Salmon to The Governor. Forwards letter from Mr. Bonnetard, Agent for Messrs. Pallio (? Pallic) of Seychelles, Paris and London. Wishes to hire Indian labour at Mauritius, as local men do not remain long at factory work. Note. There is no clue as to what the factory does.	47
19.05.1876 153.	Salmon to Colonial Secretary. Gives particulars about the Glorioso group of Islands.	63
23.05/1876 157.	Salmon to The Governor. Long report on tables forwarded with report of Acting Inspector of Africans on 29.2.76.	66
4.06.1876 166.	Salmon to The Governor. Sending copy of his report on the four schools whose managers have asked for grants. Copy of report follows the page of letter, (many pages).	80
22.06.1876 178.	Salmon to Colonial Secretary. Suggested ideas for proposed coal depot.	105
23.06.1876 186.	Salmon to The Governor. Sends some letters from Dr. Brooks. Comments upon	

Date	Subject Matter	Page
	various matters connected with vaccination.	110
23.06.1876 187.	Salmon to The Governor. Gives reasons for desirability of amendment to law on vaccination.	114
25.07.1876 201.	Salmon to Crown Agents. Ordering 12 Snider rifles with bayonets, 500 rounds ammunition, 12 pouches and belts.	125
5.08.1876 212.	Salmon to Colonial Secretary. Sends, in duplicate, Deed, of Lease of Glorioso Islands, (Mellish & Co.,) for approval.	135
19.08.1876 222.	Salmon to Colonial Secretary. On the matter of having a printing press.	141
8.09.1876 227.	Salmon to Colonial Secretary. Relative to taking a census of Mahe, Praslin, La Digue, Silhouette Islands.	146
9.09.1876 235.	Salmon to Governor. Sending proceedings of Local Rate Committee.	153
9.09.1876 237.	Salmon to the Governor. Dealing with complaints made by Dr. Brooks.	157
11.09.1876 238.	Salmon to Colonial Secretary. Comments upon amount of litigation which goes on.	160
14.09.1876 250.	Salmon to The Governor. More about Dr. Brooks.	169
16.09.1876 276.	Salmon to The Governor. Reports on various aspects of Administration, and refers to attitude of Dr. Brooks.	193
14.10.1876 287.	Salmon to Colonial Secretary.	

Date	Subject Matter	Page
	On matters connected with vaccination arrangements (existing, and suggested).	202
18.10.1876 295.	Salmon to The Governor. 33 liberated Africans whose wages were retained during their minority have been traced.	210
18.10.1876 297.	Salmon to The Governor. Someone to serve the Praslin district as a medical man and a justice of the Peace is wanted.	212
18.10.1876 299.	Salmon to Colonial Secretary. The Crown Agents have requested a report on the Seychelles for the Commissioners of the Philadelphia Exhibition. One will be sent to arrive London about 10 th Jan. A copy will go to the Governor.	213
25.10.1876 303.	Salmon to The Governor. A report on Felicité Island.	216
25.10.1876 306.	Salmon to Colonial Secretary. The wharf for de Fressinet & Co., commenced. Site is to the end of the large jetty.	221
30.10.1876 307.	Salmon to Governor. Long letter on Customs matters.	222
6.11.1876 313.	Salmon to Colonial Secretary. The system of keeping all public accounts by rupees and cents will be in operation on 1st. Jan. 1877.	234
8.11.1876 315.	Salmon to Colonial Secretary. On the duties and fees of Dr. Brooks.	235
11.11.1876 320.	Salmon to Governor. Sending for approval, a regulation for protection of cocoa-de-mer trees.	239
12.11.1876 323.	Salmon to Governor. Says he has received from Dr. Brooks a letter of	

Date	Subject Matter	Page
	26 pages for transmission to the Governor. There may not be time before next mail (soon) to go into it, and provide H.E. with information.	243
23.11.1876 324.	Salmon to Governor. Forwards, with comments, Dr. Brooks letter.	244
27.11.1876 326.	Salmon to Colonial Secretary. Expenditure required for establishment connected with printing press will be £ 100 a year. May cost more later, but not for sometime.	250
5.01.1877 9.	Salmon to Colonial Secretary. Sends lease in duplicate of lands for the Industrial School of African race.	269
6.01.1877 15.	Salmon to Governor. Forwards petition of certain inhabitants. He makes some pertinent comments upon its statements and some of those who signed.	272
6.01.1877 24.	Salmon to Governor. Sends Official return of Religious sects at the three principal islands - Mahe, Praslin, La Digue.	280
1.02.1877 40.	Salmon to Governor. Relates to various aspects of the law concerning employment of minors and liberated Africans.	295
3.02.1877 53.	Salmon to Governor. Forwards with comments letter from Dr. Brooks to Secretary of State on the matters of grievances to which he considers he has been subjected through the action of the Local Authority.	306
3.03.1877 65.	Salmon to Colonial Secretary. Returns two copies of lease of Glorioso Islands to Mellish & Co., for two years ; £ 20 for 1st. year and £ 30 for 2nd year.	316
3.03.1877 69.	Salmon to Governor. Long letter (about 18 pages) making remarks on	

Date	Subject Matter	Page
	Petition H.E. his forwarded. These pages are stained, and parts in a very delapidated and fragile state. Note. All the pages following the above ones are in same condition, and also stuck together.	318
16.05.1877	Salmon to Dr. Brooks. Encloses a letter having reference to a proposed modification of Vaccination Laws.	18
Sept. 1877 Original date 30th Aug, is deleted and "September" (only) substituted.	Salmon to G. Barrow. Regarding special accounts to be kept of disbursements in connection with State prisoners.	29
1.09.1877	Salmon to Dr. Brooks. Sending copy of letter 2.8.1877 from Colonial Secretary to Salmon conveying to him final orders of the Governor and the Secretary of State about Dr. Brooks fees.	31
25.10.1877	Salmon to Civil Chaplain. The Board of Civil Commissioners voted Rs. 520.41 for the Protestant Schools. This, with Rs. 1070.84 already received, makes Rs. 1591.25, which the examiners recommended.	40
25.10.1877	Salmon to Rev. Père Ignace. The Board of Civil Commissioners voted Rs. 1694.07 for the Roman Catholic Schools. This, with Rs.3429.16 already received, makes Rs. 5123.25, which the examiners recommended.	41
26.11.1877	Salmon to Dr. Brooks. Information regarding vaccination stations and days of attendance.	53
24.12.1877	Salmon to President, Prison Committee. The goaler is sending out men to work for the Public Works Dept. who are not physically fit for it.	59
16.01.1878	Salmon to Governor. Concerning Long Island and Mr. Gebert's wish to	

Date	Subject Matter	Page
	lease it (assuming that the Quarantine Station is to be removed).	340
19.01.1878	Salmon to Governor. Forwards report from Inspector of Africans on the Church Missionary Establishment for Africans "Venns Town", and makes comments on need to teach trades.	360
22.01.1878	Salmon to Major Grattan, Secretary to Governor. Regarding construction of coal wharf for Fraissinet & Co.	357
23.01.1878	Salmon to Major Grattan. Relative to Dr. Brooks taking advantage of his position as pratique officer, to trade.	356
29.01.1878	Salmon to President, Prison Committee. Concerning prisoners on P.W.D. labour.	70
4.02.1878	Salmon to Dr. Griffiths. Vaccination matters.	77
4.02.1878	Salmon to Dr. Brooks. Vaccination matters.	78
17.02.1878	Salmon to Governor. Forwards letter from Mr. de Lapeyre asking that he may be transferred to Natal.	332
5.03.1878	Salmon to Jules Cauvin. On his duties as surveyor.	88
17.06.1878	Salmon to President, Prison Committee. Several matters concerning building and prisoners.	105
3.08.1878	Salmon to H. Leipsic, Chief of Police. French naval vessel "Cursieur" (?) 85 men, from Java, has typhoid fever. A strict quarantine.	113

Date	Subject Matter	Page
12.09.1878	Salmon to Dr. Brooks. Concerns some accounts received from collector of Dues and Taxes to be forwarded to Naval Commander in Chief for collection.	121
9.10.1878	Salmon to Dr. Brooks. Information on arrangements for vaccination.	131
21.10.1878	Salmon to Inspector of Africans. Mentions the principle that all minors baptised and brought up as Roman Catholics should, during their minority, not be realloted into other denominations, and similarly with minors brought up as Protestants.	147
30.10.1878	Salmon to Dr. Brooks. Concerns vaccination returns asked for, and which have been refused.	151
6.12.1878	Salmon to Dr. Brooks. Certain communications have been received from Mauritius about vaccination. The Board of C.C. will consider them at end of year or beginning of next.	172
14.12.1878	Salmon to ex-Sultan of Perak. His petition to H.M. the Queen, with letter to Secretary of State for Foreign affairs, and several enclosures, were forwarded to the Colonial Office, London. The duplicates will be sent to Mauritius. Exact copies of all these papers should be supplied for record in Mahe.	177
16.12.1878	Salmon to Dr. Brooks. He still has not provided the Vaccination returns.	178
24.12.1878	Salmon to Dr. Brooks. As Dr. B's letters point to his inability to perform regularly vaccination at Anse Royale and Anse Boileau, Mr. Pasnin has been appointed to do it (pending approval of the Governor) to avoid further breaches of the law.	188
17.01.1879	Salmon to Messrs. Lanier, Bonnetard, and Others. The new Customs House will be started shortly.	194

Date	Subject Matter	Page
19.02.1879	Salmon to Dr. Brooks. With reference to the numerous letters and voluminous enclosures sent by him for transmission, all of which contain charges of serious nature against various Public Officers and Private Persons, copies of every statement and document reflecting on their character and acts will be furnished to them, in order that they may take the measures they shall judge fit to clear their characters.	205
22.02.1879	Salmon to Dr. Villemont. Dr. Brooks, about to be suspended from all his functions, Dr. V. is to be G.M.O. and Pratique Officer from 25 th inst., pending decision of Govt. of Mauritius.	207
25.02.1879	Salmon to Dr. Brooks. Informs him that because of his conduct (which is set out) he is interdicted from all his functions under Government from after to-day.	209
3.07.1879	Salmon to ex-Sultan of Perak. His petition has been laid before the Queen. The Secretary of State was unable to advise her to cause the decision now being carried out, to be re-considered.	226
17.10.1879	Salmon to Jules Cauvin Surveyor General. Instructions about an expedition to Aldabra Islands.	242
18.10.1879	Delapeyre, Acting C.C.C. to Dr. Brooks. By decision of Secretary of State he is removed from his appointment.	244
18.10.1879	Delapeyre to Dr. Villemont, Asst. G.M.O. Dr. Ward has been appointed G.M.O. and Dr. V. is to resume duties as Asst. G.M.O. and J.P. for Praslin and La Digue.	245
9.12.1879	First letter signed by A.E. Havelock. New Chief Civil Commissioner.	287
18.12.1879	Havelock to Chief Officer of Police.	

Date	Subject Matter	Page
	Acknowledges letter about accident to two men of Force while firing salute on Havelock's arrival. More thorough instruction needed.	294
18.12.1879	Havelock to District Judge. Sending extract from Colonial Secretary's letter of 6.12.79 on subject of bearing and conduct of the members of the Bar practising before the Court.	295
22.12.1879	Havelock to Chief Officer of Police. On various Police matters.	297
26.12.1879	Havelock to Chief Officer of Police. As quarters at Police Station were provided, were occupied for several years, vacated by own accord, and could again be occupied, his application for quarters or allowance in lieu, cannot be considered. Nor for reasons given can he have a horse and horse allowance.	306
2.01.1880	Havelock to E. Sauzier, J. Petit, H. Wilson. Acknowledges petition to Secretary of State, praying for re-instatement of Dr. J.H. Brooks as Govt. Medical Officer. A duplicate and a Triplicate copies are required.	318
3.01.1880	Havelock to Dr. Brooks. Replies to a letter claiming fees and allowances.	320
6.01.1880	Havelock to Dr. Ward. Replying to a letter enclosing one for the Colonial Secretary in which he tenders his resignation as Govt. Medical Officer.	328
6.01.1880	Havelock to Chairman of Prison Committee. Long letter dealing with conditions, and alterations proposed.	329
2.12.1878 216.	To Governor. Relates to unauthorised and illegal possession of Govt. lands at Praslin.	13

Date	Subject Matter	Page
3.12.1878 218.	To Governor. Explanations about Dr. Brooks and fees from Navy.	16
15.12.1878	To Colonial Office. Forwarding petition from ex-Sultan of Perak.	36
23.12.1878 236.	To Colonial Secretary. Dr. Villemont, Asst. M.O., arrived 11th. He will live at La Digue.	39
30.12.1878 249.	To The Governor. On conditions respecting Aldabra, Cosmoledo, Astove, and Assumption Islands.	46
31.12.1878 252.	To Colonial Secretary. Long letter about statements by Mr. Barrow, and the Public Accounts.	52
28.01.1879 25.	To Crown Agents. Asking for 6 copies of Survey and Plan of Port Victoria made in 1877 by H.M.S. "Fawn", and published by Hydrographical Dept. of Admiralty.	72
31.01.1879 30.	To ? (not stated, but apparently to Col. Sec). Sending letter from Dr. Brooks appealing from decision of Governor. From C.C.C's comments it appears dispute concerns use of boats.	73
20.02.1879 44.	To Administrator, (F. Napier Broome), Mauritius. Four page letter dealing with statements in a letter from Dr. Brooks dated 7th Feb. to Sec. of State, which is sent for transmission.	81
24.02.1879 45.	To Administrator, Mauritius. Four pages commenting upon 2 letters from Dr. Brooks to Secretary of State dated 8th Feb. (Copies were only received after originals had been forwarded).	85
27.02.1879 53.	To Colonial Secretary. Forwards letter from Dr. Brooks, and comments upon its statements.	92

Date	Subject Matter	Page
28.02.1879 54.	To Administrator, Mauritius. He has had to interdict Dr. B. from Govt. duties. Gives reasons, and reports on a so-called "petition" (in fact a document of a slanderous and defamatory nature on the C.C.C., District Judge, Chief of Police and Force, and others).	93
1.03.1879 57.	To Administrator, Mauritius. Forwards copy of above-mentioned "Petition". The original will go to Downing Street by next mail. He writes at length on the nature of it. Many were misled by a French version on 2 sheets of paper. Some have withdrawn signatures. At least 120 of the 162 who signed do not know English.	98
1.03.1879 61.	To Administrator, Mauritius. Sends various documents for the S of S in order that charges made against C.C.C. by Dr. Brooks direct to Downing Street may be refuted, and his general conduct to C.C.C. known there.	102
6.03.1879	Report by C.C.C. on a petition to the S of S. dated 8th Jan. 1879. 12 pages.	106
7.03.1879	To Under Secretary of State for Colonies. Sends letters and papers conveying complaints by Dr. Brooks against C.C.C. and Officers of the Govt. sent direct by him to S of S. Here follows copy of Salmon's letter 12.2.1879 to U.S. of S about Dr. Brooks, 7 1/2 pages.	118
7.03.1879	To Under Secretary of State for Colonies. Sends letters referring to interdiction of Dr. Brooks.	120
18.03.1879 63.	To Administrator. 9 1/2 page report on Schools, Education, and the difficulties in way of teaching English.	129
26.03.1879 66.	To Administrator. Vaccination affairs.	142
2.04.1879 76.	To Governor (Sir G. Bowen)	

Date	Subject Matter	Page
	The efforts of Brooks and Barrow to bring discredit on Collard.	148
23.04.1879 91.	To Governor. Sends duplicate of letter forwarded by Dr. Brooks to S of S. last mail. Comments thereon.	164
23.04.1879 92.	To Governor. Forwards letter with enclosure, from Dr. Brooks, dated 18th inst. Two pages by Salmon, dealing with contents.	166
25.04.1879 95.	To Governor. Sends letter from Dr. Brooks dated 19th inst. 3 1/2 pages of comment upon his statements.	169
26.04.1879 101.	To Governor. Alterations to prison buildings.	177
3.05.1879 108.	To Under Secretary of State. A report about the ex-Sultan of Perak and his fellow prisoners.	181
19.05.1879 112.	To Governor. Remarks on Ordinances to do with fishing matters.	184
21.05.1879 118.	To Governor. Sends map of Mahe showing roads, bridle paths and footpaths. Refers also to La Digue and Praslin.	193
15.08.1879 175.	To Colonial Secretary. Forwarding minutes of Board of Education, and report of Inspector of Schools.	223
16.08.1879 182.	To Colonial Secretary. Replying to some complaints from a Political prisoner on Felicite Island.	234
11.10.1879 192.	To Colonial Secretary. Sends, at request of Chief Officer of Police, to	

Date	Subject Matter	Page
	be passed to Procureur General, report and evidence about a murder at Round Island, Praslin.	242
4.11.1879 197.	de Lapeyre, Acting C.C.C. to Colonial Secretary. Mentions that decision of S of S has been signified to Dr. Brooks and Mr. Barrow ; both have handed over to the gentlemen appointed to replace them.	245
5.12.1879 220.	Acting C.C.C. H.E. Desmarais, to Col. Sec. Taken over from de Lapeyre to-day Capt. Havelock expected to-morrow.	260
6.12.1879 223.	A.E. Havelock, C.C.C. to Col. Sec. Has arrived to-day and taken over.	261
27.12.1879 238	Havelock to Colonial Secretary. On the Law regulating Licenses.	270
1.01.1880 1.	Unless otherwise stated, letters are from Havelock. To Colonial Secretary. Report on Estimates 1880.	273
2.01.1880 2.3.	To Colonial Secretary. Sends petition from some inhabitants for reinstatement of Dr. Brooks. Also application from him. Havelock does not recommend.	278 279
15.01.1880 15.	To Colonial Secretary. Forwards claim for fees and allowances sent by Dr. Brooks.	287
18.01.1880 19.	To Colonial Secretary. Relative to prison matters.	291
23.01.1880 20.	To Colonial Secretary. Remarks on Educational System.	292
23.01.1880 22.	To Colonial Secretary. Report on Fishing Laws.	296

Date	Subject Matter	Page
24.01.1880 24.	To Colonial Secretary. On custody of Public moneys.	300
28.01.1880 31.	To Colonial Secretary. Introduction of Metric system.	305
19.02.1880 59.	To Colonial Secretary. Complaints of Political prisoners at Felicité.	323
8.03.1880 75.	To Colonial Secretary. Acknowledges letter 19/2 issuing amended instructions about custody of Public moneys.	334
12.03.1880 79.	To Colonial Secretary. Adoption of metric system of weights and measures.	336
15.03.1880 83.	To Colonial Secretary. Report on new Labour Law.	340
19.03.1880 89.	To Colonial Secretary. Submitting amended Hospital tariff. One of the causes given for the little use made of the Hospital is the existing high tariff.	344
25.03.1880 101.	To Colonial Secretary. Forwards a letter from Dr. Brooks to Secretary. of State on the subject of certain claims for fees.	353
13.04.1880 107.	To Colonial Secretary. Ex-Sultan of Perak requests increased allowance.	356
15.04.1880 111.	To Colonial Secretary. Improvements to prison ; and suggestions for future.	359
16.04.1880 115.	To Colonial Secretary. Report on Crown Lands.	363

Date	Subject Matter	Page
		VOL. B/38.
7.05.1880 129.	Proclamation declaring special Ward in Hospital assigned to sick prisoners to be a legal prison.	2
13.05.1880 140.	Rev. J.F. Grandjean arrived on 24th April, and entered at once on his duties as Civil Chaplain.	9
17.05.1880	Remarks on Blue Book Return for 1879, 7 1/2 pages.	14
19.05.1880 149.	To Colonial Secretary. Reclamation and Lease of portion of foreshore in Victoria.	25
11.06.1880	Sending a report on the Memorial of the Board of Civil Commissioners dated 31.01.1879 advocating certain changes in the Government and Administration.	37
6.07.1880 168.	Dr. Robert Lepper arrived 19th June and began duty as Government Medical Officer on 21st.	44
6.07.1880 171.	Acknowledging letter raising allowance of ex-Sultan of Perak to Rs.400 a month from 1st. May.	45
6.07.1880 173.	Letter of 17.6 sending copy of one from Govt. of Straits Settlements, received. The increased allowance to the Shabandar of Perak, from 1st. May being paid.	47
10.07.1880 191.	A woman lunatic, Remy Mimi, accompanied by a Police Constable, sent in Barque "Laconia".	62
7.08.1880 213.	On rapidly spreading disease in cocoanut trees.	80
13.08.1880 221.	Arrangements consequent on departure of C.C.C. A.E. Havelock.	85
13.08.1880 224.	Forwards petition from ex-Sultan of Perak to H.M. The Queen, that a fresh investigation of his case be made. C.C.C. says he has been banished for 3 years now, and pays a tribute to his excellent conduct.	87

Date	Subject Matter	Page
	Note :- H.C. Desmarais becomes Acting C.C.C.	
28.09.1880 252.	Desmarais, Acting C.C.C. to Col. Sec. As per instructions of 7th he has paid to Dr. Brooks in the terms of the Sec. of State's decision, and after approval by local audit officer, the sum of Rs. 3018.60 for fees allowed for period between interdiction and dismissal.	104
	Note :- A letter dated 23.10.1880 is signed by the new C.C.C., F.J. Blunt.	
26.10.1880 269.	M.O. is badly needed in Praslin and La Digue. (And to serve as Stipendiary Magistrate).	113
17.12.1880 297.	Concerning the Admirante Islands.	130
27.01.1881 15.	An application from Mr. Leipsic, Chief Police Officer, has been received, accompanied by Medical Certificate. He wishes to retire. Papers not sent by this mail, as not been verified. Hopes to send next mail.	160
22.02.1881 36.	Sending for Procureur General, an enquiry made by Chief of Police into a murder reported to have been committed, evening of 16th.	170
23.02.1881 38.	Desmarais, A.C.C.C. Forwards 2 public notices published by C.C.C. which will inform Governor of the change in the administration in consequence of Capt. Blunt suffering from a severe attack of dysentery.	171
24.02.1881 39.	Acting C.C.C. (Desmarais) to Col Sec. Reporting death of Capt. Blunt, C.C.C., at 8.20 a.m. to-day from dysentery.	171
25.02.1881 45.	The Acting C.C.C. proposes to ask the Board of Civil Commissioners to vote Rs. 3,000 for passages to England of widow and family of the late C.C.C.	173
4.03.1881 50.	The Board of C.C. at a meeting yesterday voted the above mentioned Rs. 3,000.	177

Date	Subject Matter	Page
4.03.1881 51.	Mr. Spencer has been appointed Chief Officer of Police and his constable incorporated with the Force.	177
18.03.1881 63.	Advises that passages to Mauritius for Mr. Spencer and constable taken in steamer "Dupleix".	184
27.03.1881	From new C.C.C., H. Cockburn Stewart., to Colonial Secretary. Reporting arrival evening of 26th.	189
20.04.1881 79.	The C.C.C. presided at Public meeting held to promote the erection by Public subscription of a suitable memorial over the grave of late C.C.C., Capt. Blunt.	194
22.04.1881 81.	Relative to the need for a Mortgage Office.	195
19.05.1881 98.	On the great want of a Govt. Saving Bank.	204
19.05.1881 99.	The recently taken Census shows an increase of population of nearly 3,000.	205
20.05.1881 103.	Messageries Maritimes ships may discontinue, calling Seychelles when new service to Australia via Mauritius begins in Jan. 82. This is less likely to happen if a lighthouse is erected shortly on Bird Island (other name Ile aux Vaches), or Denis Island, about 60 miles north of Mahe.	207
17.06.1881 112.	Relates to Draft Ordinance proposing to bring certain islands under the jurisdiction of Seychelles.	215
17.06.1881 113.	Concerns the spread of disease affecting cocoanut trees, and mentions "I imagine that the appearance of this insect is caused by the dirty and neglected state in which the cocoanut trees are left by the majority of the inhabitants of this place".	218
17.06.1881 114.	For increased agricultural development roads much needed. Suggests a loan of £ 12, 000 for the purpose.	220

Date	Subject Matter	Page
18.06.1881 116.	A long report on agricultural conditions and problems.	223
19.06.1881 117.	Long report on administrative and legal changes proposed (as per a copy of letter from Sec. of State) to enable more matters to be dealt with at Mahe instead of referred to Mauritius.	237
6.06.1881	Long report on the Blue Book returns of 1880.	254
7.07.1881 123.	Requests that Dr. Lepper be confirmed as G.M.O. having satisfactorily completed 12 months probation.	273
6.07.1881 127.	On revenue and expenditure matters.	279
14.07.1881 133.	A society of Acclimitization (at present 9 members) formed, to advance agriculture. A piece of ground for Nursery and Botanical Garden provided at back of Govt. House.	289
15.07.1881 136.	Forwards application from ex-Sultan of Perak requesting increased allowance.	292
15.07.1881	Long report on prison buildings and conditions, with alterations proposed.	293
2.08.1881	The great need for better and constant communication with outer islands. C.C.C. believes Admiralty would lend a gunboat no longer in commission.	306
25.08.1881 59.	A report on the state of education. (Of particular interest).	321
27.08.1881 160.	Urging the need for a Medical Officer for Praslin, La Digue, Curieuse.	326
29.08.1881 164.	A letter (following up one of 19th May) on the need for a Govt. Savings Bank.	329
1.09.1881 167.	Reporting results of a meeting to discuss problem of cocoanut tree disease.	332

Date	Subject Matter	Page
5.09.1881 171.	Sending Draft Estimates of Revenue and Expenditure for 1882, with explanations thereon.	341
7.09.1881 172.	Report on Forests and Crown Lands. Long.	352
8.09.1881 174.	Sanitary conditions in Victoria.	362
9.09.1881 175.	Acknowledges letter 9th Aug. with one from Procureur General on proposed administrative and legal changes.	364
23.09.1881 177.	On the state of the Records in Office of C.C.C.	369
2.10.1881 183.	Advocating that guards in charge of gangs of prisoners working on roads should be armed because of escapes made. (Prison Committee claim illegal). Criticises the management of Prison. Recommends it should be placed under Chief Officer of Police, under the control of the C.C.	379
7.10.1881	The need of a reformatory method of dealing with juvenile offenders instead of sending to prison.	388
8.10.1881 198.	The ex-Sultan of Perak wishes to visit Mauritius. Request is recommended.	392
8.10.1881 200.	The French barque "Francis", Motiac, Master, Bourbon for Pondicherry, having 395 coolies on board, has put in, in distress, making 17 inches of water an hour. Only anchored 2 or 3 hours ago. It is said that vessel will probably be abandoned.	393
26.10.1881 207.	It has been unanimously resolved by Board of Commissioners to borrow Rs.150,000 (the equivalent of £ 12,000) from Mauritius surplus balance, as directed by the S of S.	397
27.10.1881 209.	Advising that Dr. Brooks ceased to perform the duties of Govt. M.O. on 25th Feb. 1879 though he was paid his full fees up to the 18th Oct. of that year.	394

Date	Subject Matter	Page
28.10.1881 214.	Suggesting the nomination of unofficial and unsalaried J.P. for the various district and outlying islands, to save persons from remote parts having to come to Victoria.	403
29.10.1881 215.	Forwarding petition from ex-Sultan of Perak to Lieut. Govt. for transmission to S of S., and paying tribute to his excellent behaviour. (It is not stated what the petition is about, but it appears probable that it could have been to ask for repatriation).	405
3.11.1881 217.	Forwards a draft labour regulation felt to be more suitable for Seychelles than Ordinance 12 of 1878. The last letter signed by H. Cockburn Stewart, C.C.C. is 4th Nov. H.E. Desmarais becomes acting C.C.C.	406
28.11.1881 232.	The French ship "St. Jacques" sailed for Pondicherry on 12th taking 283 of the coolies landed at Long Island in Oct. from French ship "Francis" (See item 8.10.1881).	411
21.12.1881 253.	Forwards statement of expenses incurred in connection with the exhumation and transport to Singapore of the body of the mother of the Datoh of Perak.	431
21.12.1881 254.	Advising that the Right Rev. Father Ignatius, Bishop "d'Aureliopolis", died on the 19th Dec.	431
27.12.1881 259.	The tower for lighthouse on Denis Island which had reached forty feet fell on the 10th inst. causing severe injury to several labourers and prisoners.	434
2.01.1882 4.	Reports death of Mr. James Davidson (late Clerk of Dues and Taxes) this day.	439
19.01.1882 14.	The "Isabelle", a vessel chartered by the Mauritius Govt. for conveyance to Madras of the coolies which were not shipped in the "St.Jacques", arrived 9th and left 14th.	444
23.01.1882 16.	Forwards petition from the Acting C.C.C. (Desmarais) for transmission to S of S. Copy of Petition follows the letter.	445

Date	Subject Matter	Page
28.01.1882 25.	Reports that A.C.S. Barkly, Chief Civil Commissioner, has arrived this day.	452
3.02.1882 28.	Barkly himself reports his arrival.	453
23.02.1882 31.	Sending correspondence on the subject of marriages of Liberated Africans, for the Procureur General.	457
18.03.1882 44.	Replies to letter of 14.02.1882 enclosing one from Col. Sec. of Straits Settlements about applications for increased allowance for ex-Sultan of Perak and ex-Mantri. Barkly does not see need for increase for latter as no family to support. For ex-Sultan suggests an allowance of about Rs.500 a month. Gives reasons for favouring an increased to present sum.	463
24.03.1882 54.	Sends the report of a commission of enquiry on the collapse of the partly-built tower on Denis Island.	472
		VOL. B/39.
21.04.1882 68.	Two addresses (one from Board of Civil Commissioners) expressing feelings of loyalty and devotion, to H.M. The Queen, sent to Secretary of State. (There had been an attempt on her life). Forwarded direct because no mail to Mauritius for some time.	1
19.05.1882 74.	Preservation of coco de mer trees.	4
19.05.1882 76.	Forwarding report on Acting Inspector of Schools, for 1881.	8
19.05.1882 77.	Forwarding report of Conservator of Crown Lands and Forests for 1881.	9
16.06.1882 96.	Ex-Sultan of Perak going on visit to Mauritius, as sanctioned.	20
16.06.1882 97.	The idea that Admiralty might lend a gun-boat to Seychelles, abandoned as too expensive. Would cost	

Date	Subject Matter	Page
	£ 1,000 to £ 1200 a year to maintain, exclusive of fuel.	21
11.08.1882 5.	Remarks and suggestions about proposed Ordinance providing for trial of capital offences. 4 1/2 pages.	40
11.08.1882 7.	Suggestions for the carrying out of the duties of a Shipping Master.	45
18.08.1882 25.	Juvenile Offenders. Only one now in the prison and during last 12 months only two had sentences exceeding 10 days. Barkly does not consider sending J.O. s to Lady Missionary in charge of Venns Town establishment, feasible. Recommends passing a Regulation on the lines of a Juvenile Offenders Act now in force at the Cape.	57
8.09.1882 28.	Concerning the Governor's view that Mauritius finances should not bear the cost of expenses in connection with cases tried in Mauritius.	60
8.09.1882 31.	On the duties of The Collector of Dues and Taxes, and the C.C.C.	63
21.09.1882 42.	A report on various conditions existing : Financial, state of Govt. House and its equipement.	71
6.10.1882 48.	A long letter on the construction of Denis Island lighthouse, and the general conduct of the Supt. of Public Works. The work on lighthouse is temporarily suspended.	81
6.10.1882 50.	Forwards letter from Supt. of P.W. to the Governor and comments further on his behaviour.	95
4.11.1882 68.	Ex-Sultan of Perak has returned from his visit to Mauritius.	107
4.11.1882 70.	Sending estimates for 1883, with remarks thereon.	109
1.12.1882 75.	Requesting a competent man from Surveyor General's Dept. be sent to take charge of te P.W.D. A method	

Date	Subject Matter	Page
	of construction for Denis Island lighthouse is proposed.	121
1.12.1882 81.	On the leasing of Cosmoledo, Aldabra, etc...	128
1.12.1882 82.	Report on proposal to establish a Govt. School at Mahe. Goes into the matter very thoroughly.	131
9.12.1882 94.	Forwarding a petition from the ex-Mantri of Laroot to S of S.	145
6.01.1883 1.	Salary and allowances of the C.C.C.	150
31.01.1883 11.	The Port Officer, Mr. B. Hibbs, wishes to retire on a gratuity.	156
3.03.1883 27.	The District Judge has committed one Joseph Joubert to take his trial in Mauritius for murder. It will be quite impossible at this time of year, for Seychelles Govt. to meet heavy expenses of transport of prisoner and witnesses, unless an advance is made, sufficient to cover.	166
3.03.1883 29.	Denis Island Light. Foundations completed. A few weeks after arrival of the structure from Mauritius will suffice to put lantern in place. A thoroughly competent and experienced man as keeper necessary. No one here. Can Mauritius supply ?	168
3.03.1883 34.	Advances to Political Prisoners, cannot be met without a quarterly advance of Rs. 5,000 from Mauritius Treasury.	170
31.03.1883 49.	Further reference to advances to Political Prisoners.	179
28.04.1883 62.	Report on Crown Lands.	
28.04.1883 64.	Further respecting salary and emoluments of C.C.C.	191

Date	Subject Matter	Page
26.05.1883 67.	Acknowledges Rs. 4,500, being an advance on account of the Political Prisoners.	194
26.05.1883 72.	Reporting for approval certain arrangements for the performance of the duties of Legal Adviser and Ministère Public under Ordinance. 14 of 1872.	198
26.05.1883 74.	Sending copy of Lease of Aldabra, Cosmoledo, Astove etc...	203
26.05.1883 81.	Forwarding annual report of Inspector of Schools on state of Primary Education during 1882.	208
26.05.1883 82.	Forwarding petition from Bishop Monard to S of S. Comments upon it made by C.C.C.	209
29.05.1883 84.	Dr. Lepper willing to replace Dr. Davidson. Dr. Brooks will do Dr. Leppers medical duties under private arrangement approved. Dr. Brooks has said he would accept any suitable Govt. appointment. If he could be provided for, it would relieve Seychelles of his pension of £ 204, which Govt. can ill afford.	212
30.05.1883 85.	Asking for an advance of Rs.10,000 for 3 months to meet temporary deficiency, and to provide for regular payment of salaries.	214
23.06.1883 86.	Nearly 2 years have elapsed since Mr. Leipsic, late Chief of Police, retired, and the amount of his pension to be paid respectively by Mauritius (where he served before Seychelles) and Seychelles has not been settled. The C.C.C. asked about this on 3.2.1883.	215
21.07.1883 107.	Remarks concerning the establishment of a Savings Bank.	229
18.08.1883 123.	Acknowledges receipt of advance of Rs.10,000.	244
15.09.1883 150.	Emoluments of C.C.C., and appointment of Clerk in his office.	257

Date	Subject Matter	Page
15.09.1883 151.	To the Governor. (As are all subsequent letters.) Respecting Varicella at Seychelles.	259
13.10.1883 160.	A very long letter (14pp) on proposed reductions in expenditure.	265
13.10.1883 162.	Further respecting Crown Lands.	280
13.10.1883 169.	Forwarding a petition signed by 11 persons as to Varicella.	288
8.11.1883 184.	Transmitting Report on Liberated Africans for 1882, and commenting thereon.	297
9.11.1883 185.	Respecting complaint of ex-Sultan of Perak against the Interpreter, Mr. Strugnell, and recommending return of the latter to Singapore.	302
28.12.1883 214.	Regarding reforestation.	321
3.01.1884 1.	Long letter concerning disease prevailing.	324
9.01.1884 12.	Petition from certain inhabitants to be sent by the mail on 3rd Feb. It contains grave statements respecting Dr. Brooks, Dr. Lepper, and the C.C.C. in relation to the epidemic and therefore needs a full and careful report.	334
30.01.1884	Observations (5 pages) on printed papers about the disease at Seychelles.	337
30.01.1884 22.	Forwards the petition referred to on 9.1.1884 and makes 3 1/2 pages of comments on it.	345
31.01.1884 29.	Sends the explanations of Drs. Lepper and Hoad as to Dr. Chartellier's report on the disease in Mahe.	351
26.02.1884 40.	Ex-Mantri of Laroot (Political Prisoner), and a follower of his, Abdoola, have been fined Rs. 50	

Date	Subject Matter	Page
	each for assulting (inflicting blows) on a woman servant of one of the other prisoners.	359
28.02.1884 49.	Forwarding report of Conservator of Crown Lands and Forests on protection of coco de mer.	364
28.02.1884 51.	Regarding Lease of Aldabra Island.	366
28.02.1884 54.	Further respecting disease in Seychelles.	370
27.03.1884 65.	As above.	375
24.04.1884 76.	Forwarding for transmission, Loyal Adress to H.M. The Queen, from Board of C.C.	380
24.04.1884 79.	The difficulties of instituting a jury system.	380
25.04.1884 83.	French Steam Vessel "Assyrien", Larretche, Master, Toulon for Tamatave, wrecked on Providence Island. Master and crew (20 in number)brought Mahe by Barque "Venezuela" which happened to be there.	385
25.04.1884 84.	Sending address from ex-Sultan of Perak to H.M. The Queen (Because of death of Duke of Albany).	386
25.04.1884 85.	On the status of the C.C.C.	387
17.06.1884 116.	Respecting Coco de Mer valley at Praslin.	407
12.06.1884 117.	Further reference to wreck of French Steamer "Assyrien". (See 25.04.1884).	409
18.06.1884 118.	Return of Mr. Strugnell (Interpreter for Political Prisoners) and wife to Singapore.	412

Date	Subject Matter	Page
19.06.1884 124.	Sending petition from ex-Sultan of Perak and remarking on his excellent conduct.	414
20.06.1884 125.	Reporting that a liberated African, Jacob, No. 397 has stabbed (on 9th inst.) four persons, two of whom died. He escaped ; Police and inhabitants searched the hills. Captured last night.	415
18.07.1884 141.	The building formerly used as Fibre factory (until failure of the Co., 4 or 5 years ago), is still unlet and getting out of repair. The C.C.C. has had one or two offers, and requests permission to lease it for 9 years on usual terms for leases here.	423
13.08.1884 153.	Jacob (see 20.6.1884), and the witnesses, will be sent to Mauritius for his trial.	430
16.08.1884 158.	Respecting epidemic of small pox.	433
12.09.1884 166.	Sending Report on Liberated Africans for 1883, with remarks thereon.	439
10.10.1884 175.	Forwarding for approval proposed Estimates, with remarks, for 1885.	449
29.10.1884 179.	Transmits report from Dr. Hoad on state of the Public Health.	454
7.11.1884 184.	Further respecting lease of Fibre factory.	456
8.11.1884 188.	Sending reports on Survey of Mahe.	459
5.12.1884 205.	The C.C.C. (A. Barkly) acknowledges being granted 3 months leave on full salary and 3 months of half salary. Proposes to leave on 30th inst, and will hand over to Mr. G.H. Griffiths (Chief of Police) who will be acting C.C.C.	468
5.12.1884 209.	Report of C.C.C's visit to Coco de Mer valley at Praslin.	471

Date	Subject Matter	Page
18.12.1884 210.	Referring to letter 205 of 5/12., The C.C.C. has been offered a passage to Colombo in H.M.S. "Osprey" leaving on 20th. Having been seriously indisposed of late, he is accepted.	472
	The first letter signed by G.H. Griffiths, the Acting C.C.C. is dated 31st December, 1883.	
31.12.1884 213.	Reports departure of Mr. Barkly, C.C.C., in H.M.S. "Osprey" on 20th inst.	474
31.12.1884 231.	After saying that a certain documents asked for is not to be found, the letter states "I may mention that the Archives of Seychelles have been found by me in a deplorable condition".	481
31.12.1884 236.	Sending copy of Minutes of Prison Committee, with remarks thereon.	483
		VOL. B/40.
15.06.1887	The C.C.C. (A. Barkly) to Mauritius. Asking for guidance as to whether the Govt of Seychelles should bank with the New Oriental Bank.	7
10.08.1887	Report on coaling wharves as now leased, and possibilities for increasing such.	8
28.12.1887	Dealing with various Police and Prison matters.	12
15.11.1889	From T. Risely Griffith, Administrator, to Mauritius. Proposed ordinance relating to Trial by jury. Judge's opinions thereon.	24
27.11.1891	From R.M. Brown, Acting Administrator, to Mauritius. Concerning complaints of increase of larcenies of vanilla and cloves, and report upon.	38
28.03.1892	Asking to be informed whether there are any grounds for the fears which seem to be entertained in local commercial circles concerning the New	

Date	Subject Matter	Page
	Oriental Bank Corporation	46
13.06.1892	**From T. Risely Griffith, Administrator to S of S.** An account of his visit to Aldabra.	49
13.11.1895	**From H. Cockburn Stewart, Administrator to Colonial Secretary.** Proposal that Seychelles be made a Naval Coaling Station, and respecting establishment of a Volunteer Corps.	66
18.12.1895	Further concerning establishment of a Naval Coaling Station. The M.M. Co., willing to sell wharf and slip.	67
16.01.1896	M.M. Coal Wharf and slip brought by Imperial Govt. for £ 1,030.	68
3.07.1896	Describes the disadvantages arising from Seychelles being a dependency of Mauritius. Since M.M. ships ceased to call 6 months ago, no communication with Mauritius except via Zanzibar or Bombay. Not possible to get a reply to any despatch sent Home via Mauritius under 6 months. Advocates time has now come for separation.	69
19.12.1896	Further to question of possibility of separation from Mauritius. The Judge has made representations to the Administrator about difficulties in carrying out Seychelles Capital Offences Order in Council.	72
21.06.1899	**From R.M. Brown, Acting Administrator.** Reporting proceedings at a meeting held to consider the question of steam communication.	86
13.01.1900	**From E.B. Sweet-Escott, Administrator.** Proposals for excluding the Seychelles from the Dependencies of Mauritius.	91
20.01.1900	Further to above despatch, a copy of a letter from the Judge of Seychelles is sent.	93

Date	Subject Matter	Page
26.02.1900	A long letter about the possibility of raising a Volunteer Force. The past views of H. Cockburn Stewart, former Administrator, and Sir Hubert Jerningham, former Governor of Mauritius - which are quoted - are of interest, particularly because of their divergence.	96
20.04.1900	Outlying briefly the preparations feasible for receiving 2,000 Boer prisoners on two islands within 25 miles of Mahe.	101
7.05.1900	More detail on above, and names Felicité and Curieuse as the two islands.	102
30.08.1900	Proposal to establish Seychelles as a separate Government. Sends information requested, and copy of Minutes by the Judge. A 5 1/2 page review of whole situation.	106
10.11.1900	Explains difficulties in constituting an Education Board with powers outside the Govt., and refers to Measures to be taken to encourage use of Englsih language. 4 interesting and informative pages.	112
12.04.1901	Explains difficulty in finding accommodation for Boer prisoners in any other place than Curieuse and asks for instructions as to whether enquiries should be made respecting Silhouette, Felicité or Frigate Islands.	123
26.05.1901	Asks for certain information in connection with raising a Volunteer Force.	125
3.10.1901	Forwards copy of Draft Regulations for Grant-in-aid Schools, as adopted by Education Committee, with Minute by the Judge (the Chairman) with special reference to the question of promoting the use of the English language in Primary Schools.	134
26.12.1901	Reports on proposal to send rebel prisoners sentenced to penal servitude, to Felicité 4 1/2 pages.	141
2.01.1902	Submits for reconsideration, proposal to separate Seychelles from the Govt. of Mauritius 6 1/2 pages.	146

Date	Subject Matter	Page
24.01.1902	Acknowledges despatch on subject of proposed transfer to Seychelles of Islands of Farquhar, Coetivy, and Agalega ; and the separation of Seychelles from the Govt. of Mauritius.	158
9.02.1902	Forwards copies of correspondence with the Governor of Mauritius on the subject of the proposed separation of Seychelles from Mauritius.	160
2.03.1902	Capt. Martyn, 1st. Battalion, Queen's Own Regt., having inspected Felicité Island, agrees with the Administrator as to suitability for Prisoners of War.	162
31.05.1902	Refers to Orders in Council, Letters Patent, and Royal Instructions, relating to Mauritius and Seychelles, and asks for reconsideration of decision that the Governor of Mauritius can issue any instructions to the Administrator of Seychelles.	170
2.06.1902	Refers to recent correspondence respecting proposal to establish a penal settlement for Cape rebels, and states local Police Force cannot be charged with duty of acting as Prison Guards.	174
7.07.1902	Penal settlement in Seychelles. Mentions arrival of Mr. Smith of Ceylon P.W.D. Recommends La Digue in preference to Felicité.	176
14.07.1902	Submits observations on views of Sir Charles Bruce (Governor of Mauritius) as to effect on Educational system and Civil Service of Seychelles, of complete seperation of Govt. of Seychelles from that of Mauritius. 8 pages.	179
17.07.1902	Forwards copy of report by Mr. W.R. Smith, of Ceylon P.W.D., on proposal to establish a Penal Settlement at Felicité.	187
17.08.1902	Reports further on proposal to transfer to Seychelles the islands of Farquhar, Coetivy, and Agalega. 4 pages.	189
31.08.1902	Forward Bill to enable the Administrator to control stations from wireless telegraphy.	194

Date	Subject Matter	Page
1.11.1902	Stating that because of the expense and of other services being more urgently required, the formation of a Volunteer Corps will be deferred.	202
17.11.1902	Acknowledges despatch that S of S has decided to drop idea of transfer of Farquhar, Coetivy and Agalega, because of strong opposition in Mauritius.	204
22.11.1902	Forwards precis of correspondence on proposed separation of Seychelles from Mauritius, and bill to establish and regulate Seychelles English scholarship.	205
13.12.1902	Long letter concerning sea transport. 6 1/2 pages.	210
16.03.1903	Returns various documents concerning Seychelles becoming a separate Colony.	226
6.04.1903	Forwarding various documents, with explanations, relative to the separation. 4 pages.	229
30.06.1903	Proposes a special stamp be issued in celebration of Seychelles.	246
20.09.1903	Submits proposals as to details in establishing a complete local subsidiary coinage for Seychelles.	255
20.10.1903	Acknowledges three Orders in Council and expresses thanks of Colony for the good wishes of Secretary of State.	258
9.03.1904	Acknowledges telegram offering Mr. Sweet-Escott the Government of British Honduras, and expresses thanks for the honour.	271

The following are from W.E. Davidson, Governor.

Date	Subject Matter	Page
3.09.1904	Reporting breakdown of the M.M. Co's Mail Service due to strikes at Marseilles.	274
8.10.1904	More on Seychelles Mail Service.	277
13.10.1904	Observations on a Military Report concerning	

Date	Subject Matter	Page
	Seychelles. 4 1/2 pages.	280
28.10.1904	Resumption of the M.M. Mail Service.	285
6.05.1906	Long letter relating to export of phosphatic rock (St. Pierre Island). 5 1/2 pages.	298
3.06.1906	Further regarding the above.	306
27.06.1906	Consideration of tentative proposals of the B.I.S. N. Co., for the trade service to Seychelles.	310
5.01.1907	Concerning possibility of improved steamship service to Seychelles. (Deutsche-Ost-Afrika Linie).	323
20.01.1907	A 3 page letter on the proposed Carnegie Library in Victoria.	327
21.03.1907	Regarding steamer service by Deutsche-Ost-Afrika Linie, and other steamer service propositions.	332
8.05.1907	The Governor reports his departure on leave tomorrow Mr. E. Blackwood Wright will administer the Government.	341
31.12.1884 250.	Recommending calling for fresh tenders for leasing former Fibre Factory.	5
26.01.1885 5.	Further respecting lease of Aldabra, Cosmoledo, etc...	9
27.01.1885 13.	Long report (29 p.) on indebtedness to Mauritius, and suggesting measures to increase revenue and decrease expenditure.	16
30.01.1885 27.	Supplying information on Primary Schools.	51
26.03.1885	Sending Report of Acting Inspector of Immigrants, on Liberated Africans for 1884.	68

Date	Subject Matter	Page
26.03.1885 71.	Forwards request from Ex-Sultan of Perak to visit Mauritius. (He was allowed to do so in 1882).	73
26.03.1885 76.	Enclosing Report of Conservator of Crown Lands and Forests.	76
26.03.1885 77.	Reporting that Dr. Brooks claiming arrears of pension, Rs.5114.37, and sending on his bill.	85
26.03.1885 78.	Report on Blue Book Returns for 1884, taking a number of pages.	86
20.04.1885 89.	Respecting acquisition of land by Roman Catholic Mission.	107
20.04.1885 91.	The Govt. Printer and Binder interdicted for embezzlement of Public moneys.	107
20.04.1885 101.	Further respecting lease of Aldabra Islands.	114
24.04.1885	Recommending former Fibre Factory be leased to Mr. G.F. Guerard.	122
24.04.1885 116.	The Board of Commissioners voted Rs.5114.37 for arrears of pension for Dr. Brooks from 1.7.82 to 31.12.84. Instructions to pay requested.	123
24.04.1885 117.	The Moitie system : a report on.	124
20.05.1885 126.	The Govt. Printer (see 20.04.1885) has left surreptitiously on 8th by French schooner "Belette" for Reunion.	132
22.05.1885 145.	Sending copies of minutes of Prison Committee and giving details of Prison rations.	143
18.06.1885 158.	Sending report, by Mr. Leduc, on Agalega island.	150

Date	Subject Matter	Page
18.06.1885 163.	Regarding leases of land to Victoria Cricket Club and old Fibre Factory.	152
18.06.1885 167.	Acting Supt. of Public Works and Govt. Surveyor arrested for drunkenness and creating a disturbance at the R.C. procession and assulting the Police.	156
27.06.1885 174.	Reporting arrival, by Brig "Alert", of Capt. Comby, 2nd mate, and 14 men of ship "Slieve More", of Liverpool, Tyne to Bombay with coal, burnt at sea on 16 th inst. The ship's second boat, with the mate and rest of crew arrived here to-day. See further letters of 2nd July (175), 14th July (184), 14 th July (185) 14th July (186), 16th July (197). 12th Aug. (207) 12th Aug (211).	160
17.07.1885 199.	A petition praying that land now used by Victoria Cricket Club be made into a Public Square.	174
14.08.1885 228.	Indebtedness of Seychelles to Mauritius. Proposed arrangements for paying off the debt.	190
14.08.1885 229.	Ex-Sultan of Perak proceeds to Mauritius.	191
9.09.1885 238.	Sending annual report on Education for 1884.	195
6.10.1885 273.	Forwarding Estimates for 1886, with remarks thereon.	216
6.10.1885	On the morning of 27th September, the body of one Joseph Abdool, a native of Mauritius, found in Morrison Street, showing marks of strangulation. The G.M.O. reports cause of death as "Violence", "the form of violence was strangulation". Five persons have been arrested. Enquiry yet closed.	223
5.11.1885 298.	Public Square. Making observations on the scheme, and asking for instructions.	236
5.11.1885 302.	Regarding the landing on Long Island of a man from H.M.S. "Bacchante" suffering from what bore suspicious resemblance to small pox.	239

Date	Subject Matter	Page
6.11.1885 311.	The District Judge has committed one Ally to stand his trial before the Assize Court at Mauritius on a charge of willful murder. Note :- This, presumably, relates to item 6.10.1885.	245
7.12.1885	Denis Island Lighthouse. Report from Acting Supt. of works. Tripod sent from Mauritius in March 1883 (rather expensive) of very inferior quality ; cannot be repaired to make safe for any length of time, timbers being rotten suggests one be made here in capucin wood, and built on outside of present one. Sketch and estimates sent.	262
31.12.1885 354.	Denis Island Light. Report from Surveyor General received and passed to Acting Supt. of P.W. whose report is now forwarded.	275
26.01.1886 11.	Education. Giving details of sums paid for grants in aid, 1885.	281
22.02.1886	States that prisoner Ally, prosecuted on a charge of manslaughter, was sentenced to 15 years imprisonment on 29th Jan. (Refer back to 6.11.1885).	295
24.02.1886	Two Indians just arrived from Reunion state they heard there from a man (former resident of Seychelles) who had arrived from Madagascar, that he had been informed while there that the Brig "Briton" had run ashore, dismasted, at a place called Mitinandree on E. Coast of Africa, and the natives had set fire to vessel, and taken Captain, crew, and passengers as slaves. "Briton" left Seychelles for Mauritius in May 1876 and has not been heard of since. Mrs. A. Nageon, and Mrs. Berlouis (?), widows, had sons on board.	307
24.02.1886 46.	Denis Island, Lighthouse. Sending report from Acting Supt. of P.W. on its condition.	308
26.02.1886 59.	The ex-Sultan of Perak arrived back from Mauritius on 20th.	316
23.03.1886 66.	Dr. W. Hoad, G.M.O. left for England on 19th.	319

Date	Subject Matter	Page
24.03.1886 72.	Dr. E. Esnouf arrived on 19th to be Acting G.M.O.	321
16.04.1886 81.	Respecting new rules as to Grants in Aid of Schools.	326
22.04.1886 91.	Primary Education. Regarding amount to be provided for this, and new rules.	331
12.07.1886 159.	Respecting complaint of certain inhabitants against the manner in which Bills of Health issued at Mahe are treated by the General Board of Health in Mauritius.	366
15.07.1886 167.	The Board of C.C. voted Rs.2045.75 for arrears of pension for Dr. Brooks, 1st. Jan to 31st. Dec. 1885.	371
21.10.1886 246.	Mr. G.A. Banbury, appointed Collector of Dues and Taxes by S of S has arrived here, and commenced duties on the 12th.	408
29.10.1886 255.	Forwards copy of Report of the M.O's of H.M.S. "Bacchante" and "Mariner" on the suitability of Long Island as Quarantine Station.	411
30.10.1886 256.	At request of the Rear Admiral, a man reported by the Acting G.M.O. to be suffering from Varioloid was landed at Long Island Quarantine Station from H.M.S. "Mariner" on the 22nd.	412
3.11.1886 257.	Stating that the above man died on the 1st.	412
23.11.1886 287.	Long letter (6 pages) relating to custody of Public Money : forwarding correspondence and asking for instructions.	429
1.12.1886 296.	Denis Island Lighthouse. Forwarding copy of report from Acting Supt. of P.W.	441
19.01.1887 7.	Enclosing application from Dr. Esnouf, Acting G.M.O. for post of G.M.O.	463

Date	Subject Matter	Page
14.02.1887	Alleged proselytism in the Public Hospital. Transmitting copies of correspondence.	475
21.02.1887 54.	Enclosing copy of Report for 1886 from the Acting Inspector of Schools.	486
21.02.1887 55.	Sending a memorial, with 8 enclosures, from the ex-Sultan of Perak to Secretary of State.	486
21.02.1887 58.	Remarks about Long Island Quarantine Station.	490
		VOL. B/42.
18.06.1889 182.	Making report on Blue Books for 1888.	5
4.07.1889 187.	Suggesting distinctive postage stamps, and forwarding estimate from De La Rue and Co.,	14
6.07.1889 189.	Sending, with observations, a signed application asking for renewed immigration of rescued Africans.	16
13.07.1889 195.	Denis Island Lighthouse. Sending report by Govt. Surveyor.	22
9.08.1889	Sending petition from two men complaining that they have been refused licences for Hotels in Hangard Street. Letter gives reasons and describes the very undesirable reputation of Hangard Street.	26
2.09.1889 214.	On the matter of duty on coal. Renewed application by M.M.Co., The letter to The Governor gives an interesting insight into shipping affairs in general as regards the M.M.Co.	34
11.09.1889 231.	Clerk in Administrator's Office ; respecting pay and Work. Describes state of the records in the office.	48
8.10.1889 248.	To the Secretary of State for the Colonies. Malay Political Prisoners. Their decision in res-	

Date	Subject Matter	Page
	pect of suggested idea of transfer to Sarawak.	66
14.10.1889 263.	To S of S. Remarks on a petition from mercantile community (relating to Custom matter) which unknown to the Administrator was sent direct to S of S. by last mail.	81
17.10.1889 268.	Messageries Maritimes. Further respecting dues on coal.	86
14.11.1889 280.	To S of S. Refers to another document (at the instigation of Mr. Galbraith as was one before, see 14.10.1889) sent to a member, or members, of Parliament.	96
14.11.1889 281.	Respecting idea of introducing trial by Jury.	98
14.11.1889 282.	Concerning proposal for reintroduction of Liberated African Labourers.	99
13.11.1890	To S of S. Requesting that enquiries be made, and support given, to idea of B.I.S.N. Co., ships calling.	116
15.01.1890 16.	Transmitting Estimates for 1890, with comment thereon.	120
11.02.1890 35.	Summary punishment of perjury. Reporting introduction of such an Ordinance to Legislative Council, with reports and recommendation from the judge.	141
11.02.1890 36.	Proposal submitted for building a new goal, and enclosing plan of present premises and suggested alterations.	143
11.02.1890 38.	Treasury and Customs and other offices. Proposal for enlargement, and enclosing plans.	149
6.03.1890 56.	Immigration Dept. sending report for 1889, and commenting thereon.	163

Date	Subject Matter	Page
12.03.1890 61.	Advising passing of Ordinance Nº.1 of 1890 to reorganize the Board of Health.	166
31.03.1890 75.	Reporting visits to Praslin, La Digue, Curieuse and Felicité.	175
10.04.1890 80.	Advising that the Seychelles Postage Stamps have arrived.	181
14.04.1890 84.	Transmitting a letter from the Pro Vicar Apostolic of Seychelles addressed to the Governor, and commenting thereon, as invited to do (The Administrator's remarks are of great interest).	183
15.04.1890 87.	On the necessity of a permanent Medical Officer for Praslin, La Digue and Curieuse.	186
8.05.1890 94.	Concerning alleged disastrous deforestation of land, and refuting the report of.	196
15.05.1890 104.	The ex-Mantri of Perak is to leave for Singapore, via Aden, in order to take up residence at Sarawak.	202
30.05.1890 112.	Transmitting, with remarks, Report on Elementary Schools for 1889.	207
7.06.1890 120.	Sending for sanction, proposed ordinance transferring power to close cemeteries from Chief of Police and Govt. M.O., to the Administrator in Council.	213
13.06.1890 125.	Proposed ideas for establishing a Govt. School. Mention made of strong protests made against the school, throughout the island, by Vicaire Apostolique threatening families will be excommunicated if they send their children to it.	220
15.07.1890 151.	Ecclesiastical grants. Views as to distribution of, and submitting proposal for entire withdrawal.	242
22.07.1890 158.	Trial of capital offences in Seychelles, transmitting opinions of Legislative and Executive Councils on proposed ordinance, and Judges' report.	250

Date	Subject Matter	Page
13.08.1890 176.	Felicité Island. Information about.	264
13.09.1890 189.	Rupee currency. Submitting proposal to demonetise the rupee and substitute British silver.	276
11.10.1890 206.	Denis Island Lighthouse. Reporting official visit to inspect. The recommendations of the Govt. Surveyor will be sent next mail.	289
14.11.1890 228.	Denis Island Lighthouse. Sending report of Govt. Surveyor, with comments.	304
15.12.1890 247.	Denis Island Lighthouse. Sending photograph.	319
15.12.1890 248.	As above, but to S of S.	319
16.12.1890 250.	British Bark "Earn", Island of Johanna for Mauritius with sugar, wrecked on Providence reef, about 17 miles from island of that name, on 29th October. Captain and crew arrived Mahe recently.	320
7.01.1891 2.	Water supply. Reporting expenditure on two pieces of work in 1890.	327
8.01.1891 6.	Ecclesiastical Grants in continuation of (see 15.07.1890 (151). A long letter on this matter.	329
13.01.1891 15.	To Secretary of State for the Colonies. Forwarding copy of report of inquiry regarding loss of British Barque "Earn". (See 16.12.1890 (250).	338
14.02.1891 33.	Forwarding Estimates for 1891, with remarks thereon.	352
3.03.1891 43.	Mr. James Driver, Headmaster of Govt. School arrived on 16th Feb.	373
12.03.1891 51.	The Govt. Undenominational School opened on 2nd inst.	376

Date	Subject Matter	Page
15.04.1891 76.	Submitting draft Order in Council for the trial of capital offences in Seychelles.	395
9.05.1891 85.	Agricultural labour. Sending a memorial from planters about obtaining liberated slaves from Portuguese East Africa.	400
14.05.1891 91.	Religious instruction at Govt. School. Asking what system is adopted in Mauritius undenominational schools.	405
14.05.1891 92.	Denis Island Lighthouse. Notifying the taking of a vote for Rs.4,000 on account of repairs to.	406
16.06.1891 113.	Proposal for new gaol dropped for the present. Immediate necessary addition to the gaol are being commenced.	422
14.08.1891 146.	Aldabra Islands. Transmitting a report.	440
16.09.1891 159.	To Secretary of State. Proposed telegraphic communication between Zanzibar and Mauritius via Seychelles.	450
8.10.1891 168.	To Secretary of State. Telegraphic communication with Europe via Zanzibar Legislative Council have passed a vote of £ 1,000 a year subsidy.	454
9.10.1891 171.	To Secretary of State. Malay exiles. On the subject of their return to Singapore, and sending a document from them.	457
10.10.1891 172.	Exhibition in Mauritius : Seychelles representation at Rs.2,000 voted.	459
9.11.1891 184.	Reporting visit to outlying islands.	466
10.11.1891 188.	Sending report on the Census.	472

Date	Subject Matter	Page
14.11.1891 191.	A severe outbreak of influenza.	476
14.11.1891 193.	Transmitting Estimates for 1892 with explanations thereon.	476
16.11.1891 194.	To S of S. from R.M. Brown, Judge. Reports departure of Administrator C. Risely Griffiths, and that he (Brown) becomes Acting Administrator as directed by the S of S. A similar notification to the Governor.	483
15.12.1891 216.	Further to epidemic of influenza (see 14.11.1891). This is now on the decline.	494
	VOL. B/43.	
15.02.1892 48.	To Secretary of State. Reference to the death of the Duke of Clarence and sending an address to the Queen from the Council.	29
15.02.1892 51.	Transmitting Blue Book reports for 1889 and 1890. For reference to Liberated Africans see p. 42 and 49. The last was introduced in 1874.	31
12.03.1892 77.	Forwarding Ordinance to consolidate and amend the law relating to Prisons.	69
14.03.1892 80.	Explaining vote in Estimates of Rs.6,500 for extension of Gaol and Judicial buildings.	74
30.03.1892 91.	Transmitting Inspector of Liberated Africans report for 1891.	91
13.04.1892 116.	Sending Annual Report of the Chief Officer of Police with remarks thereon.	100
14.05.1892 138.	Report on the Seychelles Blue Books for 1891.	117
14.05.1892 139.	Report on the working of the Vagrancy Ordinance.	129

Date	Subject Matter	Page
14.05.1892 141.	Submitting for decision whether Seychelles Govt. liable for expenses of maintenance in a foreing land, and repatriation to this Dependency of a native of Seychelles who has left the place years ago, and of a wife and family not native of Seychelles.	132
17.05.1892	C. Risely Griffity, Administrator, reports his arrival from Europe to-day.	135
17.05.1892 146.	Referring to news of a devastating hurricane in Mauritius. Rs.5,000 voted by the Govt of Seychelles for relief purpose, and a fund opened for private subscriptions.	136
9.06.1892 150.	Mr. Abdool Rassool's offer to lease the Admirantes Islands.	138
13.06.1892 152.	The Administrator describes his visit to Aldabra Island in H.M.S. "Redbreast".	141
15.06.1892 158.	Mr. Brodie, Govt. Auditor and etc... interdicted from 1st. June (There have been a number of letters to Mauritius over months past about his inattention and dilatoriness, and ignoring remonstrance).	147
15.07.1892 176.	The New Oriental Bank closed its doors 17th June.	159
15.08.1892 190.	St. Paul's Boys'School. Replying to enquiry as to its formation and composition.	168
13.09.1892 196.	New Oriental Bank's premises. Proposals for dealing with the same under the lease.	174
14.10.1892 219.	Chief Officer of Police, Relating to the filling up of appointment, should it become vacant.	191
14.10.1892 220.	Sending petition to S of S signed by 61 persons, asking for a new form of constitution and sundry other matters. 10 pages of comments.	192
12.11.1892 234.	Alteration in postal rates. The Legislative have adopted the suggestions for assimilation of postal	

Date	Subject Matter	Page
	rates with United Kingdom, Mauritius, etc...	209
17.12.1892 255.	Respecting office of Chief Officer of Police and selection of someone to fill the appointment.	227
12.01.1893 8.	Assimilation of Postage Rates to U.K. and Mauritius, reasons for delay in bringing into operation.	235
14.01.1893 15.	Forwarding Estimates of Revenue and Expenditure for 1893, with explanations.	240
14.01.1893 19.	Educational Report for 1892.	252
8.02.1893 28.	Assimilation of postage rates to United Kingdom ; further to.	261
11.02.1893 33.	To S of S. Transmitting the offer of Seychelles. Govt. for the buildings of the New Oriental Bank.	264
13.03.1893 56.	Frauds on Treasury Dept. Transmitting correspondence thereon, and showing system of Treasury Dept. work in connection therewith.	282
14.03.1893 61.	Suggesting desirability of a Botanical Station, the Officer in charge being also Conservator of Crown Lands.	285
4.04.1893 71.	Gigantic Tortoises at Aldabra ; in reply to an enquiry respecting.	294
4.05.1893	To S of S. Telegraph cable, Seychelles. In reply to an enquiry as to place of landing.	310
10.05.1893 98.	Postage Stamps. Transmitting specimen of a new overprint 12c stamp.	316
12.05.1893 102.	To S of S. Felicite Island. Information as to claim for ownership of part, and offer of compromise	319

Date	Subject Matter	Page
14.06.1893 121.	Denis Island Lighthouse. Notifying vote of Rs.4,000 additional for repairs, and asking approval.	337
15.06.1893 124.	To S of S. Postage Stamp Dies and new stamps. Enclosing requisition for, and asking approval.	340
13.07.1893 142.	Botanical Station at Capucin. Further respecting proposed establishment of.	352
9.08.1893 159.	Denis Island Lighthouse. Further respecting the method of rebuilding.	365
13.09.1893 178.	Relating to the acquirement of the Bank premises by Govt., and the temporary occupation of a portion by the Eastern Telegraph Co.,	380
13.10.1893 201.	Asking for approval of establishment, on trial, of Inland Post.	397
15.11.1893	To S of S. Sending copy of telegram despatched upon completion of Seychelles and Zanzibar cable.	408
12.12.1893 223.	Asking to be allowed to introduce legislation to protect cocos de mer trees at Praslin.	411
16.12.1893 237.	Schooner "Lighter" brought 50 persons (British Indian subjects) survivors from native dhow "Dolut Pasa", Mossé Bé, Madagascar, for Bombay, wrecked Cosmoledo Island 10th Sept.	419
10.01.1894 3.	Forwarding estimates of revenue and expenditure for 1894, with explanations.	423
15.02.1894 28.	To S of S. Notifying passing of Ordinance to amend Regulation N°. 1 of 1889, relating to better preservation of coco de mer trees, and asking authority by telegraph to assent to same.	453

Date	Subject Matter	Page
5.03.1894 33.	Ex-Sultan Abdullah accepts conditions named relating to his proposed visit to England.	456
12.03.1894 38.	Removal of Govt. School, Audit Office, Warden's Office, to new premises, and asking approval of a Legislative vote of Rs.1500 consequent on changes.	459
15.03.1894 41.	Seychelles Govt. Savings Bank opened on 5th inst.	462
14.04.1894 53.	To S of S. Botanical Station. Remarks upon the proposals of Mr. Scott, Director of Forests and Gardens, Mauritius.	468
12.05.1894 63.	Letter concerning the temporary suspension, by the Acting Judge, of a notary unable to find acceptable security. It also gives an enlightening picture of several of the notaries in the town.	476
14.05.1894 64.	To S of S. Reporting departure, for England, of Ex-Sultan of Perak.	477
25.06.1894	To S of S. Rendering congratulations to Prince and Princess of Wales on the birth of a son to the Duke and Duchess of York.	492
30.06.1894 81.	Sending report on Primary Education for 1893.	492
12.07.1894 90.	Because of financial loss, inland postal service discontinued after a trial of 9 months.	499
12.07.1894 91.	To S of S. The premises of the late New Oriental Bank have been acquired. Raising question as to removal or redistribution of certain Judicial Offices.	500
14.07.1894 97.	Education. Legislative Council vote for expenses in connection with the affiliation of two Schools to the Royal College, Mauritius, and asking approval of	504

Date	Subject Matter	Page
13.10.1894 134.	To S of S. Notifying illegal removal of "Pierre de Possession", by a resident, and its conveyance to France by General Frey.	531
19.10.1894 140.	Transmitting an Ordinance "to provide for the creation of slaughter houses", and asking authority to assent thereto.	536
15.11.1894 150.	Dr. J. Monnier, Acting G.M.O. (pending either the return of Dr. Esnouf or appointment of another permanent official), having fallen ill, and being unable to continue his duties, (also probably going Reunion for change of air), Dr. J.H. Brooks appointed in his place.	545
15.11.1894 151.	New Govt. premises. Notifying transference of Treasury, decision to move Law Courts, and asking approval of vote of Rs.2,500 in connection with alterations.	546
		VOL. B/44.
12.12.1894 163.	Sending Estimates for 1895 with remarks thereon.	4
7.02.1895 20.	Communication between India and Seychelles direct : suggested proposals for.	29
14.02.1895 26.	General survey of Seychelles. Replying to despatch asking that steps should be taken. An interesting account which shows the great difficulties presented.	34
14.02.1895 27.	Botanic Station. Concerning scheme for establishing.	36
14.02.1895 28.	Coco de mer ravine, Praslin. Negociations for purchase of a portion.	37
16.02.1895	To S of S. Ex-Sultan of Perak and family leaves to-day for Singapore.	39

Date	Subject Matter	Page
14.03.1895 38.	Forwarding Education Report for 1894, with remarks.	46
16.03.1895 40.	Transmitting drafts of Prison Regulations.	48
16.03.1895 42.	Coco de mer valley, Praslin. Notifying purchase of Mrs. Germains'half share.	50
16.03.1895 49.	C. Risely Griffiths, Administrator, reports his departure to-day, having accepted administrator-ship of St. Kitts	53
17.04.1895 51.	R.M. Brown, now Acting Administrator, reports departure of Mr. Griffiths.	54
1.04.1895 61.	Forwarding copies of deeds for purchase of some coco de mer land at Praslin. (See 16.3.1895. N° 42).	64
17.04.1895 76.	Advising departure for Singapore of last of the Political prisoners.	77
17.04.1895	To S of S. Reporting that Pierre de Possession was returned last Nov. and is in Govt. House grounds (see 13.10.1894. n° 134).	77
13.05.1895 83.	Reporting discussions by Board of Education upon the Report for 1894. Reference made to the pros and cons of teaching French and English.	82
13.05.1895 85.	Forwarding a letter from Mr. H. Baty concerning necessity of a new line of steamers.	85
14.05.1895 89.	Submitting for approval, suggestions for legislation concerning squatters.	88
15.05.1895 93.	Deforestation of Seychelles mountains. Asking for views of Mr. Scott, Mauritius Director of Forests.	91

Date	Subject Matter	Page
15.05.1895 96.	Submitting for the opinion of the Procureur General, a case of an alleged squatter.	94
22.05.1895 105.	Felicité Island. Asking for advice as to leasing.	100
15.06.1895 123.	The Acting Administrator reports Mr. Henry Cockburn Stewart has arrived to be Administrator. (Note. he was here before ; left in Nov. 1881).	109
17.06.1895 125.	H. Cockburn Stewart reports having assumed the Administration to-day.	110
26.06.1895 129.	To S of S. Same as above.	112
6.08.1895	To S of S. Respecting the calling of British India Steam Navn. Co's steamers (on the Bombay/Zanzibar service) which has been arranged.	120
7.08.1895 147.	Concerning the devastation of cacao plantations	121
8.08.1895 150.	Further respecting the teaching of two languages in Primary Schools.	123
12.08.1895 155.	Concerning Seychelles Bacca Ordinance Nº 13 of 1893.	127
4.09.1895 159.	H.M.S. "Bonaventure", having arrived on 27 th Aug, leaves for Aden to-day.	131
9.09.1895 161.	Calls by B.I.S.N. Co., Ships. Sending pro forma time-table.	133
14.09.1895 164.	Long report about misconduct of certain prison officers.	134
3.10.1895 173.	Dr. Monnier, Acting G.M.O., given a month's leave to go to Port Said in medical charge of a Russian	

Date	Subject Matter	Page
	Man of War. (Surgeon lost a few hours before arrival Mahe). Dr. Denman appointed to act until Dr. M's return.	142
10.10.1895 183.	Adoption of increased postal rates. New stamps required.	149
4.11.1895 194.	Forwarding Estimates of Revenue and Expenditure for 1896, with remarks thereon.	156
15.11.1895 205.	"An Ordinance to provide for the levying of Harbour and Light Dues". Submitting for assent.	167
16.11.1895 207.	Respecting guano deposits in some of the islands.	168
17.12.1895 222.	Relating to M.M. Co's decision to cease calling at Mahe.	177
13.01.1896 13.	Regarding the raising of a loan of £ 15,000 for the Making of roads.	185
15.01.1896 18.	More about M.M. Co's ships ceasing to call.	189
8.02.1896 28.	Respecting the working of guano deposits in some of the islands.	195
14.02.1896 31.	"Clan Graham" was stranded on Cosmoledo Island. "Clan Ross" arrived Mahe 8th January to endeavour to float her off. "Clan Graham" floated off at high tide before "Clan Ross" had returned to her.	197
14.02.1896 32.	To S of S. Quarantine in Seychelles : problems arising from.	198
15.02.1896 34.	The large number of out patients having free treatment at Hospital greatly reduced (by one third). Administrator, believing many, well able to pay, were getting free treatment, directed that to obtain it, a ticket from Chief Officer of Police, stating unable to pay, must be produced.	200

Date	Subject Matter	Page
10.03.1896 49.	Respecting postal service between Europe and Seychelles.	210
17.03.1896 56.	To S of S. Asking whether a gunboat not in service could be lent to Seychelles for communication with the islands. (Note. This idea was raised some years back, but it did not develop).	214
17.04.1896 71.	To S of S. Necessity of a clerk to relieve Govt. Surveyor of so much office work, and enable him to give more time to outside duties.	226
30.04.1896	To the under Secretary of State. Sending drawing and notes (including a design for flag) made by General Gordon in 1881, for Colonial Office Library.	229
6.05.1896 81.	To S of S. Respecting guano deposits in the group.	234
8.06.1896 89.	To S of S. Reporting death (after a month's absence from duty) of Dr. Jules Monnier, Acting Govt. Medical Officer. Recommending Dr. Denman (who has twice acted as G.M.O. and is doing so now) be appointed.	239
9.06.1896 90.	To S of S. Irregularity of calls by B.I.S.N. Ships.	240
16.06.1896	To S of S. German Man of War "Condor" arrived from Zanzibar on 14th to remain 3 or 4 days.	242
1.07.1896	To S of S. Dumont Camille presented (publicly) with medal and certificate of Royal Humane Society. (He saved 5 men from drowning at La Digue in 1894 which, on learning of it, was reported to S of S on 22.2.1896).	244

Date	Subject Matter	Page
3.07.1896	**To S of S.** Rear Admiral Durmmond Naval Commander in Chief East India Station, arrived on 20th June in H.M.S. "Bonadventure", accompanied by "Cossack" and "Redbreast", and leaves this day for Mauritius.	245
9.07.1896 100.	**To S of S.** In accordance with telegram received Dr. Denman appointed Govt. Medical Officer.	248
13.07.1896 103.	Dr. Portal arrived on 3rd inst. to be Assistant G.M.O.	248
8.08.1896 121.	**To S of S.** Forwarding memorials from Dr. Brooks and Mr. Harrison on the subject Harbour regulations.	259
8.08.1896 123.	**To S of S.** Transmitting with remarks, a Memorial from Mr. Harrison respecting a printed circular from the Judge relative to a certain pamphlet abusing the Govt. (Printed in Bombay, and a considerable number of copies received from there, but evidently concocted in Seychelles).	262
31.08.1896	**To S of S.** A long report of the Administrator's visit to Praslin, La Digue, Curieuse, and Felicité.	267
19.10.1896 146.	**To S of S.** Transmitting, with comments, a Memorial from Mr. S. Galbraith, relative to the management of the Hospital. Accusations proved unfounded.	281
27.10.1896	**To S of S.** Respecting overprinting of certain postage stamps	287
3.11.1896	**To S of S.** Relative to appointment of an Engineer from Ceylon to report on roads. Mr. Creasy arrived from Bombay yesterday.	290

Date	Subject Matter	Page
12.11.1896	**To S of S.** Proposal that as there is no public pharmacy in the town, and no signs of private enterprize providing one, the Govt, should open a public paying dispensary, No one. unless a pauper (who are treated at the Dispensary), can obtain medicine unless they go to a Doctor, and pay a fee in addition to cost of medicine.	294
11.11.1896	**To S of S.** Sending with remarks, petition asking that the M.M. Co., should resume calls.	296
23.11.1896	**To S of S.** Respecting Exhibition in Paris in 1900.	300
23.11.1896	**To S of S.** Forwarding, with comments, Estimates of Revenue and Expenditure for 1897.	301
16.12.1896	**To S of S.** Respecting supply of new postage stamps.	313
31.12.1896	**To S of S.** Concerning exportation of guano.	321
23.01.1897	Asking to be supplied with a plan of a gallows, also a model.	326
1.02.1897	**To S of S.** Concerning the teaching of 2 languages in all Govt. Schools.	329
20.02.1897	Concerning charge of murder against Robert and others.	334
22.02.1897 10.	**To S of S.** As above.	334
12.03.1897 12.	**To S of S.**	

Date	Subject Matter	Page
	Acknowledging despatch approving that medicines should be sold at Government dispensary (because no pharmacy in the town). See 12.11.1896. Page 294.	338
10.04.1897 18.	To S of S. Relating to measures taken to present introduction of bubonic plague.	344
19.04.1897 19.	To S of S. Concerning proposed general survey.	345
1.05.1897	As above.	350
14.05.1897	To S of S. The Administrator applies for 5 months leave, to begin between July and end of year.	353
30.06.1897 32.	To S of S. Forwarding an address from the Liberated Africans to H.M. the Queen.	364
30.06.1897 33.	To S of S. Respecting loan for the construction of roads.	364
10.07.1897 39.	To S of S. Rear Admiral Drummond, H.M.S. "Eclipse" arrived 19th June and left 5th. German man of war "Condor" left on 23rd inst. (presumably ultimo, letter being dated 10th) having stayed a month.	368
12.07.1897 40.	To S of S. Describing celebrations of the 60th year of the Queen's accession to the throne.	368
23.07.1897 45.	To S of S. Relating to raising of loan for roads. Suggesting that a foreman of works could be obtained from Aberdeen to teach how granite should be worked.	374

Date	Subject Matter	Page
19.08.1897 54.	To S of S. Respecting cessation of the affiliated classes in Seychelles.	384
20.08.1897 55.	To S of S. Annual inspection of Praslin, La Digue and Curieuse.	385
28.08.1897 59.	To S of S. Scheme for a Botanic Station. Recommending that because of financial situation, it should be postponed.	387
1.10.1897 68.	To S of S. On the advice of Executive Council, the sentence of death passed on Joseph Robert, Charles Robert, and David Robert, altered to Penal Servitude for life. The Judge recommended this, as in his opinion premeditation had not been clearly established. See 20.2.1897. Page 334.	395
1.10.1897	To S of S. Farquhar Island. Executive Council have no particular wish that it be included with Seychelles group, but if Mauritius Govt. wish it, there would be no objection. No expense of a magistrate could be incurred, and only such measures as taken for other outlying islands, would be made applicable.	396
11.10.1897	Asking if Mr. Hobbs can be spared to undertake the survey.	398
1.12.1897 87.	To S of S. Respecting loan for road making.	413
29.12.1897 99.	To S of S. Forwarding the Estimates for 1898, with remarks.	422
30.12.1897 103.	To S of S. Mr. Hobbs, who is to do survey, arrived from Mauritius on 24th.	428

Date	Subject Matter	Page
30.12.1897 104.	**To S of S.** Reporting purchase of a further area of the coco de mer valley at Praslin.	430
5.01.1898 7.	**To S of S.** Concerning a case of small-pox, (25th Nov.) and action taken. Man now quite recovered, and no other cases.	433
28.01.1898 15.	**To S of S.** Full powers of Governor having now been conferred, the question has arisen whether the Administrator should not be styled "His Excellency the Administrator", instead of "His Honour the Administrator".	438
18.02.1898 18.	**To S of S.** Mr. George Waddell, the Engineer for Road works arrived las mail, and has begun duty.	440
18.02.1898 19.	**To S of S.** Part of Govt. House condemned by the Surveyor as uninhabitable.	440
15.03.1898 24.	**To S of S.** Sending 3 ordinances relating to scheme to amalgamate offices of Police Magistrate, Crown Prosecutor, and Conservator of Mortgages.	443
21.03.1898 25.	**To S of S.** Long letter regarding scheme of getting labour from India or Ceylon for road making.	444
10.05.1898 35.	**To S of S.** Concerning whether M.M. Co., ships would again serve Seychelles.	454
14.05.1898 38.	**To S of S.** Respecting Mr. Creasy's estimate for road and Mr. Waddell's views thereon.	456
7.06.1898 45.	**To S of S.**	

Date	Subject Matter	Page
	Respecting Civil Chaplain's claim to Private Entree at Levees. Sending copy of letter.	461
8.07.1898 47.	To S of S. Acknowledging sanction of special vote for repair of Govt. House later in year.	463
10.06.1898 48.	To S of S. Sending another letter, as above.	464
2.07.1898	Rear Admiral Douglas. H.M.S. "Eclipse", arrived 15th June and left 27th.	465
7.07.1898 52.	To S of S. A report against the Rev. S.E. Walters, Civil Chaplain.	465
13.07.1898 54.	To S of S. On the 12th June Rinderpest occurred in cattle (introduced from Mombasa on 9th). Twenty animals had to be destroyed.	468
13.07.1898 56.	To S of S. Transmitting an Ordinance for raising the sum of £ 20,000 for construction of roads, and a general survey.	470
15.07.1898 57.	To S of S. Forwarding with comments, a memorial from the Rev. S.E. Walters, Civil Chaplain.	471
18.07.1898 58.	To S of S. Sending Petitions relative to precedence of the Civil Chaplain. The Administrator's remarks thereon, and upon some of the supporters are most enlightening.	473
30.07.1898 60.	To S of S. Reporting Mr. Waddell's departure for Bombay to recruit labour for road constructions.	479

Date	Subject Matter	Page
30.07.1898 61.	**To S of S.** Requesting permission to order some small iron bridges from Bombay : Mr. Waddell proceeding there to-day to hire labour for road works.	480
23.09.1898 71.	**To S of S.** Forwarding Education Report for 1897.	485
3.10.1898	**To S of S.** Acknowledging receipt of new seal.	485
13.10.1898 77.	**To S of S.** Further respecting memorial from Civil Chaplain sending letter from Mr. Boustead.	487
13.10.1898 78.	**To S of S.** As above, and sending another letter from Mr. B.	489
12.10.1898 80.	**To S of S.** Concerning the moitie system contract.	492
18.10.1898 81.	**To S of S.** Reporting return from Bombay of Mr. Waddell, bringing 320 coolies.	494
26.10.1898 83.	**To S of S.** Relating to question of M.M. Co. ships resuming calls, and giving details as to B.I. services.	495
15.11.1898 91.	**To S of S.** Asking approval of vote of Rs. 1500 to continue the work of erecting a new Public Works Office and workships.	504
15.11.1898 92.	**To S of S.** Giving an account of prison matters and difficulties.	505
15.12.1898 96.	**To S of S.** Reduction of letter postage rate as from 25th Dec.	

Date	Subject Matter	Page
	One penny (that is six cents) per half ounce.	508
22.12.1898 103.	To S of S. Forwarding, with remarks, Estimates for 1899.	511
30.12.1898	To S of S. Transmitting Ordinance N°. 15 of 1898 to reduce export duty on guano from Rs.5/- a ton (ordinance N°. 5 of 1897) to Rs.1/- a ton. This because it has been found that Seychelles guano is of a low class not worth more than L 2.10 a ton, not L 10 to L 12 as Administrator thought at time of sending Despatch 65/185 of 21/12/96.	517
	Unless otherwise stated, letters are to The Secretary of State. The Administrator is E.B. Sweet Escott, who, in 1903, became the first Governor of Seychelles	
19.01.1901 20.	Refers to proposal of B.I. Co., for a mail service.	1
19.01.1901 21.	Suggests issue of a paper currency.	3
29.01.1901 31.	Forwarding resolution from Legislative Council ament the death of Queen Vistoria.	12
13.02.1901 39.	Forwards copy of letter from French Consular Agent covering one from Director General of M.M.Co.	18
14.02.1901 40.	Mr. R. Dupont to be Curator of Botanic Station, arrived from Mauritius on 4th.	19
14.02.1901 43.	Recommends acceptance of conditions proposed by Seychelles Club for lease of piece of land.	20
16.02.1901 45.	Sending copy of letter from Unofficial Members of Legislative Council suggesting Duke and Duchess of York be invited te visit Seychelles on return passage from Australia.	24

Date	Subject Matter	Page
16.02.1901 47.	Forwards design, prepared by Mr. Dupuy, Head-master Victoria School, for a flag for Seychelles.	26
16.02.1901 49.	Sends 2 photos of Political Prisoners from Ashanti. Enquires as to possibility of Ashanti Labourers being recruited.	29
16.02.1901 50.	Concerning regulations for Victoria School, and amendments. (An informative insight into scholastic matters).	31
3.03.1901 58.	Report a tour of inspection of the roads in Mahe.	42
11.03.1901 63.	Reports arrival of Rev. F.J. Fuller, Civil Chaplain.	49
15.03.1901 70.	Refers to proposal that the ex-King of Uganda may be deported to Seychelles.	53
20.03.1901 75.	Forwards rules and conditions for apprentices at Botanic Station.	63
5.04.1901 87.	A detailed account of visit to Silhouette Island and North Island.	69
8.04.1901 90.	Concerning proposed Infant School, in connection with the Victoria School.	76
13.04.1901 100.	On the matter of overseas shipping services.	84
27.04.1901 106.	Concerns recent correspondence on subject of obtaining labourers from India, explains reasons for want of labourers, and recommends 20 coolies be imported from Madras for road work.	94
7.05.1901 109.	About scheme, suggested by Messrs. Baty, Bergue & Co. (Copy Bros. Agents and Lighter Owners), for a light tramway (for goods) on Long Pier, and in main street.	99

Date	Subject Matter	Page
9.05.1901 112.	Reviewing local postal arrangements.	102
11.05.1901 115.	Long letter relating to proposed alterations in French Customs Tariff.	108
24.05.1901 122.	Advising that Baty, Bergue & Co., have withdrawn proposal for tramway. Comments made upon this.	118
22.06.1901 137.	Urging (as previously) the need for information about negociations with the M.M. Co., for a mail service.	140
22.06.1901 138.	The additional Ashanti Political prisoners arrived in transport "Dwarka" to-day. With servants and interpreter, 21 in party.	142
15.07.1901 148.	Sending copy of agreement leasing Curieuse Island for 30 years.	148
17.07.1901 149.	Forwards notice and prize list for agricultural and Industrial Exhibition to be held 12 th, 13 th, 14 th Sept. The Administrator says "The Exhibition will be useful if it only serves as a topic for reasonable conversation".	149
19.07.1901 151.	Informative letter dealing with relative strength of the C of E. and R.C. adherents ; the number of children in the schools ; duties of Civil Chaplain; and other matters.	150
27.07.1901 158.	Forwards with explanations, statement of Assets and Liabilities on 31 st December, 1900.	158
28.07.1901 159.	Sending an account of a tour of the roads.	161
28.07.1901 160.	Submitting plans, with estimates, for converting Post Office into a Central Police Station ; and Victoria School Room, Public Works Store, and Seychelles Club premises into Post Office, Infant School and Victoria School, respectively.	163

Date	Subject Matter	Page
30.07.1901 162.	Long letter about problems connected with transport (mails and cargo) because of lack of opportunities.	166
29.08.1901 191.	Report vote of Legislative Council for L 500 as Seychelles Contribution to Imperial Memorial to Queen Victoria.	203
30.08.1901 192.	Sending 2 copies of agreement for lease of the Aldabra group to Baty, Bergue & Co.	204
5.09.1901 204.	Relates to proposed establishment of a note Currency issue.	220
20.09.1901 214.	Respecting mail service for Seychelles. Long letter dealing also with cargo matters.	229
21.09.1901 218.	The need for a Lunatic Asylum. Opportunities of transport to Mauritius a difficulty ; also costly.	235
29.10.1901 247.	Forwards copies of regulations for grant-in-aid schools.	265
3.11.1901 251.	Forwards copies of Resolutions of Public meeting to consider the erection of a Public Memorial to Queen Victoria.	272
5.11.1901 254.	This letter amongst other matters mentions that a Volunteer Fire Brigade has been formed.	274
5.11.1901 256.	Sends petition from ex-King Prempeh and Ashanti Chiefs praying that they may be allowed to return.	276
16.11.1901 260.	H.M. Transport "Armenian" has brought 1017 Boer prisoners.	283
21.11.1901 264.	Concerning proposals to increase and improve the Police Force.	286
3.12.1901 269.	Submits for approval, action in having arranged importation, from Mauritius, of 25 Malagache labourers.	293

Date	Subject Matter	Page
6.12.1901 271.	Forwarding Estimates of Revenue and Expenditure for 1902, with remarks.	296
17.12.1901 280.	Further remarks as to a design for a flag for Seychelles.	314
23.12.1901 281.	Forwarding copies of correspondence with the Governor of Mauritius connected with filling appointment of Postmaster, Seychelles. In conclusion the Administrator mentions the desirability of the Govt. of Seychelles being entirely separated from that of Mauritius.	315
27.12.1901 287.	Sending copies of correspondence with the Governor of Mauritius relating to wreck of schooner "Maggie Low".	322
17.01.1902 19.	Concerning appointment of a 2nd Master of Victoria School, and other scholastic matters.	337
30.01.1902 25.	Botanic Station. Sending report by Curator on analysis of soils of the station and of North Island.	344
28.02.1902 44.	Sending Annual Report of Savings Bank, with remarks.	359
1.03.1902 47.	Concerning proposal to render obligatory the payment of fees in Grant aided schools.	361
6.03.1902 48.	Forwarding, with observations, Annual Report by Inspector of Schools, on Primary Education in 1901.	363
7.03.1902 49.	Vessels of Messageries Maritimes Co., accorded status of men-of-war.	366
5.04.1902 75.	Submits proposals for establishing, from January, 1903, industrial training at the Victoria School.	386
25.05.1902 100.	Refers to the relative positions of the Administrator of Seychelles and the Governor of Mauritius as constituting a further argument in favour of the separation of Seychelles from Mauritius.	408

Date	Subject Matter	Page
3.06.1902 104.	Queen Victoria Memorial. Reports that amount (Rs. 3223.81) collected, and vote of Legislative Council for similar sum. Forwards for transmission to Crown Agents - indent for Clock Tower.	414
4.06.1902 106.	Refers to existing arrangements for mail service to Seychelles, and enquires whether B.I.S.N. Co., could not be approached again.	419
6.06.1902 109.	Forwards programme of events to take place to celebrate coronation of King Edward VII.	423
24.06.1902 119.	Submits, for consideration, papers relating to insufficiency of labour, and proposes that labourers for Govt. and for planters, be introduced from Ceylon. 9 pages.	434
27.06.1902 123.	Sends report on the census of Seychelles for 1901.	445
4.07.1902 131.	Forwards resolution of sympathy of Legislative Council at illness of H.M. The King.	452
24.07.1902 143.	Reports that Seychelles has been made a centre for the Cambridge Local examinations.	464
31.08.1902 163.	Reports representation at La Digue to Gustave Charles Mirabeau and Ange Payet, of Royal Humane Society's testimonials for saving life on 26th Dec. 1901.	482
5.09.1902 174.	Forwards accounts of Coronation Celebrations in Seychelles, copies of addresses presented, and 13 photographs.	494
1.10.1902 183.	States that Ceylon Govt. decline to allow Indian labourers to be recruited in Ceylon, and application has been made to the Govt. of Madras.	508
21.10.1902 202.	Reports result of First Examination for the Seychelles Scholarship, and explains conditions relating to the Victoria School.	528

Date	Subject Matter	Page
31.10.1902 219.	Reference is made to progress in English language made in Schools.	540
		VOL. B/47.
28.11.1902 233.	Schools. R.C. Bishop of Victoria proposes to open a school for boys at Anse Royale, and-later-one at La Digue. Both conducted by Marist Brothers.	5
1.12.1902 236.	Forwarding, with comments, the Estimates for Revenue and Expenditure for 1903.	7
31.12.1902 247.	Refers to telegram of 15th advising arrival of Steam Launch "Alexandra", from Bombay (Towed by B.I. "Nuddea". See letter 29.11.1901), and reports on two trial trips.	22
27.02.1903 32.	Submits suggestions as to disposal of remaining stock of Victorian Postage stamps.	48
1.03.1903 34.	Forwards amended regulations for the Victoria School, and regulations for Victoria Infant School.	50
6.03.1903 40.	Sends, with remarks, report of the Inspector of schools (and Head master of Victoria School).	57
12.03.1903 42.	Forwards Annual Report of Police Force for 1902, and refers to qualifications required of an Officer appointed as Inspector of Police.	60
2.04.1903 52.	Reports unveiling of Tower Clock erected in memory of Queen Victoria.	71
2.05.1903 74.	Forwards adopted minute N°. 2 of 1903 as to the purchase of a property as Govt. Sanatorium.	94
8.05.1903 87.	Advises death of Muanga, ex King of Uganda.	105
27.05.1903 99.	Gives account of visit of inspection to Denis Island and islands included in Praslin district.	119

Date	Subject Matter	Page
10.06.1903. 112.	Reports destruction of Victorian stamps and bringing into circulation of stamps bearing the King's head.	135
1.07.1903 129.	On the matter of teaching staff at Victoria School, and proposed salary increases.	153
3.07.1903 135.	Submits scheme for improving Victoria prison.	159
4.08.1903 151.	Further concerning need for a Lunatic asylum.	171
7.08.1903 157.	Submits proposals for transferring Pauper Camp from Round Island to the African Camp, near Victoria.	179
22.08.1903 161.	Submits for approval vote of Legislative Council for Rs. 100 for a survey of the town of Victoria.	185
3.09.1903 177.	Inquires whether the S of S would be prepared to consider the question of establishing a Government Agricultural Bank, and applies for information regarding the working of such Banks.	195
4.09.1903 178.	In connection with copies of a Police Instruction Manual printed in French and English, the Administrator considers it deplorable that although Seychelles has been a dependency of the British Crown for 107 years, the language should be French or a debased French patois.	196
7.09.1903 182.	Submits for approval action respecting importation from Madras of 60 male and 20 females for the service of the Govt. (Note. Letter 1.10.1903 reduces 60 to 50).	201
22.09.1903 187.	Reporting results of examination for Seychelles scholarship.	207
7.10.1903 200.	Regarding proposed transfer to lease of Aldabra Island for Baty, Bergue & Co., to Mr. A. d'Emmerez.	218
8.10.1903 201.	Long letter on proposed construction of a road from Baie St. Anne to Grand Anse, Praslin, and	

Date	Subject Matter	Page
	difficulties in acquiring necessary land.	218
20.10.1903 205.	Acknowledges receipt of new Letters Patent, Commission as Governor and Commander-in-Chief of Seychelles, and Royal Instructions for Seychelles and Mauritius.	227
2.11.1903 215.	Deals with the difficulties and disadvantages of substituting out door relief (as suggested by S of S) for present Pauper establishment on Round Island.	235
6.11.1903 219.	Reports on 2nd Agricultural and Industrial Exhibition, Distinct advance on one of 1901. 391 exhibits, whereas there might have been 3,000. Many did not exhibit because they thought they might not be awarded prizes. Comments upon lack of sporting spirit, and the lethargy in which planters, and their forefathers have been content to live during the last hundred years.	239
19.11.1903 223.	An account of the proceedings on the 9th inst. celebrating Seychelles Islands becoming a separate Colony.	244
19.11.1903 224.	Refers to proposal to make instruction in Agriculture a part of Grant in Aid system in Schools, and asks for copies of Regulations in force and reports presented by other Colonies, and names of text book used.	246
6.12.1903 239.	Forwards petitions for establishment of a Bank ; report on present agricultural position ; suggests raising of a loan of Rs. 500,000. Lengthy letter.	255
24.12.1903 247.	Forwards Estimates of Revenue and Expenditure for 1904, with remarks.	267
6.01.1904 12.	Sends a map of Mahe showing road work done from 1899-1903.	282
11.02.1904 28.	Forwards petition from some traders, planters and landowners against increase of ad valorem duty on goods coming from gold-using countries. With explanations.	295

Date	Subject Matter	Page
24.02.1904 32.	Reports visit of inspection to islands in the Praslin District.	307
2.03.1904 44.	Advises arrival on 12th Feb. in B.I. Co's "Itna", of 106 male adults, 42 fenale, 4 boys, 2 girls, 1 male infant, being immigrants from Madras.	313
8.03.1904 50.	Concerning possibility of extending cultivation of cotton.	317
25.03.1904 63.	Long letter about agriculture, and the Govt's action in endeavouring to foster cultivation of new products.	327
1.04.1904 67.	Forwarding Report on Education for 1905, with comments thereon, including a tribute to "the un-wavering support received from R.C. Bishop, Mother Superior of Convent, and the Sisters of St. Joseph de Cluny, in making English the real subject of instruction in all Grant-in-Aid Schools.	338
3.04.1904 69.	Acknowledging instructions that the Governor has been appointed as Governor of British Honduras, and should leave for England on 9th May.	341
7.04.1904 74.	Acknowledging advice that Mr. W.E. Davidson, C.M.G., late Colonial Secretary, Transvaal, is to be Governor of Seychelles.	344
9.05.1904 88.	F.A. Herchanroder advises that the Governor left at 1 a.m. to-day, and he has assumed the Administration of the Govt. pending arrival of Mr. W.E. Davidson.	353
31.05.1904 90.	W.E. Davidson, Governor, advises that the arrived on 30th and assumed administration of the Colony	354
7.07.1904 102.	Transmitting request from ex-King Prempeh and his followers that they may be allowed to return to their country.	358
5.09.1904 110.	Concerning illness of Rev. H. Johnson, Civil Chaplain.	363
1.10.1904 123.	Express thanks for cotton gin lent by British	

Date	Subject Matter	Page
	Cotton Growing Association, and asks to be supplied with Sea Island cotton seeds.	372
7.12.1904 138.	Transmit Estimates of Revenue and Expenditure for 1905, with comments.	383
1.03.1905 24.	Mr. F.A. Herchenroder, Chief Justice, will leave on 12th to take up the appointment of Procureur General, Mauritius.	399
10.03.1905 37.	Enquiring whether any possibility of Prince and Princess of Wales (who are to go to India), visiting Seychelles Outwards or Homewards.	405
24.03.1905 39.	Transmits, with remarks, annual report by Inspector of Police.	409
30.03.1905 40.	Notifies suspension of appointment of Rev. E.R. Ward (newly arrived) as Civil Chaplain, and states that an inquiry into charges (which are referred to) will be held by Bishop of Mauritius.	409
6.04.1905 47.	Sending Reports on Prisons by Supt. of Prisons and Chief Medical Officer.	416
7.04.1905 50.	Forwards annual report on Outlying Islands for 1904.	418
2.05.1905 56.	Reports arrival of B.I.S.N. Co's "Nuddea" with two cases of small pox on board.	423
6.05.1905 58.	Reports judgement by Bishop of Mauritius in the case of the Rev. E.R. Ward (See 30.03.05).	425
5.07.1905 79.	Submits proposals regarding Water Supply to Victoria.	436
31.08.1905 93.	Forwards Local Rate Recovery Ordinance Nº 5 of 1905, with explanations.	448
1.09.1905 94.	Sending with remarks, report on Seychelles exhibits at Zanzibar Exhibition.	452

Date	Subject Matter	Page
9.12.1905 109.	Forwards, with comments, Draft Estimates of Revenue and Expenditure for 1906.	463
5.01.1906 12.	In this letter reference is made to copies of original state documents 1742-1810 received from Mr. Fauvel in Paris ; compiled by him since 1889.	472
30.01.1906 19.	Concerning the various facets of the further education of "Laureates of Seychelles" (the boys who gain the two annual scholarships) : how and where they should continue their studies.	476
5.02.1906 24.	On the matter of an Ordinance concerning Lunacy.	480
7.02.1906 25.	Forwards further documents in connection with records compiled by Mr. A.A. Fauvel (See item 5.1.1906).	481
7.02.1906 26.	States reasons for non-adhesion by Seychelles to the Paris Sanitary Convention.	482
20.02.1906 29.	Forwards Annual Report on Education, and on Dec. examination of the Victoria School.	485
22.02.1906 30.	Forwards Annual Report for 1905 on the Savings Bank.	486
28.02.1906 32.	States that application for a coat of arms for the Colony must be deferred because of expenses.	488
12.03.1906 38.	Lengthy informative letter replying to despatch concerning the Estimates for 1905, and gives explanations thereon, with a survey of the financial position.	492
17.03.1906 42.	The Governor states he would be glad to be permitted to publish, at his own expense, the historical records and maps. (See 5.01.1906). (7.02.1906).	498
23.03.1906 47.	Details about Export in 1904, 1905.	505

Date	Subject Matter	Page
27.03.1906 49.	Informative account of visit to the Outlying Islands.	510
20.04.1906 59.	Sending with remarks, Annual Report on the Police Dept.	517
26.04.1906 63.	Sending with remarks, Annual Medical Reports for 1905.	519
3.06.1906 83.	On the subject of Port improvements.	536
4.06.1906 85.	As above.	538
5.06.1906	As above.	538
18.06.1906 91.	With further reference to historical records compiled by Mr. Fauvel. (See 17.03.1906). S of S has no objection to Governor publishing at own expense. Permission sought for the printing being done by Govt. Printing Press, Mahe, provided no outlay incurred by Govt.	541
21.06.1906 96.	Long letter about proposed amendments to Local Rate Ordinance N° 16 of 1900.	545
		VOL. B/48.
1.08.1906 112.	Reporting discovery of wrecked sailing vessel on Providence Bank, 10 miles from the settlement on Providence Island. Investigation is being made.	7
4.09.1906 120.	Sending report made by the Investigator (Mr. J. Spurs) concerning above wreck.	12
20.12.1906 131.A.	On certain aspects arising from the detention of Political Prisoners and their followers.	21
31.10.1906 132.	Sending with comments, Estimates of Revenue and Expenditure for 1907.	23

Date	Subject Matter	Page
7.11.1906 138.	Considerable further information about the wreck on Providence Bank (See items 1.08.1906) and 4.9.1906).	27
17.12.1906 146.	Asking for papers dealing with the constitution and regulations of the sponge and Fisheries Board of Bahamas.	34
7.02.1907 16.	Advises loss on 25th Dec., of S.S. "Endeavour", 124 tons net, on Providence Bank. Owners -Mahe Syndicate Ltd., vessel a total loss. Crew and passengers saved. Master and Officer exonerated.	42
16.02.1907 21.	Annual Report of Port, Marine, and Lighthouse Dept. for 1906.	44
24.02.1907 25.	Franco - British Exhibition, London, 1908. Desirability of Seychelles taking part in it.	47
2.03.1907 31.	Sending Police Report for 1906, with comments.	51
6.03.1907 38.	Forwarding Report on Education for 1906, with comments.	58
7.03.1907 39.	Concerning state of Denis Island lighthouse.	59
7.03.1907 40.	On the matter of importation of labour for outlying Islands.	60
22.03.1907 44.	Relative to the mangrove bark industry.	63
23.03.1907 45.	Sending with remarks, Medical Dept. Report for 1906.	64
28.03.1907 48.	Forwards, with explanations, Financial statement for 1906.	67
30.03.1907 49.	Forwards, with remarks, Prison report for 1906.	71

Date	Subject Matter	Page
6.04.1907 60.	Outlying Islands. Pratique Ordinance N° 3 of 1907. A scheme to enable exploitation of the islands by steamships without having to come to, and return to, Victoria, for clearance papers.	78
26.04.1907 68.	Concerning scheme for High level water supply.	84
4.05.1907 74.	Reports wreck of Norwegian barque "Norden" on night of 1st. March on reef off St. Pierre Island with the loss of six lives. Nine survivors arrived Mahe 1st. May in Schooner "Zipporah".	90
11.05.1907 78.	E. Blackwood Wright advises that he took over as Administrator on the 9th, Governor Davidson having left that day.	93
7.06.1907 88.	Concerning repairs being done to Govt. Houses, and House Rent of Administrator.	97
4.07.1907 91.	Re : the establishment of a Quarterly journal by Mr. Mercer.	100
4.07.1907 96.	Long letter, forwarding Ordinance n° 10 of 1907 (to amend Civil Status Ordinance n° 4 of 1903), and explaining need for it.	102
6.08.1907 101.	Dr. J.B. Addison appointed Asst. Medical Officer, Seychelles as from 16th July.	107
7.08.1907 105.	Medical Report on outbreak of beri-beri. From Dr. Denman, C.M.O.	109
11.11.1907 128.	Governor W.E. Davidson. Reports arrival back to-day.	123
18.11.1907 130.	Regarding exports of Vanilla.	124
25.11.1907 132.	Submitting with explanations, draft Estimates of Revenue and Expenditure for 1908.	125

Date	Subject Matter	Page
26.11.1907 133.	On the matter of the water supply of Victoria (Grand St. Louis).	130
6.01.1908 7.	Denis Island Lighthouse, and methods of transport of material.	139
14.01.1908 10.	Dr. R. Denman accepts post of Health Officer for the State of Perak. Governor suggests Dr. J. B. Addison as Chief Medical Officer.	142
4.02.1908 17.	Transmits copy of letter from ex King Prempeh requesting that two of his wives with a servant and their children, and the wife of one of his chiefs, be sent back to Kumasi.	145
13.03.1908 41.	Forwarding Annual Report on Port Office for 1907, with remarks.	160
21.03.1908 46.	Plans for Govt. buildings in connection with Victoria Harbour.	163
21.03.1908 47.	Forwards, with comments, Police Dept. Report for 1907.	165
23.03.1908 49.	Forwards, with comments, Report on Public Works for 1907.	167
1.04.1908 55.	Forwards, with comments, Report on Post Office for 1907.	170
3.04.1908 56.	Submits proposals for organization of a "Friend-in-Need" Society.	171
3.04.1908 57.	Rebuilding of Denis Island Lighthouse.	172
2.05.1908 66.	Relative to Revenue from guano.	177
3.05.1908 67.	Cinnamon bark. Report on future prospects.	180

Date	Subject Matter	Page
1.06.1908	Transmits, with remarks, Financial statements for 1907.	197
1.07.1908 91.	Transmits correspondence regarding mail contract with M.M. Co.	204
1.07.1908 92.	Further to Denis Island Lighthouse.	205
25.07.1908 103.	Long letter on matters arising - and likely to arise - from presence of Ashanti Political prisoners.	220
3.08.1908 108.	Reports completion of the printing of the Seychelles Historical Records. (1743-1810).	230
6.08.1908 115.	Reporting on scheme for a Carnegie library, L 1750 having been given, and the formation of a Committee.	241
10.08.1908 116.	Long letter regarding Mahe syndicate, St. Pierre Island, and guano export.	245
25.08.1908 117.	Crown rights over marine products other than fish on the banks of the Seychelles Archipelago.	250
27.09.1908 128.	Ashanti Political Prisoners. Refers to some financial aspects, also to repatriation of two of Prempeh's wives and their children, the son of a deceased Chief, and the servant of another.	271
22.10.1908 140.	Acknowledges receipt of sanction of purchase of collection of ancient maps from Mr. Bergue, and their reproduction in colour for 1 46 for 200 copies.	279
4.11.1908 146.	Allowances to widows and orphans of deceased Political Prisoners.	283
4.12.1908	Forwards, with remarks, Estimates for 1909.	309
5.12.1908 172.	Proposals for a Boarding House for Victoria School.	312

Date	Subject Matter	Page
16.12.1908 176.	Further to reconstruction of Denis Island Lighthouse.	316
28.01.1909 21.	Sending with remarks, Prison Dept. Report for 1908.	345
4.02.1909 24.	Forwarding with Governor's comments, Report of a Committee to enquire into Fishery Laws.	350
18.02.1909 32.	Transmit letter from Mahe Syndicate notifying establishment of regular steam communication with St. Pierre.	363
25.02.1909 37.	Forwarding, with Governor's comments, Report on the working of the Post Office for 1908.	368
27.02.1909 39.	Denis Island. New Lighthouse will be finished during this year. Suggested that materials from other one be used for St. Anne Island.	371
27.02.1909 41.	Sending with Governor's comments, Report on the Savings Bank for 1908.	373
8.03.1909 47.	Reports suppression of outbreak of small pox. 8 cases among 27 (29?) Indian passengers ex Bombay on 4th Feb. No deaths.	378
25.03.1909 55.	Forwards copies of telegraphic correspondance with Crown Agents about Denis Island Light, and suggests that new optical apparatus should be erected on St. Anne Island.	385
27.03.1909 56.	Regarding commutation of allowances of Ashanti Political Prisoners.	387
30.03.1909 57.	Reports inauguration of Grand St. Louis water supply for Victoria.	388
31.03.1909 58.	Sending with Governor's comments, Police Dept. Report for 1908.	390
31.03.1909 59.	Reports completion of printing of volume of Archives of Seychelles.	392

Date	Subject Matter	Page
31.03.1909 60.	Reports publication of historical maps of Seychelles.	393
3.04.1909 63.	Further to suppression outbreak of small pox.(see 8.03.1909. page 378).	397
7.04.1909 68.	Transmits, with Governor's comments, Financial statements for 1908.	400
16.04.1909 70.	Forwards, with Governor's comments, Report on Public Works for 1909.	402
5.05.1909 78.	Transmits Ordinance N° 5 of 1909, "The outlying islands Labour Ordinance", Long letter about it.	409
22.05.1909 85.	Sends, with Governor's comments, Medical Report for 1908.	418
26.05.1909 88.	Concerning giant land tortoises on Aldabra Island.	421
4.06.1909 97.	Renewal of contract with Mahe Syndicate for the extraction of guano from St. Pierre Island.	425
5.06.1909 103.	Submits, for approval, scheme for extension classes for young men.	428
14.06.1909 109.	Transmits, with Governor's Comments, report on the Botanic Station and Crown Lands for 1908.	432
14.07.1909 122.	Reporting the death of Mr. F. Hodoul, C.M.G. (letter dated 14th says - according to the copying - death occurred "on the 16th inst". (should it be "16th ulto" or 6th inst).	439
4.08.1909 137.	Proposed light on St. Anne's Island. Also a reference to Denis Island.	448
5.08.1909 139.	Concerns acquisition of Central mountains in Mahe for afforestation and conservancy of water supply.	450
20.08.1909 144.	More about the Giant Land Tortoises on Aldabra.	455

Date	Subject Matter	Page
16.09.1909 160.	Relative to proposed scheme for fishing of Mother of pearl in Seychelles waters.	464
27.09/1909 167.	Reviewing what has been done for education, and by whom : sets forth various aspects of educational matters as at present : suggests ideas to facilitate higher educational opportunities. Long and informative letter.	468
13.10.1909 172.	On the matter of development of fisheries, and amendment of Fishery law.	482
4.11.1909 177.	Forwards draft estimates of Revenue and Expenditure for 1910, with comments.	486
7.12.1909 185.	Raising the question of a new Govt. House.	491
7.01.1910 9.	Reports the death in Paris on the 6th inst. of the Right Rev. Mare Hudrisier, R.C. Bishop of Victoria appointed 1890. "He had done excellent work as a Bishop, and was, moreover, a loyal and reliable supporter of the Government.	498
3.02.1910 21.	Recommending (and giving very sound reasons) a system of leave privileges for the Nursing Sisters at the Victorial Hospital.	503
4.02.1910 23.	Transmitting copy of letter to Mr. Andrew Carnegie, reporting opening of the Carnegie Library (Note : - No date is given. Was it this day ?)	505
7.02.1910 24.	Sending copy of a letter to the Board of Trade about alterations to Denis Island Lighthouse.	505
24.02.1910 32.	Reports the death, on the 17th of the Hon. Mr. F.E. Savy, the Senior Unofficial Member of the Legislative Council.	513
22.02.1910 34.	Transmits, with Governor's comments, the Savings Bank Report for 1909.	515
7.03.1910 39.	Reports on purchase of central mountain zone.	517

Date	Subject Matter	Page
8.03.1910 41.	A long letter concerning Secondary Education, and scheme for a new College.	519
9.03.1910 45.	Reports outbreak of beri-beri on Coetivy Island.	525
10.03.1910 47.	Submitting for approval, a vote of the Legislative Council for Rs. 1,000 to provide show cases for a nucleus museum in Carnegie Public Library.	
16.03.1910 51.	Forwarding, with Governor's comments, Report of Port, Marine, and Lighthouse Dept for 1909.	530
23.03.1910 53.	Transmits, with Governor's comments, Report of Victoria Prison for 1909.	532
24.03.1910 55.	Forwards a Memorial from the priest administering the R.C. Diocese of Port Victoria, setting out the work done by the Capuchin mission in aid of Education in Seychelles.	533
31.10.1910 60.	Sending, with Governor's comments, Medical Report for 1909.	536
6.04.1910 67.	Forwards papers relating to Carnegie Library.	542
7.04.1910 68.	Advising that arrangements will be made for the exhumation of body of ex-King Muanga, and removal to Uganda.	542
30.04.1910 77.	Submits proposals for legalising and regulating the sale of the juice of sugar cane "bacca". 5 pages.	547
5.05.1910 78.	Submits plans and drawings of the proposed new Govt. House.	552
7.05.1910	Acknowledging news of the death of King Edward VII.	554

Date	Subject Matter	Page
	VOL. B/49.	
7.08.1908	This letter from E. Blackwood Wright, Administrator.	
	Secondary Education. An informative picture of certain facets of education, including the lack of knowledge of English.	1
14.01.1908	The following letters are from W.E. Davidson, Governor. A 4 page letter dealing with the general administration of the Hospital. Refers to the efficiency and devotion to duty of the Sisters of Mercy.	7
19.03.1908	Further to Secondary Education 4 page review of the matter.	11
25.01.1909	Reporting that on the occasion of the King's Accession Day a special service was held in all the R.C. Churches.	31
2.06.1909	Leave of absence granted to Bishop of Victoria, Father Mark Hudrisier, on the ground of ill health. Submits for consideration certain issues resulting from the apparent improbability that he will be able to resume duties.	33
14.07.1909	Reviewing a report on Aldabra Island by Mr. Spurs which has been received from the S of S.	35
28.04.1910	Concerning Royalty and Export Duty on guano from St. Pierre.	40
30.04.1910	A lengthy letter being a general review of the different deposits of guano in the Seychelles groups.	41
25.07.1910	Relative to Royalty and Export Duty on guano.	45
6.09.1910	A lengthy letter dealing with the appeal, by the new R.C. Bishop, against the new Education laws, and advising S of S that a petition is being got up.	47
26.09.1910	Sending a report, by Mr. R. Dupont, Curator of Botanic Station, on guano deposits on Assumption	

Date	Subject Matter	Page
	Island.	49
7.10.1910	Refers to petition (see 6.09.1910). The Governor makes pertinent comments about methods by which it was got up, signatures forged, etc...	53 B.
7.02.1911	Further observations regarding secondary education.	59
5.04.1911	The Governor reports that he will leave the Colony by the mail of the 8th inst. on 6 months leave. Mr. A.K. Young, Chief Justice, will administer the Govt. A footnote to letter says M.M. Agents have advised ship been delayed at Reunion, and will probably arrive 4 or 5 days late.	61
6.12.1911	Long letter concerning allegations against Mr. R. Dupont, Curator, Botanic Station.	71
2.06.1912	Enclosing various papers relative to the above matters.	84
26.06.1912	Copies of the State portraits of the King and Queen, asking if they could be ready for installation at the ceremonial opening of the New Govt. House to the public (6th May 1913, the anniversary of His Majesty's accession to the throne).	87
21.08.1912	Regarding Mr. Dupont (see 6.12.1911 and 2.06.1912) being fined and reprimanded.	92
		VOL. B/50.
16.05.1910 81.	The Governor proclaimed the accession of King George V on the 9th inst.	1
17.05.1910 83 (apparently should be 82).	Transmits Annual Report on Public Works for 1909, with comments.	1
21.05.1910 83.	Refers to the death of King Edward VII	4

Date	Subject Matter	Page
30.05.1910 87.	Submits proposal for the establishment of a Maternity Home.	Pasted in between 5 and 6.
1.06.1910 89.	Notes on Land Tortoises.	7
24.06.1910 101.	Advises (in connection with some communications received) that no system of mechanical transport has been introduced.	17
19.07.1910 112.	Lengthy letter (4pp) dealing with proposals for improving means of communication with the outlying islands.	22
5.08.1910 124.	Steamship "Tai Wan", 1072 tons register, Port Louis for Hong-Kong, with 256 Chinese passengers, lost tail end shaft and propellor on 23rd July, 658 miles from Mahe, arrived under sail on 1st. inst. Govt. steam launch "Alexandra" towed her into harbour. Ship is being repaired here by Parc, Newsam & Parc.	30
5.08.1910 130.	Further to the idea of the original Light on Denis Island being used on St. Anne's Island.	33
2.09.1910 137.	Reports completion of the Denis Island Lighthouse.	37
5.09.1910 139.	Long letter (8 pp) forwarding, with comments Education Ordinances, and letter of protest from Bishop of Victoria.	38
25.09.1910 145.	Notifies arrival, on 11th, of Miss. A.M. Beedie to Nursing Supt. and Matron in charge of Maternity Home.	48
3.10.1910 152	Transmits estimates for new Govt. House.	53
7.10.1910 156.	Forwarding with Governor's lengthy explanations, petition against the new Education Ordinances. The Governors dissection and analysis of the numerical facets of this petition is most enlightening, and shows the real value of the petition as compared with the superficial value.	55

Date	Subject Matter	Page
7.10.1910 157.	Forwarding a further petition regarding the Educational Ordinance.	59
12.10.1910 159.	Providing information regarding loss of the "Sea Queen". Letter refers to Governor's "despatch N° 117 of 22nd July last". (There is no N° 117 in this book ; 116 of 21st. July, and 118 of 23rd).	61
7.11.1910 169.	Construction of new Govt. House. After considering tenders, decision made that work be done by P.W.D.	66
7.11.1910 170.	Submits for approval vote for Coronation Festivities	67
1.12.1910 174.	Concerning some structural alterations and improvements required in the building to become the Maternity Home.	72
1.12.1910 175.	Further to proposals for improving means of communication with the Outlying Islands.	72
3.12.1910 180.	Outlining proposed preparations for celebrating the Coronation of the King.	74
22.12.1910 186.	Transmits Ordinance n° 19 of 1910 "Levying of Harbour Dues", and gives a detailed report on shipping affairs.	80
3.01.1911 1.	On the financial condition of the Colony.	86
4.01.1911 10.	Sending, with Governor's comments, copy of the offer from E. Lanier & Co. to undertake the lighting of Victoria by electricity.	90
7.01.1911 13.	Inquiring whether it would be possible to recommend for the King's favourable consideration, an advancement of Sister St. Landri, Matron of the Victoria Hospital, in the order of St. John of Jerusalem. She was appointed an Honorary Serving Sister of the Order in 1901. She entered the Hospital on the 1st. January 1876, and in the 35 years has never been absent for a single night.	93

Date	Subject Matter	Page
22.01.1911 18.	On the subject of a proposed Bill to control the manufacture and sale of bacca. 4 pages of information.	97
1.02.1911 21.	Secondary Education. H.M. the King has approved of the new Govt. College being given the name of "King's College". It opened on 23rd January, and some Boarders can be taken.	102
14.02.1911 24.	Transmits report on vital statistics for 1910. Governor Davidson remarks that the population (22620 estimated at end of 1910) is rapidly approaching limit which resources of Colony can support, and it is of vital importance that the growing generation should be so trained as to be able to maintain themselves, if necessary, in the larger world outside the Colony.	
22.02.1911 25.	A 7 page letter on Export trade for 1910.	106
28.02.1911 26.	Reports the death, on the 26th of Mr. G.H. Griffiths, Treasurer, after a brief illness ; was due to retire on pension on 23rd March when he would have completed his 72nd year.	113
2.03.1911 31.	Concerning scheme, by Lanier & Co., to develop fishing industry.	117
3.03.1911 32.	Sending with comments, Report of the Port Department for 1910.	119
17.03.1911 39.	Forwards, with comments, Police Dept. Report for 1910.	125
18.03.1913 43.	Two page letter accompanying Report on Education for 1910.	126
20.03.1911 43.	Puts forward the scheme by which a Boarding House for King's College is to be started.	130
22.03.1911 44.	Transmists, with comments, the Report of the Medical Dept. for 1910.	131

Date	Subject Matter	Page
23.03.1911 45.	Presents an informative account of the imports during 1910. 3 1/2 pages.	133
23.03.1911 46.	Forwarding with comments, the Report on the Savings Bank for 1910.	137
3.04.1911 52.	A 3 page letter concerning the Annual Report of the Judicial Report for 1910 which is sent.	140
4.04.1911 55.	Transmits with comments, Annual Report of the Post Office for 1910.	144
5.04.1911 57.	Forwarding with explanations, Ordinance n° 3 of 1911 relating to Moitie System of Contracts.	145
12.04.1911 59.	Mr. A.K. Young. Reports he has assumed the administration of the Govt. the Governor. W.E. Davidson, C.M.G. having left on leave last night.	148
6.06.1911 64.	Tobacco, cultivation of. Almost negligible. A report by Acting Curator of Botanic Station is sent.	151
8.07.1911 76.	A preliminary report on the census of 2nd April last.	158
4.09.1911 93.	Concerning resignation of Miss. Reedie, late Nursing Supt. of the Maternity Home, and the circumstances connected therewith (see item of 25.09.1910), reporting arrival).	172
13.11.1911 106.	The Governor, W.E. Davidson, reports his arrival in Mahe from leave on the 11th.	186
24.11.1911 108.	A letter dealing with the functions of the Auditor. Mr. W.H. Smith the recently appointed Auditor from England has objected to continuing certain things done by former Auditor. Governor's letter refers to extraneous duties willingly undertaken by Govt. Officials - one Dr. making roads, another manages rifle Association., and other similar cases.	185
28.11.1911 114.	Reporting on the satisfactory progress of Secondary Education ; also refers to Boarding House for King's College.	192

Date	Subject Matter	Page
27.12.1911 127.	An account of the transfer of the old lighthouse on Denis Island to Mamelles Island.	203
4.02.1912 22.	Refers, with details, to unprecedented rainfall during January.	221
13.02.1912 26.	Transmits, with Governor's comments, Prison Report for 1911.	225
29.02.1912 33.	Forwards, with Governor's comments, Port and Marine Dept. Report for 1911.	230
29.02.1912 34.	Reporting action taken regarding alleged theft of a boat and cargo by Master and crew.	232
4.03.1912 36.	Forwards, with comments, Report of the Police Dept. for 1911.	237
21.03.1912 49.	Sending with comments, Report on the Savings Bank for 1911.	248
22.03.1912 50.	Transmitting, with comments, Report on Public Works for 1911.	249
26.03.1912 52.	Forwards, with comments, Report on the Civil Status for 1911. Note : - For details about 1910, see p. 104.	251
26.03.1912 53.	Transmitting, with comments, Report of Medical Dept. for 1911.	252
23.04.1912 73.	Concerning project for building a road in Praslin to connect Grand'Anse and Baie St. Anne.	Pasted in after 275.
1.05.1912 78.	Census Report. 1911. This letter amends one dated 8.07.1911.	278
2.05.1912 81.	Reports, that the 6 men concerned in stealing boat and cargo (see 29.02.1912) were arrested in Dar-es-Salaam and are now in Mahe awaiting trial.	280

Date	Subject Matter	Page
7.05.1912 84.	Applying for approval to buy a house adjoining Maternity Home in order to extend, because it is proving such a success.	287
7.05.1912 85.	The Editor and the Printer of weekly newspaper "Le Reveil", prosecuted because of attacks of an outrageous character on the Governor in issues 23rd and 30th March. Practically no defence, and no attempt to substantiate insinuations. Editor sentenced to 3 months and fines amounting to Rs. 1,250. Printer (who pleaded guilty, and tendered apology), to pay fines amounting to Rs.250.	289
16.05.1912 90.	Concerning the holding of an examination in January 1913 for the Seychelles English Scholarship.	298
17.05.1912 92.	Sending with comments, the Education Report for 1911.	300
20.05.1912 96.	Reporting the completion of the lighthouse on Mamelles Island.	304
22.05.1912 98.	Further convictions of the Editor and Printer of "Le Reveil".	305
1.06.1912 105.	Raises the question of proposed contribution for the rebuilding of the Roman Catholic Cathedral which is in a very bad state.	315
4.06.1912 106.	Reporting result of the trial of the men who stole a lugger and cargo (see 29.02.1912 and 2.05.1912).	319
4.07.1912 119.	Concerning the installation of a light on Capucin Point.	328
12.08.1912 126.	Sending a copy of M.M. Co's new timetable, and commenting thereon.	339
10.10.1912 141.	Regarding proposed scheme for a Government Rest House in Victoria for travellers and visitors.	351
19.10.1912 147.	Forwarding with comments, the draft Estimates of Revenue and Expenditure for 1913.	355

Date	Subject Matter	Page
19.10.1912 149.	The Governor acknowledges appointment to the Governorship of Newfoundland. He will leave on the 17th December.	358
28.11.1912 179.	Mentions that it is proposed to begin a complete survey of Praslin in 1913.	384
11.12.1912 186.	Gives a long report on guano deposits on St. Pierre Island, and other matters to do with that and other islands.	392
13.12.1912	A lengthy report on the financial position of the Colony.	398
		VOL. B/52.
29.07.1898	Wreck of French Barque, Providence Island. "Under art. 36 of Ord. 38 of 1888, in case of wreck of foreign ships, the Consul is to be deemed the Agent of Owner, so far as relates to the custody and disposal of any articles belonging to or forming part of the ship or of the cargo thereof. This, it is submitted, is the answer to the question asked".	4
13.02.1899	Water supply : raises various questions in connection therewith.	28
1.03.1899	Naturalization of Aliens. Deals with the matter of whether, having regard to the laws of Mauritius, the Administrator of Seychelles can, or cannot confer naturalisation. The L.A. thinks a special ordinance necessary to cover Administrator's being able to do so.	36
27.12.1899	Outlines to the Administrator, the various proceedings followed regarding an application for naturalization.	63
6.01.1900	Information as to requirements expected from anyone wishing to practise Medicine or Surgery in Seychelles.	72
15.12.1900	Refers to an Ordinance to provide, for the service of the Local Board of Health for the Central	

Date	Subject Matter	Page
	District, for a period of 15 months from 1st. January 1901 to 31st March 1902, the sum of Rs. 22,719.50.	139
8.01.1901	Advising prosecution of a Chinese for having a larger quantity of opium than he should possess.	149
1.02.1901	Draft proclamation naming 30th May as the day for taking the census.	161
1.02.1901	Proposed amendment of regulations concerning passengers going to Quarantine.	162
25.03.1901	Inquiries into Wrecks, Ceylon ordinance amended to suit local circumstances.	202
17.04.1901	Outlines what Lanier & Co. should do as regards application to get Indian Labourers from Madras.	210
19.06.1901	Raises matter of proposal to establish a Govt. note issue.	249
6.08.1901	Concerning the possibility of calling for tenders for mother of pearl and pearl fishery rights ; and the Legal Adviser's views.	270
2.09.1901	Relating to request from Secretary of state to be informed of conditions and restrictions regarding Coasting Trade.	281
8.10.1901	Concerning Mr. Spurs wishing to have a lease of Isle aux Cerfs and half of Providence Bank. Necessary to obtain copy of deed of concession of Providence Island from Mauritius to make sure Isle aux Cerfs was not included.	298
15.10.1901	Draft regulations for the licensing and tariffing of vehicles in Victoria.	302
30.10.1901	Detailed report concerning Parcel Post Conveyed by M.M. Co Ships.	313
11.12.1901	Parcel Post (insured) between France and Seychelles.	334

Date	Subject Matter	Page
31.12.1901	Sending draft Regulations under Section 45 (1) of Ord. N° 12 of 1897 concerning the Police Force.	349
7.01.1902	Submits remarks on the turtles Bills.	354
15.01.1902	Submits comments on alleged disturbance near the English Church at Anse Royale.	357
24.01.1902	Expresses opinion that the Govt. of a British Colony would have no right to detain a foreign ship for unseaworthiness.	363
10.02.1902	Alteration to a Bill concerning the sale and consumption of intoxicating liquors.	379
		VOL. B/53.
15.02.1904	Requesting that a competant Interpreter be appointed to serve in Court (Supreme and Police Courts). For French and Creole. Arrangement hitherto in Police Court (using a Constable) is open to very grave objection ; also interpretation most indifferent, and at times quite unintelligible.	12
2.04.1904	Advises that the lease of a portion of Crown Lands adjoining Victoria Cemetery for the erection of a School, should be in the name of "The Church of England Authorities" ; Mr. Johnson, Civil Chaplain, and any other member or members of the Committee can sign in their official capacities.	49
16.04.1904	Refers to a Circular from the Secretary of State forwarding translation of rules issued by Russia to be observed during the war with Japan.	67
21.06.1904	Gives information as to what must be done regarding registration of a private cemetery in La Digue.	108
20.07.1904	Answers, in the affirmative, an enquiry as to whether the Bishop of Victoria is legally entitled to receive a legacy.	136
21.07.1904	Forwarding statement of witnesses concerning the	

Date	Subject Matter	Page
	loss by fire of the steamer "Sir Celincourt Antelme" in the roadstead of Marie Louise island (one of the Admirantes) on 8th July.	139
18.02.1905	Report as to whether Immigrant Labourers pass with the Estate on transfer thereof.	293
6.04.1905	Persons who are harmless imbeciles, with no visible means of subsistence, or relatives or friends willing and able to look after them may be sent to Round Island as paupers. Persons of unsound mind and who ought to be put under restraint, should only be dealt with as lunatics and detained in a place proclaimed to be a lunatic asylum.	322
28.04.1905	An enquiry to the Legal Adviser as to what powers the Quarantine Committee has in the event of passengers refusing to be vaccinated. He says the law is that a person before landing from a small-pox infected or suspected vessel, should be vaccinated; further than this the law does not go. Once allowed to land, and placed in a Quarantine Station, and having remained for the statutory period (15 days), there is in his opinion, no power to detain them any longer, whether they submit to or decline to submit to vaccination.	336
		VOL. B/54.
9.08.1905	Encloses Draft Regulations concerning Public Cemetery desired at Bay St. Anne, Praslin.	60
9.04.1906	Opinion of the Legal Adviser on the matter of Medical attendance to new Immigrants.	164
26.12.1906	Approves of passing of Bill to amend the Civil Status Ordinance 4 of 1893, and to enable the Court to presume the death of persons who have disappeared.	269
19.03.1907	E. Lanier and Co. ask to be allowed to land labourers from Zanzibar for work on guano islands. The Legal Adviser says this depends mainly on willingness of Authorities of Zanzibar and the Foreign Office to allow labour to be exported. Al vessels carrying labourers from Zanzibar, or any place not in the Colony, should receive pratique at Victoria.	316

Date	Subject Matter	Page
		VOL. B/55.
27.01.1908	Introduction of Indian Immigrants from Madras. The L.A. states in reply to enquiry from Governor, that under M.O. 12/1878. Sec. 51 the proportion required was 50 women for every 100 males, but this ordinance (except chapter 6) has been repeated by O. 6/1902, and there is now no provision in force. The Indian Govt. shoud be informed of this fact.	178
20.02.1908	Reply from Legal Adviser to Governor about circular letter from S of S regarding information desired by a Committee of the General Council of Medical Education and Registration of the United Kingdom.	
		VOL. B/56.
7.01.1914	The L.A. reports that from searches made in Civil Status Registers as far back as 1794 he finds that Mrs. Bossy is not a member of the Queau de Quincy's family as she alleges in her letter. She is the great granddaughter of one Auguste Vaulbert, whose divorced wife, Marie Joseph Dubail, subsequently married Governor Queau de Quincy. He submits a genealogical table showing how the two families Vaulbert and Queau de Quincy are connected.	Not numbered.
		VOL. B/57.
13.02.1918	Concerning a submitted Bill relating to changes in the Moiete System.	
1.04.1918	Arising from the above.	
19.02.1923	The Governor enquires as to the legal responsibility of the Government for repairs to Carnegie Library, and gives certain facts. Following copy of letter is a note to effect that the Legal Adviser attached his report to original letter.	354
22.02.1923	Suggestion that as requested by Bishop of Victoria - the chapel outside the grounds of the Fiennes Institute should now be legally transferred to him. He would be prepared to spend money on it, and enlarge it if necessary ; a chapel is badly wanted in the locality.	357

Date	Subject Matter	Page
7.03.1923	Further regarding the above.	369
		VOL. B/60.
8.05.1923	Rest House. Lease of by Seychelles Club. The leases of the Club Tennis Courts and Rest House registered on 5th May 1923.	40
		VOL. B/64.
10.04.1929	In the course of a letter of this date from the Legal Adviser to the Governor, reference is made to letter books of 1812 "of considerable historic interest" kept in a room off the Registry, and being eaten by insects.	
		VOL. B/65.
2.03.1932	Draft rules for registration of bicycles.	

MINUTES OF THE BOARD OF CIVIL COMMISSIONERS

		VOL. B/66.
1872 to 1882.	Minutes.	

MINUTES OF EXECUTIVE COUNCIL

		VOL. B/67.
1898 to 1902.	Minutes.	
		VOL. B/68.
1902 to 1911.	Minutes.	

Date	Subject Matter	Page
		VOL. B/69.
1911 to 1923	Minutes.	
		VOL. B/70.
1923 to 1933.	Minutes.	
		VOL. B/71.
1933 to 1936	Minutes.	
	LETTER BOOK (LOCAL)	VOL. B/72.
1839	Letter Book.	
		VOL. B/72 (A)
1840	Letter Book.	
		VOL. B/72 (B)
1880	Letter Book.	
		VOL. B/73.
1886 to 1887.	Letter Book.	
		VOL. B/74.
1887 to 1888.	Letter Book.	
		VOL. B/75.
1888 to 1889.	Letter Book.	

Date	Subject Matter	Page
		VOL. B/76.
1889 to 1890.	Letter Book.	
		VOL. B/77
1890 to 1891.	Letter Book.	
		VOL. B/78.
1891 to 1892.	Letter Book.	
		VOL. B/79.
1892.	Letter Book.	
		VOL. B/80.
1895 to 1899	Letter Book.	
		VOL. B/81.
	CROWN AGENTS LETTER BOOK.	
1889 to 1895.	Letter Book.	
		VOL. B/82.
	EDUCATION (LOCAL)	
1916 to 1919.	Letter Book.	
		VOL. B/83.
1921 to 1923.	Letter Book.	

Date	Subject Matter	Page
1835	COMPENSATION PAID TO SLAVE OWNERS. Letter Book.	VOL. B/84.
1861 to 1872	REGISTER OF LIBERATED AFRICANS. Register.	VOL. B/85.
1890 to 1934.	MEDICAL REGISTER. Register.	VOL. B/86.
1892 to 1900.	PROCEEDING OF THE PRISON BOARD. Letter Book.	VOL. B/87.
1891 to 1898	Oath Book.	VOL. B/88.
1892 to 1904.	Oath Book.	VOL. B/89.
1904 to 1920	Oath Book.	VOL. B/90.
1920 to 1941	Oath Book.	VOL. B/91.
1941 to 1956	Oath Book.	VOL. B/92.
1956 to 1972	Oath Book.	VOL. B/93.

DOCUMENTS OFFICIELS SELECTIONNES DE L'ADMINISTRATION

BRITANNIQUE A PARTIR DE 1867

- CLASS C -

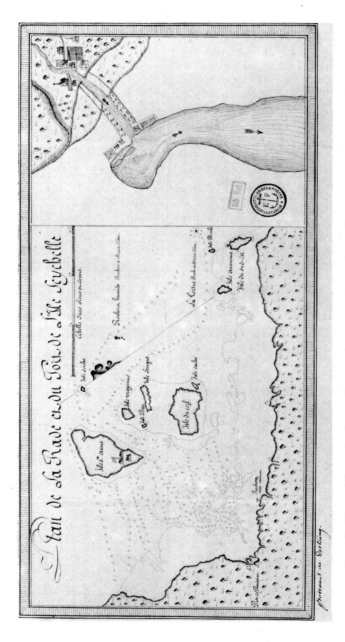

Seychelles. Plan de la rade et du port 18e siècle (Cli. B.N. C. 96508).

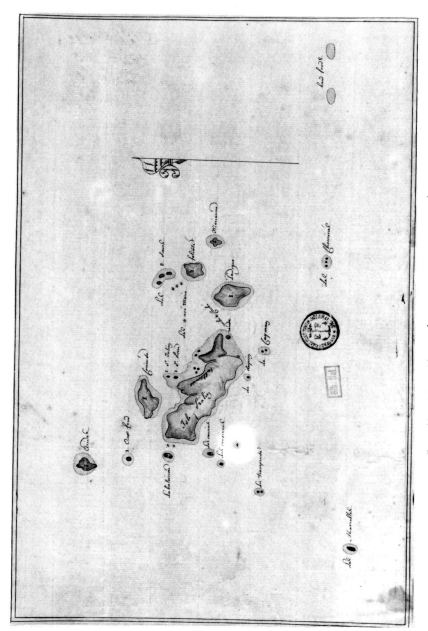

Praslin 18e siècle (Cli. B.N. C. 89523).

CLASS C

SELECTED OFFICIAL RECORDS FROM UNBOUND FILES OF BRITISH PERIOD OF
ADMINISTRATION AFTER 1867

With the introduction of a system of individual files as opened to bound
books of all letters received or despatched, the task of selecting those
of permanent value for transfer to the Archives became easier. It did, however, raise one problem of its own - how to devise a system of numbering suf-
ficiently simple for the type of staff available. Much thought was given to
the subject.

It was decided finally that this class (C), to which additions would continue
to be made indefinitely, should be divided into 3 sections as under :

Section 1

Miscellaneous correspondence by years under the Code Number C/AM/1 (onwards).

Section 2

Files of World Wars I and II under the Code Number C/W/1 (onwards).

Section 3

Special Subject files, under the Code Number C/SS/1 (onwards). Wherever the
size or importance justifies it, the emphasis should be on Section 3. In fact
Section 1 contains those records unsuitable for binding as separate subjects,
but having a claim for permanent preservation. In the case of special subjects
there may be any numbers of volumes under any one head and additional volumes
can be added as documents in the Central Records are selected for transfer to
the Archives. Such subjects as "Constitutional Changes" (C/SS/39) ;
"Seychelles Postal Service" (C/SS/62) ;"Educational Policy" (C/SS/36) may run
to many volumes.

Note : - Where additions are insufficient to form a new bound volume, they may
be kept temporarily in a loose cover and placed with previous volume till

sufficient have been collected to warrant permanent binding.

In the index below the contents of Section 1 are printed in full for easy reference. For Section 3 only the subject headings are given.

SELECTED OFFICIAL RECORDS FROM UNBOUND FILES OF BRITISH

PERIOD OF ADMINISTRATION AFTER 1867

Subject Matter	Code N°
CONTENTS OF SELECTED CORRESPONDENCE FILE FOR 1867 TO 1934	C/AM/1 to C/AM/2

CONTENTS OF SELECTED CORRESPONDENCE FILE FOR 1867 to 1885   C/AM/1

Correspondence re : illegal occupation of St. Juan de Nova (alias Farquhar) Island by a French fishing vessel.

Letter from Private Secretary, Mauritius relative to increasing French influences in Seychelles.

Mr. F. Cheyron's views on economic possibilities of Mahe.

Memorandum recording decision that expenses of trials of Seychellois in Mauritius Courts shall be borne by Government of Mauritius.

Correspondence concerning fees to be levied for registration of deeds.

Correspondence from Colonial Secretary Mauritius and asking for report on deficiency in Seychelles Treasury of L 557 - 17s - 3d. Note : The report submitted is missing.

Correspondence re : report that French Consul in Mahe was opening, on instructions from French Government, a naval sanatorium in Seychelles.

Proposal that meteorological observations should be recorded at Mahe.

Report from Chief Civil Commissioner of Seychelles to Governor of Mauritius re : frequent visits of French warships to Mahe.

Correspondence concerning security of notarial deeds.

Original of oath of allegiance signed by the Revd. Père Ignace, Prefet Apostolic of Seychelles, before Civil Commissioner Mr. Swinburne Ward.

CONTENTS OF SELECTED CORRESPONDENCE FILE FOR 1887 and 1891   C/AM/2

Alleged cases of proselytism in the Civil Hospital, Victoria.

Letter from Governor of Mauritius re : the opening of a branch of the New Oriental Bank at Victoria.

Subject Matter	Code Nº
Correspondence re : slave trade between Madagascar and Reunion involving Seychelles.	
Report of Sanitary Inspector for 1891.	
Report on Crown Lands for the year 1889.	
CONTENTS OF SELECTED CORRESPONDENCE FILE FOR 1892 to 1896.	C/AM/3
Annual Report of Sanitary Inspector for 1892.	
Alleged removal by French General of the "Pierre de Possession" and its recovery.	
Letting condemned prisoners out of goal at night.	
Proposal to introduce the mongoose into Seychelles for destruction of rats.	
Governor of Mauritius approves introduction in Seychelles of system of "Cantonniers" as an experiment.	
Correspondence re : powers of the Collector of Customs to register uncertificated Masters of vessels.	
Lease of Old Fibre Factory to Seychelles Club.	
Acknowledgement by Government of Mauritius of copies of the first issue of the Seychelles Almanack for 1896.	
Re : Supply of Reuter's Telegrams to Seychelles.	
Correspondence re : loan of a Gun Boat for the use of the Seychelles Government.	
Award of Royal Humane Society's Bronze Medal and Certificate to Dumont Camille for gallantry.	
Public petition against Local Rate Ordinance, rejected by S of S	
Correspondence re : establishment of a Public Dispensary.	
CONTENTS OF SELECTED CORRESPONDENCE FILE FOR 1898 and 1899.	C/AM/4
Naturalization of Messrs. Low-Shang, Ahwaye and Alexander Ahsain.	
Lease of land to Lawn Tennis Club.	
Payment for Anse Royale property bought by Church of England.	
Opening of Private Pharmacy in Seychelles.	

Subject Matter	Code N°

Re : Closing of the Government Pharmacy.

School books supplied to Seychelles and cost.

Re : Appointment of a Government Dispenser.

Mr. Hodoul's resignation from Legislative Council and good services rendered by him.

S of S's refusal to impose heavy protective import duty to help Seychelles Coffee industry.

CONTENTS OF SELECTED CORRESPONDENCE FILE FOR 1898 and 1899. (Contd) - C/AM/4

"Seychelles Judicature Order in Council 1899".

Measures for the prevention of Bubonic Plague.

CONTENTS OF SELECTED CORRESPONDENCE FILE FOR 1900. Vol. I. C/AM/5 VOL. I.

Copy sent to Secretary of State of Regulations for open competitive examinations for appointment of Copyists in Government Departments, introduced to remove charge that former appointments had depended on favouritism and not on merit. Also correspondence concerning and results of first examination held in May 1900.

Forwarding to S of S six copies of the Seychelles Almanack for 1900 compiled by Dr. Denham, Chief Medical Officer, Seychelles.

Permission sought from S of S to lay before the Legislative Council a plan for stationing at Anse Royale a Medical Officer and for opening there a hospital and dispensary, a police station, court room, and sub-registrar's office.

Despatches to S of S re : selection of Civil Chaplains of Seychelles and the unsuitability of a number of those who had been appointed by the Bishop of Mauritius by reason of their age, lack of knowledge of English etc...

Correspondence concerning contribution by public of Seychelles to the Widows and Orphans (South African War) Fund.

Repayment of Rs. 55,000, which Seychelles was indebted to Mauritius.

Relief of Mafeking - Colony's hearty congratulations cabled to S of S and to Colonel Baden - Powell, and acknowledgements of ame.

Proposal made to S of S that a steam launch should be purchased for Seychelles, and setting out advantages to be derived.

Subject Matter	Code N°
Correspondence concerning proposal to impose a heavy protective duty on coffee imported into Seychelles, and S of S's refusal to agree on grounds that it would benefit planters only at expense of the poorer section of the community.	
Report of failure to obtain tenders for supplies for Government Departments, and difficulty of finding persons to undertake contracts for building.	
Visit of Lord Brassey's Yacht "Sunbeam".	
S of S forwards for adoption by Seychelles of "Instructions for the guidance of Financial and Accounting Officers in the Colonial Service".	
Petition from certain inhabitants of South Mahe that an Englishman be appointed as Assistant Medical Officer and stationed at Anse Royale.	
CONTENTS OF SELECTED CORRESPONDENCE FILE FOR 1900, VOL. II.	C/AM/5 - VOL. II.
Request to S of S to sanction additional vote of Rs. 1000/- for reclaiming land at end of long pier, Victoria, for making a turtle pool there.	
Return of 36,264 rats destroyed in the Colony as a precaution against introduction of bubonic plague for first 7 months of 1900, of which nearly half were killed in Victoria.	
S of S's approval of grant of subsidy to M/s J and J. Petit for opening an ice - factory in Victoria.	
Correspondence with S of S concerning amendment and consolidation of laws relating to Local Rates, the chaotic condition of which had made possible certain dishonest practices by the Warden of North and South Mahe.	
Requests approval of S of S to a Bill entitled "An Ordinance to amend and consolidate the Customs Tariff", and mentions recent large influx of Indian traders into the Colony.	
Acknowledgement of Code of Financial Instruction sent by S of S, and intimating that it will be enforced in Seychelles and that financial year in future be from 1st. April to 31st March.	
Report to S of S proposal for exchange of land at Baie St. Anne, Praslin, between Government and Bishop of Victoria, and asks approval of vote for building office and quarters for Assistant Govt : Medical Officer and S of S's approval thereto.	

Subject Matter	Code N°.
Correspondence re : resumption by Government of certain buildings leased to Seychelles Club. Noting throws light on early history of this club.	
Report to S of S on various suggestions made to improve conditions in Praslin and La Digue. Provides good picture of conditions existing there in 1900.	
Proposal to S of S to build new offices for Governor and chambers for Legislative and Executive Councils.	
Despatch from S of S suggesting that in future Crown Lands in Seychelles should be leased instead of sold.	
CONTENTS OF SELECTED CORRESPONDENCE FILE FOR 1901.	C/AM/6
Governor's comments on estimates of revenue and expenditure for 1901 submitted to S of S. Contains some interesting administrative history.	
Quantity of vanilla and its values exported to various countries between 1898 and 1900, and some ealier correspondence on subject of French tariffs on tropical produce from British Colonies.	
S of S's despatch on subject of adjustments of accounts between Seychelles and Mauritius.	
Lease of land for use of Seychelles Club and terms.	
CONTENTS OF SELECTED CORRESPONDENCE FILE FOR 1901 (Contd.)	C/AM/6
Proposal that TRH. the Duke and Duchess of Cornwall and York should visit Seychelles on their return voyage from Australia.	
Proposals for conversion of certain Government buildings and some interesting comments by S of S concerning these.	
Report of number of persons naturalized in Seychelles from 1895 to 1900.	
Re : Seychelles Section of Mauritius Court at the Imperial Institute and recommends appointment of a separate governor to represent Seychelles at the Institute.	
S of S's approval of purchase of a steam launch for Seychelles.	
Sister St. Landri, matron of Victoria Hospital, honoured by Order of St. John of Jerusalem.	
Proposal to increase salaries of Bishop of Victoria and	

Subject Matter	Code N°

Civil Chaplain Seychelles, and S of S's disapproval. Contains some administrative history.

Informations as to contributions paid by Seychelles in connection with the marine cable between Seychelles and Zanzibar and Seychelles and Mauritius.

Interesting despatch to S of S on the problem of drunkenness in Seychelles.

Creation of Local Boards of Health in Praslin and La Digue.

S of S sanctions establishment of Lunatic Asylum in Seychelles, and correspondence concerning proposal.

Mr. François Hodoul created C.M.G.

Transport "Armenia" calls at Victoria with 1017 Boer prisoners of war on board.

Proposals for increasing Police Force on grounds that existing force "utterly insufficient for duties they have to perform".

Tenders for materials for new Government Offices. Provides interesting comparison with costs in 1962.

Local Board of Health Praslin. Estimates of Revenue and Expenditure for 1902.

      - do - La Digue

SEYCHELLES ALMANACK FOR THE YEAR - 1901.

CONTENTS OF SELECTED CORRESPONDENCE FILE FOR 1902.   C/AM/7

Proposal by Committee of Lloyd's to establish at Seychelles a heliographic signalling station for passing ships.

Report to S of S on Regulations for Victoria School. Contains interesting comments concerning pressure to teach French History and French.

CONTENTS OF SELECTED CORRESPONDENCE FILE FOR 1902 (Contd.)   C/AM/7

Report to S of S on Seychelles Savings Bank and attempt to instil thrift.

Proposal to render obligatory the payment in Grant-aided Schools of school fees. Some interesting suggestions for making pupils British Empire-minded.

Proposal to establish industrial training at Victoria School.

Subject Matter	Code N°

Lease of a house at Sans Souci for Administrator and raises question of purchase of a house in the mountains for use as a sanatorium for public officers.

Report to S of S on resolutions passed at a public meeting concerning revised Local Rates, and demanding an increase in number of members of Legislative Council. Contains some interesting sidelights on local mentality.

Proposal to establish a small library in the Prison.

Report to S of S that Seychelles has been made a centre for the Cambridge Local Examinations.

Report to S of S of measures in force to protect Coco-de-mer Palms and Giant Tortoises.

Presentation of Testimonials of the Royal Humane Society awarded to Justan Jacques, Charles Mirakan and Ange Payet of La Digue.

Forwards to S of S letter of Seychelles merchants on infrequency of visits paid to Mahe by H.M's Ships of war.

Reports closing down of Ice Factory at Victoria due to lack of local support.

Proposes to S of S that in future breaking of stones should not be permitted as work for female prisoners.

CONTENTS OF SELECTED CORRESPONDENCE FILE FOR 1903.   C/AM/8

Forwarding report to S of S on Education in Seychelles in 1902. Interesting comments on very low salaries being paid to teachers

Forwarding to S of S Report on Criminal Statistics for 1902. Comments on great increase in drunkenness.

Concerning Seychelles' representative in Imperial Institute, and suggests Sir Francis Lovell for the post.

Further correspondence re : purchase of a property as a Government Sanatorium for public officers.

Certains comments on shortage of houses in Victoria for officers and uncertainty of tenure when houses are leased.

Provision of water-supply to inhabitants of Pointe Connan.

Subject Matter	Code N°
CONTENTS OF SELECTED CORRESPONDENCE FILE FOR 1903. (Contd.)	C/AM/8

Provision of water-supply to inhabitants of Port Glaud.

Report to S of S of Governor's visit to Denis Island, La Digue, Praslin and satellite islands of Praslin. Interesting descriptions of conditions prevailing in those islands at that time.

First Seychelles Civil Servant to receive Imperial Service Order.

Her Majesty's acceptance of fancy work of coco-de-mer leaves presented by Mrs. P. Lefevre.

Report to S of S of phenomenal rainfall in April, May and June of 1903 and damage caused thereby.

Final recommendations for establishment of a Lunatic Asylum in Seychelles.

Proposal to transfer Pauper Camp from Round Island near Praslin to African Camp near Victoria ; S of S's counter-proposal to institute system of out-door relief : Governor's report on difficulties of this alternative, and S of S's final approval of transfer to Victoria.

Requesting S of S's approval of vote for a survey of the town of Victoria.

S of S's approved of vote to cover cost of Mr. Dupont's Mission to Ceylon and the East, and arrangements for publishing his reports.

Report to S of S of arrangements made for teaching carpentry in Victoria School and refers to possibility of agricultural instruction being given in rural schools.

Enlistment of foreigners in Seychelles Police Force.

Recruitment of 100 Indian Coolies for work in Seychelles.

Despatch to S of S on proposed construction of a public road from Baie St. Anne to Grand'Anse, Praslin, and outrageous demands being made by some planters for compensation.

Request to S of S for information as to probable effects on vanilla prospects of the manufacture of "Vanillin".

Report on process of curing vanilla by evaporation.

CONTENTS OF SELECTED CORRESPONDENCE FILE FOR 1904. VOL. I.	C/AM/9 - VOL. I.

Despatch to S of S on great improvement to roads of Mahe during

Subject Matter	Code Nº

past four years.

Correspondence concerning Port Victoria being constituted as a port for the registry of British ships.

Refers to importance of Seychelles being represented at the Imperial Institute.

CONTENTS OF SELECTED CORRESPONDENCE FILE FOR 1904. VOL. I.
(Contd).

C/AM/9 - VOL. I.

Correspondence concerning a Bill authorising the loan to planters from surplus balances of a sum not exceeding Rs. 100,000.

Report of Director of the Imperial Institute on samples of flour from Bread Fruit.

Governor's report on visit to islands in Praslin district, and the great improvements recently introduced there.

Concerns possibilities of extending cultivation of cotton especially in outlying islands.

Interesting despatch to S of S concerning report received on Vanillin and its probable effects on Vanilla exports, and discourses on need of planters to concentrate on other crops.

CONTENTS OF SELECTED CORRESPONDENCE FILE FOR 1904. VOL. II.

C/AM/9 - VOL. II.

Order-in-Council conferring on the Supreme Court of Mauritius the right to hear and determine appeals from the Supreme Court of Seychelles.

Concerns reasons for abolition of a close season for taking turtles (Carets).

Concerning deficiencies in water supply for Victoria as experienced in years of drought such as 1904.

Concerning proposed visit of Mr. Stanley Gardiner on a scientific mission to Seychelles.

Report of unprecedented drought of 1904 and the resulting damage to the Colony's agriculture based on questionaire to 40 leading planters.

Concerning hand power gin and press for cotton gifted by British Cotton Growing Association for demonstration to Seychelles planters.

Permission for Snake Charmer to exhibit in Victoria.

Subject Matter	Code Nº

Despatch to S of S on falling revenues due to drought.

Correspondence regarding Meteorological Observations in the Indian Ocean.

Request from Secretary of State for list of medicinal plants growing in Seychelles and reply enclosing such a list.

CONTENTS OF SELECTED CORRESPONDENCE FILE FOR 1905   C/AM/10

Annual Report on the Outlying Islands for 1904. Contains reference to preservation of Giant Tortoises.

Despatch to Secretary of State stating that Seychelles does not consider it necessary to adhere to international agreement on the white Slave Traffic.

Forwarding to S of S Annual Report on Criminal Statistics for 1904. Para 6 refers to high percentage of convictions and gives interesting explanation.

Dismissal of Revd. E.R. Ward, Civil Chaplain of Seychelles on charges of immorality etc...

S of S supplies copy of Convention with France extending minimum tariff to Seychelles.

Concerning management of Imperial Institute and publication of Bulletin.

Despatch to S of S on continued depression in Vanilla market and need to encourage other crops to replace it. Returns to proposal to encourage coffee growing by placing heavy duty on imports. S of S's objection to duty and alternative suggestion.

Proposal regarding improved water supply for Victoria, and S of S's comments and acceptance in principle.

Despatch to S of S re : Local Rate Recovery Ordinance, and some interesting commenting on difficulties inherent in recovering from labour class.

Concerning Seychelles exhibits at Zanzibar Exhibition.

Letter from Mr. Rothschild on subject of giant tortoises.

Request from Natural History Museum for a collection of blood sucking flies found in Seychelles.

Founding of Circle Litteraire de L'Anse Royale.

List of Estate Owners and acreages of estates for year ending March 1906.

Subject Matter	Code N°
<u>CONTENTS OF SELECTED CORRESPONDENCE FILE FOR 1906.</u> Correspondence on legislation regarding sale of goods under false trade description. This links up with proposal to place heavy duty on imports of coffee, vide file of Selected Correspondence for 1905. Concerns abandonment of cotton-growing in Seychelles. S of S's instruction to discontinue loans to planters from Colony's cash balances owing to Colony's unfavourable financial situation ; his strong criticism of loan proposed to be given to a planter to enable him to meet arrears of taxation ; and his rejection of suggestion to raise a loan.	C/AM/11
<u>CONTENTS OF SELECTED CORRESPONDENCE FILE FOR 1906</u> (Contd.) Correspondence relative to acquisition of land, etc.., in Seychelles by foreing companies. Concerns correspondence between British Police Officials in other colonies regarding criminal cases. **Concerns unusual proposal made to S of S to combine posts of Legal Adviser and Colonial Secretary in Seychelles, and S of S's rejection of ides.** Encouraging report by Imperial Institute on sample of citrate of lime prepared on Silhouette Island. S of S approves of acceptance in Seychelles of English gold and Bank of England notes as revenue. S of S asks for plans of new harbour works at Victoria, for purpose of correcting Admiralty Charts, and copy of plan. Concerns reservation of rights as to mineral oil in leases of Crown Lands. Proposed transfer of Coetivy and Farquhar Islands to Seychelles. Forwards letter from Admiralty relative to association of East Indies and Cape Commands, with Governor's comment on page 60. Interesting correspondence re : importation by Messrs. E. Lanier and Co of Seychelles of large number of Maundy Money coins, and seized by Customs as counterfeit coins as they had been gilded. Strangely no question seems to have been asked as to why the Company had made such an unusual importation. Request to S of S for information re : cultivation of sponges, with view to introduction in some of the Outlying Islands.	C/AM/11

Subject Matter	Code N°
CONTENTS OF SELECTED CORRESPONDENCE FILE FOR 1907.	C/AM/12

Proposal by Messrs. Lanier and Co to import labourers from Africa for working guano deposits on St. Pierre and Alphonse Islands.

Correspondence concerning Mr. Carnegie's gift of £ 1750 for establishing a free Library in Victoria and S of S's approval of annual grant by Government of Rs. 1500 for unkeep of library. Original estimates for expenditure of the gift of £ 1750.

Cases of Beri-Beri on Outlying Islands. S of S calls for further details and Chief Medical Officers' report.

Report by Imperial Institute on samples of Essential Oils produced in Seychelles and sent for examination.

Despatch to S of S concerning grave deficiences of the Code Napoleon as in force in Seychelles, and need to bring this antiquated code to the leval of modern ideas. (Vide also C/AM/16).

| **CONTENTS OF SELECTED CORRESPONDENCE FILE FOR 1907.** (Contd.) | C/AM/12 |

Report by Imperial Institute on sample of Seychelles Lemon Grass Oil sent for examination.

Increase of salary approved for Mr. Dupont and a note concerning his valuable services rendered to Seychelles.

| **CONTENTS OF SELECTED CORRESPONDENCE FILE FOR 1908.** | C/AM/13 |

Details of 1908 Vanilla exports and prices received as compared with 1907.

Despatch to S of S re : Seychelles collections of blood-sucking insects which might cause spread of disease.

Transfer of Coetivy to Seychelles.

"Friend in Need Society" founded in Victoria with S of S's approval for assistance of destitute persons of European origin for whom Pauper Camp not suitable.

Despatch from S of S re : proposed second scientific expedition of Mr. Stanley Gardener to Seychelles.

S of S's approval of an export duty on Cinnamon Bark, and his reply to a petition from the inhabitants protesting against this tax. The letter contains some interesting comments concerning taxation.

Subject Matter	Code N°

S of S transmits report from India on Beri-beri ; and comments thereon by Seychelles medical officers concerning cases which had occured in Outlying Island.

Publication by Mr. E. Blackwood Wright, Chief Justice of Seychelles, of English translation of French Civil Code, with explanations and historical notes.

Despatch to S of S concerning appointment of Mr. H.P. Thomasset, a British-born planter and mentions that it has been the practice that one of the three unofficial members of Council should be of British birth.

CONTENTS OF SELECTED CORRESPONDENCE FILE FOR 1909.   C/AM/14

Proposal approved by S of S to send Mr. Dupont and an assistant on mission to Ceylon to study modern methods of cultivating coconuts and Para rubber. Governor's comments on backwardness of Seychelles planters, and reasons for this.

S of S approves establishment of a boarding house in connection with Victoria School.

Correspondence concerning extension of loans to planters under Ordinance N° 4 of 1904 (vide also correspondence of 7/4/1909 below).

Three despatches to S of S concerning work done by Mortgage and Registration Dept : between 1909 and 1911. Some interesting comments on financial condition of agriculture.

CONTENTS OF SELECTED CORRESPONDENCE FILE FOR 1909.(Contd).   C/AM/14

Interesting claims by a Seychellois to heirship of a settler in San Dominigo who perished in the massacre of the French in that island in 1793.

Concerns consignment of samples of Seychelles products sent for exhibition in Seychelles Court of Imperial Institute.

Sanction to make a new road between Anse Royale and Anse Louis.

Further correspondence re : extension of loans to planters, and also important D/o correspondence between the Governor and Mr. Fiddes on the present and future trading position of the Colony.

Reports inauguration of Grand St. Louis water supply for Victoria and plans for further development of water supply from central chain of mountains.

Concerns report by Imperial Institute on Cinnamon Bark Oil from Seychelles.

Subject Matter	Code N°

Despatch to S of S concerning incidence of Leprosy in Seychelles, and attributing it to evils too frequent inter-marriage between old families of French colonists.

Despatch to S of S forwarding Mr. Dupont's report for 1908. Interesting comments on various pests, including Melittomma and black ants, deafforestation and need to open up fertile valleys of interior of Mahe.

Report from Imperial Institute on samples of Cardamon Oil and Vitex trifolia from Seychelles.

Reports death of Mr. François Hodoul, C.M.G.

Copy of despatch from the Governor of Bahamas concerning the Turtle industry.

CONTENTS OF SELECTED CORRESPONDENCE FILE FOR 1910.   C/AM/15

International Scientific Conference on Leprosy ; list of lepers in Seychelles, and need for amended regulation for segregation.

Balance sheet of Imperial Institute ; and Seychelles contribution of £ 30.

Govt. of U.S.A. admits Seychelles to benefits of minimum Tariff.

Decision that accounts of revenue and expenditure of Seychelles are to be audited locally.

Closing of Victoria School Boarding House owing to lack of support by parents, and its conversion to a maternity home.

Correspondence concerning loss of "Sea Queen" and repatriation of sole survivor Josue Greene.

CONTENTS OF SELECTED CORRESPONDENCE FILE FOR 1910. (Contd.)   C/AM/15

Circulars with instructions concerning taking of census and census of H.M. Ships in Colonial waters.

Request from Managing Committee of Emigration for information concerning Seychelles for benefit of intending settlers there.

S of S forwards copy of a note by Professor Ronald Ross on prevention of mosquito-borne diseases in tropical colonies.

CONTENTS OF SELECTED CORRESPONDENCE FILE FOR 1911.   C/AM/16

Despatch to Secretary of State concerning financial condition of the Colony in 1910, a year in which revenue, despite reduc-

Subject Matter	Code N°

tion of taxation, was highest on record and despite a large drop in value of vanilla exports.

Despatch to S of S concerning transport of turtles from the Outlying Islands and giving statistics of heavy losses by death on voyage, in 1909 and 1910.

Report to S of S on accident to H.E. Mr. Davidson by collapse of flagstaff at Government House.

Further honour for Sister Landri, Matron of the Government Hospital.

Despatch to S of S giving statistics of great increase in exports from "The harvest of the sea" chiefly owing to export of calipee.

S of S approves estimates for alterations to the Maternity Home and announces early sailing from England of Miss. M.G. Halkett as Nursing Superintendent.

Report from Imperial Institute on samples of Minerals sent from Seychelles.

Correspondence concerning distillation of oil from Vetiver roots and report from the Imperial Institute on sample examined.

Interesting despatch to S of S on Colony's export trade for 1910 when copra replaced vanilla as the main crop, and observations on other crops being grown, and probable effects of changes on planters' habits.

Correspondence with S of S on subject of development of fisheries·in Seychelles.

Interesting comments on shipping in Seychelles waters (local and calling) during 1910.

Report by Imperial Institute on samples of Para rubber produced in Seychelles.

Analysis of Seychelles imports in 1910

CONTENTS OF SELECTED CORRESPONDENCE FILE FOR 1911. (Contd.)   C/AM/16

Despatch to S of S on the subject of the work of the Judicial Dept in 1910, and which contains some interesting comments on the shortcomings of the Code Napoleon and of earlier surveys. (Vide also C/AM/12).

Despatch to S of S relating to Moitie System contracts and some history concerning the origin of the system.

Correspondence concerning the loss of the Seychelles fishing

Subject Matter	Code N°

vessel "Sea Queen".

Despatch to S of S concerning cultivation of tobacco in Seychelles, a crop which although Mr. Dupont had recommended it as suitable to local conditions, the planters made no serious effort to grow.

Despatch to S of S re : proposal by the Commercial Bank of Mauritius to open a branch bank in Victoria.

Football on croquet days in Victoria.

CONTENTS OF SELECTED CORRESPONDENCE FILE FOR 1912.   C/AM/17

Report to Secretary of State on Victoria Prison in 1911, with explanation as to why 74 % of all committals were for default in payment of fines.

Theft of a Seychelles boat, "La Haine" and its cargo by the master and crew and their arrest and conviction at Dar-es-Salaam.

Correspondence concerning arrangements by which the London University will conduct examination of candidates for Seychelles Scholarships.

Two despatches to S of S reporting excellent results from establishment of a Maternity Home in Victoria, and proposing measures for training midwives there under an amended Ordinance.

Conviction of the Editor of "Le Reveil" for attacks on the Governor and the publication of obscenities.

Forwards to S of S the Education Report for 1911 with comments on poor quality of instruction given in the primary schools.

Report to S of S the completion of a Lighthouse on Mamelles Island, and an earlier report concerning its construction.

Suggestion to Advisory Committee for Tropical Diseases Research for inclusion of Ankylostomiasis as a tropical disease, since the malady is wide-spread in Seychelles.

Despatch to S of S re : laying-out of grounds surrounding new Government House.

Forwards to S of S annual Report on Agriculture for 1911, with comments on the prospects of the new industry of rearing Carets (tortoise-shell turtle) in captivity.

Subject Matter	Code N°

<u>CONTENTS OF SELECTED CORRESPONDENCE FILE FOR 1912.</u> (Contd.)   C/AM/17

Despatch to S of S re : international Opium convention Mentions
that Chinese community in Seychelles bound themselves since
1910 to abandon the use of Opium.

Concerns the establishment in Seychelles of a Society for the
Protection of Animals.

Forwarding to S of S copies of printed report by Mr. Dupont
on his visit to Ceylon and the East.

Report to S of S regretting that time has not yet arrived for
introduction of policy of sending teachers from Seychelles to
undergo a course of training in the United Kingdom.

Special Report to S of S on the Educational System of
Seychelles.

<u>CONTENTS OF SELECTED CORRESPONDENCE FILE FOR 1913.</u>   C/AM/18

Circular concerning Uniform to be worn by officers who are
members of the Executive Council and white evening dress
prescribed for officers.

Governor calls for statement respecting officers engaged in
private concerns or business, and his report to Secretary of
State of glaring instances of infringement of regulations.

Note concerning information of an intended attack on person of
Governor Davidson.

Correspondence between Governor and S of S on subject of retren-
chment of establishment in bad years.

Father Justin's objection to system of bathing at School House,
King's College, or "when cleanliness is not next to godliness".

Account of H.E.'s visits to various islands of the Seychelles
group, and an inspections note concerning the attempt on
Curieuse Island to rear caret or hawksbill turtles in captivity
(vide page 40).

Minute on shortage of rupee coins in Seychelles due to Indian
and Chinese merchants remitting specie to India instead of
drafts, and measures to meet the situation.

Circular to Heads of Departments observing that Minute Papers
are frequently retained for months and sometimes for years, and
fixing 2 weeks as the maximum period for the future.

Correspondence concerning proposed closing down of Seychelles
Branch of Bank of Mauritius owing to lack of public support,

Subject Matter	Code N°

and final decision to carry on for another year as a further trial provided Government ceases giving loans to planters at rates with which no bank could compete.

<u>CONTENTS OF SELECTED CORRESPONDENCE FILE FOR 1913.</u> (Contd).　　　C/AM/18

Report carcase of a dead whale adrift off North Island and a danger to shipping.

A prisoner petitions His Excellency for a biscuit for breakfast.

Inspector and Sergeant Major of Police found guilty of grave dereliction of duty.

Steps proposed for safeguarding the Colony's heritage of freedom from endemic disease, and S of S's reply.

<u>CONTENTS OF SELECTED CORRESPONDENCE FILE FOR 1914.</u>　　　C/AM/19

Governor proposes to Secretary of State some promotion for officers who have served a number of years in Seychelles without advancement, and so remove impression that Seychelles is a backwater for those who once enter it.

Serious incidence of venereal disease in Seychelles and measures to deal with it.

Revival of whaling industry in Seychelles waters, and an interesting minute of 1911 (pages 37 to 39) prepared by Governor Davidson on the industry.

Correspondence re : objections by certain persons to discontinuance of Government loans to planters, and refers to certain misuses of those loans.

Petition that Government should establish a motor service between Victoria and Anse Royale.

Petition against appointment of Mr. S.A. Scott to the Legislative Council, and Governor's report to S of S throwing some light on Seychelles mentality and methods.

Adverse report on working of the Grant-in-aid Scheme to schools, by the Inspector of Education, and some comments on this report by Members of the Executive.

Early war-time measures introduced for curtailment of Government disbursements, cessation of road work, and employment of Government labour on growing of foodstuffs on Crown Lands.

Subject Matter	Code Nº

Correspondence concerning obligation of a Government Medical Officer to disclose the nature of the disease of an official send to him for examination, despite provisions of Seychelles Penal Code.

Halt at Mahe en route for Madagascar of a number of Officers and Non-Commissioned Officers of the French Colonial Army, their treatment as guests of the Colony and their fine gesture in return.

Notes prepared by Mr. Dupont on the small black ants which had become a serious pest in the Colony.

CONTENTS OF SELECTED CORRESPONDENCE FILE FOR 1915.   C/AM/20

Correspondence concerning the erection of a wireless telegraph station for naval purposes in Seychelles.

Motion in Legco by Hon : F. Savy relating to the punishment of juvenile offenders.

Dogs and other animals - protection of. Correspondence with Miss. Best, founder of local branch of R.S.P.C.A. asking for further legislation.

Despatch to Secretary of State re : wireless message intercepted and believed to have been sent by German Raider "Konigsberg".

Concerns violent anti-British propaganda and by Mr. Leite, a Swiss resident of Seychelles.

Alleged traffic in prostitutes between Seychelles and East Africa.

State Portraits of Their Majesties the king and Queen for Government House.

Inquiry respecting dog found hanging close to Bel Air Road. (Vide also correspondence of 12.4.1915 above).

Decision of Bank of Mauritius to close its Branch in Seychelles.

CONTENTS OF SELECTED CORRESPONDENCE FILE FOR 1920.   C/AM/21

Return of Capital Sentences carried out in 1919.

List of Barristers and Attornies-at-Law on roll of Supreme Court of Seychelles as at 31.12.1919.

Despatches from Secretary of State concerning Ordinance Nº 24 of 1919 allowing for the appointment as Acting Chief Justice

Subject Matter	Code N°

of a Notary, who would concurrently continue the exercise of his own profession, and expressing opinion that resort to its provisions should only be made in cases of extreme urgency.

Despatch from S of S concerning Ordinance N° 26 of 1919, entitled "An Ordinance to provide for a Tax on Incomes". Agrees that, while many of its provisions open to criticism, Royal Commission for United Kingdom Income Tax, whereafter Colonial Income Tax Laws will come under revision in light of their recommendation.

Public notice concerning H.R.H. The Prince of Wales' Birthday celebrations.

Report of death of Father J.D. Lachavane, R.C. Bishop of Victoria, transmitted to Secretary of State with request that the Vatican be asked to appoint an Englishman as his successor.

CONTENTS OF SELECTED CORRESPONDENCE FILE FOR 1920 (Contd.) C/AM/21

Papers concerning a serious embezzlement of Government money (Rs. 5000/-) by a Treasury Clerk with the complicity of the Audit Clerk.

Despatch from S of S forwarding copy of the Report of a Committee to inquire into certain questions connected with the Colonial Medical Services and calling for Governor's observations on the Committees recommendations.

First cinematography performance in Seychelles.

CONTENTS OF SELECTED CORRESPONDENCE FILE FOR 1921. C/AM/22

Application for extension of certain buildings in Royal Street, Victoria, supported by plan of central area of Victoria in 1921.

Letter from Mr. Collet on subject of desirability of encouraging local fisheries by introducing up-to-date methods.

Despatch from Secretary of State transmitting copies of an Act to amend the Official secrets Act 1911, and a memorandum prepared by War Office concerning modern methods of spying.

Permission granted to open a private cemetery by person against whom the Bishop of Mauritius had pronounced a Major Excommunication.

Report to S of S wreck of Norwegian barque "Dagmar" on reef of Providence Island.

Correspondence between H.E. and the Inspector of Police re : rounding up of prostitutes during visits of ships of Royal Navy.

Subject Matter	Code N°

Theft of Rs. 760/- from Post Officer safes.

Request from Director of Horticulture, Egypt, for two seeds of the Coco-de-mer ; their despatch and safe arrival.

Despatch from S of S asking that the death of any member of the Order of the British Empire occuring in any Colony may be reported with place and date of death.

Public petition for reamalgamation of Seychelles with Mauritius telegraphed to Secretary of State ; H.E' comments thereon ; and S of S's rejection of suggestion as not being in the best interests of the Colony.

CONTENTS OF SELECTED CORRESPONDENCE FILE FOR 1922-1925.　　　　　　C/AM/23

Despatch from Secretary of State on subject of encouraging purchase of British cars in Colonies and asking for information concerning numbers of cars and lorries in Seychelles. (See also Despatch of 16.12.1925 below).

Despatch of S of S stating that there are at present in the Colony no motor lorries and only two cars, and that future scope for cars very limited as there is only one road of about 12 miles in length.

Despatch from S of S concerning supply of Law Reports and Digests of Colonial Governments, and H.E.'s reply that hitherto it had not been the practiee in Seychelles to prepare full reports and digests, but that in future all important judgements would be collected in annual volumes. (Note :- This practice seems to have been continued only up to 1933).

Interesting correspondence concerning necessity to increase existing strength of two Medical Officers ; difficulty of getting a Medical European Officer on salary offerred ; and objection of Unofficial Members of Legco is engaging and Indian doctor.

Burning question as to whose duty it was to sweep out the office of the J.P. South Mahe.

An unusual case of suspected miscarriage of justice and the remedy applied.

Gift by a former Bishop of Mauritius of a plot of land adjacent to the Parsonage House of St. Paul's at the corner of Royal and Albert Streets, Victoria.

Correspondence concerning the threat of "Bud-rot" disease among coconut palms raised by Mr. Stephen Lyne, the Director of Agriculture.

Subject Matter	Code N°

Despatch from Secretary of State acknowledging and commenting upon the Colony's Annual Medical Report for 1924, and, inter alia, suggesting that for the treatment of Leprosy by the "Tai Fong Chee" method, steps should be taken to plant Chaulmoogra Nut trees.

Despatch to S of S concerning a reference from the Committee of Civil Research as to the mineral content of natural pastures, and forwarding a report on the natural pastures in Seychelles.

Letter with report to the International Geological Congress, Madrid, on guano deposits of Seychelles.

Correspondence concerning alleged undue interference with religious convictions of members of Church of England while in hospital.

Request by Naval Intelligence Centre, Colombo, for information concerning suitability of Assumption, Astove, Cosmoledo and Farquhar Islands for use as landing grounds for seaplane stations, and copy of report prepared by the Port Officer.

CONTENTS OF SELECTED CORRESPONDENCE FILE FOR 1922-1925 (Contd.)   C/AM/23

Proposal to abolish temporary export duties on Copra and Essential Oils, and to raise import duties on wines and spirits, and Secretary of States approval.

Telegram from S of S announcing death of Her Majesty Queen Alexandra ; telegram of condolence and arrangements in Victoria for Memorial Services.

Complaint by Church Warden of St. Paul's Cathedral, Victoria, that, for purpose of the Memorial Services, "the Church of Rome had been given precedence over the Church of England" ; ensuing correspondence involving Bishop of Mauritius and S of S ; and S of S's acceptance of H.E's explanation.

Despatch from S of S concerning import of British motor cars into Seychelles ; Memorandum concerning condition of roads and list of cars already in the Colony. Also correspondence on the subject with the President of the Moto-Auto Club, Mahe.

CONTENTS OF SELECTED CORRESPONDENCE FILE FOR 1926-1927.   C/AM/24

Practice of requiring ladies to curtsey to the Governor to be discontinued. Despatch from Secretary of State.

Correspondence with S of S concerning reorganization of the Agricultural Dept. and S of S's approval.

Subject Matter	Code Nº

Further correspondence with S of S concerning the abolition of export duties on Copra and Essential Oils, and H.E!s hope that it would never be necessary to reimpose them since he would prefer to raise extra revenue by other means rather thah by taxing the Colony's main exports (Note :- For earlier correspondence see File for 1925).

Proposal to appoint an Indian, Mr. Sorabji. J. Olia as an Unofficial Member of Legco, his unwillingness to accept, and request by Mr. M.S. Natarajan Chetty for nomination, which was not approved.

Proposal to appoint Major H. Kenworthy as Official Member of Legco and Exco ; a local intrigue to prevent this ; H.E!s defence of Major Kenworthy and S of S's approval of appointment.

Proposal from S of S that an officer from Seychelles be deputed to attend a short course of study in England on prison administration, and H.E's reply that there was no one suitable to send, but that such a course would prove useful to the Governor who has to deal more minutely with the various branches of the Administration".

Epidemic of burgularies and steps taken to deal with them.

Despatch to S of S relative to increased duties on wines and spirits with statistics of the effects of these increased duties.

CONTENTS OF SELECTED CORRESPONDENCE FILE FOR 1926-1927. (Contd.) C/AM/24

Report by the Imperial Institute on a sample of seaweed sent from Seychelles, which was considered to be comparable with the best grades of Irish moss.

Despatch to S of S concerning a memorandum prepared by the Imperial Marketing Board, and enclosing a note on fruit-growing and irrigation possibilities in Seychelles.

Correspondence concerning the death of His Excellency Sir Malcolm Stevenson.

Sad story of a senior clerk of the Postal Dept. who lost his job by trying to be obliging to all.

Request through the Bishop of Mauritius that the 25 th January should be observed in Victoria as a public holiday, being St. Paul's Day, the patron Saint of St. Paul's Cathedral.

Subject Matter	Code N°
CONTENTS OF SELECTED CORRESPONDENCE FILE FOR 1928-1930.	C/AM/25

Despatch to the Secretary of State concerning information called for by the Empire Marketing Board and enclosing a reply prepared by the Director of Agriculture to the questionaire regarding agricultural education and fruit growing in the Colony, together with a memorandum on the agricultural problems which await solution in the Colony.

Despatch from S of S calling for information concerning conditions and prospects in Seychelles for settlers from the United Kingdom, H.E's reply and some earlier correspondence on this subject.

Correspondence concerning purchase from U.K. of a motor-boat with auxiliary sails to replace the auxiliary Ketch "The Florence", which had been built locally and had proved a complete failure.

Despatch to S of S acknowledgeing receipt of a Report entitled "Tropical Agricultural Research in the Empire with special reference to Cacao, Sugar Cane, Cotton and Palms", prepared by Empire Marketing Board, and stating that Director of Agriculture is issuing information from the report in a condensed form to planters.

Despatch from S of S concerning the retirement of Judges on the ground of age, and stating that the decisions contained in the Despatch will apply to all judges serving in the Colonies.

Proposed road development in Mahe at an estimated total cost of Rs. 578,500 and the allocation in 1929 of Rs. 60,000 from surplus revenues for this purpose ; S of S's approval ; and counter-proposal of Unofficial Members of Legco that the cost of this work should be met from money raised by a loan and that surplus funds should be lent to the planters for the improvement of agriculture.

CONTENTS OF SELECTED CORRESPONDENCE FILE FOR 1928-1930. (Contd).	C/AM/25

Complaint from a resident concerning reckless motor driving in Mahe and H.E's reply.

Correspondence concern return to original owners of land occupied by dis-used roads, leading to legislation to deproclaim unwanted roads.

Smart detection by Police of smuggling of rum from a French steamer into Anse Etoile.

Despatch from S of S re : question of appeals in criminal cases in the Colonies, calling for report of position in Seychelles and asking for proposals for bringing the position into accord

Subject Matter	Code N°

with provisions of Criminal Appeal Act 1907 ; H.E's reply with memorandum prepared by Legal Adviser, and S of S's decision that in circumstances explained, no action is possible at present in Seychelles.

Development of Coir Fibre industry in Seychelles ; memorandum from British Research Association on this subject ; and noting by Director of Agriculture as to propects in the Colony.

Correspondence concerning proposal by owners and lessees of Outlying Islands to be permitted to supply their labour with cheaper rations to set off the fall in price of copra, and Government's rejection of the suggestion.

CONTENTS OF SELECTED CORRESPONDENCE FILE FOR 1931 and 1932.   C/AM/26

Circular Despatch from Secretary of State notifying decision of His Majesty that no official recognition should be given in Colonies to the style of "Excellency" reported to have been conferred by the Pope upon Archishops and Bishops of the Roman Catholic Church.

Letter from Chief Justice to H.E. concerning possibility that Mr. C. Serre of Port Glaud had been convicted as a result of a Police conspiracy and organized perjury. Inquiry, conviction of two policemen, and grant of free pardon and compensation to Mr. Serre.

Application by H.E. Governor Honey for medal of Boer War in which he took part as a sergeant of Mounted Scouts in the Rhodesian Regiment.

Appointment of the Rev. J.A.F. Ozanne as Civil Chaplain of Seychelles and two telegrams of later date.
Note :- He had previously voluntarily left the Church of Rome to join the Aglican Church and had published "Creoles and Coconuts", a book on Seychelles which was critical of the R.C. Mission in Seychelles.

Circular despatch from S of S calling for information concerning the Colony as required by the Colonial Advisory Council for Agriculture and Animal Health ; and replies sent on these and other matters.

CONTENTS OF SELECTED CORRESPONDENCE FILE FOR 1931 and 1932.   (Contd.) C/AM/26

Interesting correspondence concerning a proposal by Herr Buchman and a party of some 30 Germans to settle permanently in the Amirante Islands or other uninhabited islands of the Coralline Group.

Subject Matter	Code Nº

Well supported petition to S of S asking that Dr. Walsh, the Chief Justice, be appointed as next Governor of Seychelles and correspondence relating thereto.

CONTENTS OF SELECTED CORRESPONDENCE FILE FOR 1933 and 1934.   C/AM/27

Resignation of Mr. J. Stravens from Printing Dept : rather than disobey orders to attend his duties on Saturdays, which he, as a Seventh Day Adventist, was unable to do on religious grounds. (Vide also pages 94 to 99).

Report sent by Secretary of State of visits paid by Commander-in-Chief of the East India Station in H.M.S. Hawkins, and his observations (page 11) on conditions in Seychelles at that time.

Proposal to experiment in growing potatoes in Seychelles.

Despatch from S of S concerning a proposal made by Council of Legco of Nations to re-settle Assyrians in Irak in parts of the British Empire, and decision that this would be impracticable in case of Mauritius and Seychelles.

Appointment of Justices of the Peace for South Mahe District and Praslin. Ordinance Nº 19 of 1933.

Circular Nº 11 of 1934 - Present practice in the public service of granting of personal advances of salary to be strictly limited in future to quite exceptional cases.

Circular Nº 8 of 1934 - Requiring strict exercise of economy in every department, and no expenditure beyond budget sanctions without special authority of Governor.

Retirement of Bishop Gumy as Lord Bishop of Victoria. H.E's appreciation of the great services rendered by him.

Despatch to S of S re : recognition of Father Joyce in succession to Bishop Gumy ; raises certain points of procedure in appointment of R.C. Bishops of Victoria and S of S's reply.

Circular concerning public officers engaging in trade, loaning money etc and despatch to S of S submitting for approval new regulations prohibiting such practices.

Letter from H.E. to Chief Justice concerning a committee of inquiring into the working of the Public Works Dept, and the Committee's report.

Subject Matter	Code N°
CONTENTS OF SELECTED CORRESPONDENCE FOR 1933 and 1934. (Contd.)	C/AM/27

Survey Memorandum with map of eastern boundary of Government House grounds. By this memorandum the spot occupied by the Stone of Possession together with a strip of ground six feet square around the Stone was abandoned to the Government of Seychelles, and free access to the stone at any time was guaranted.

Bi-centenary of founding of Port Louis, Mauritius, and an invitation from the Mayor to Seychelles to participate in these celebrations. H.E's letter of regret that, owing to serious financial difficulties, the Colony would be unable to participate.

Tourism - first step in the development of Seychelles as a resort for visitors and tourists. Grant of loan to the hotel "Les Palms" from the Colonial Development Fund.

Despatch to S of S on religious rioting in Victoria on Good Friday of 1934, when certain Seventh-Day Adventists and Anglo-Catholics were attacked by a mob of Roman Catholics instigated by a leading planter. Also correspondence concerning Religious-Processions.

Despatch from S of S concerning Table of Precedence ; H.E's reply with propose amended Table for Seychelles ; and S of S's approval.

Retirement of Mr. J.D.E. Harter and the S of S's and Governor's high appreciation of his long and valuable services to the Colony.

| **CONTENTS OF SELECTED CORRESPONDENCE FOR 1935 to 1940.** | C/AM/28 |

Inquiry from Society for the Preservation of the Fauna of the Empire re : Aldabra tortoises.

King's Silver Jubilee Medal and list of recepients in Seychelles.

New salary scales for Seychelles Clerical and Technical Services, based on recommondation of Reid Report.

Publication of new journal - "Action Catholique".

Laws to regulate the printing and publishing of newspapers within the Colony.

Agricultural Experimental Station - notes on visits by planters.

Seychelles Agricultural and Industrial Exhibition.

Subject Matter	Code N°
Despatch from S of S with comments on Planter's lack of interest in Government's experimental work in Agriculture.	
Replacement of Seychelles currency notes of 50 cents and one Rupee by metal coins of low silver content.	
CONTENTS OF SELECTED CORRESPONDENCE FOR 1935 to 1940.(Contd.)	C/AM/28
Inquiry from Governor of Kenya and Tanganyika as to whether lack of English among Seychelles immigrants there is a handicap. Information required in connection with educational policy. Handicap confirmed.	
Revised table of average duration of voyages by ships plying between Seychelles and neighbouring islands and E. Africa.	
Despatch for S of S re : specimen of four new coins for Seychelles, and certain suggestions as to style of lettering.	
Departmental circular re : submission in future of references to the Secretary to Government, and not to the Governor direct.	
Scale of fees chargeable by Government Medical Officers for services performed in Government hospitals.	
Memorandum by Governor on reorganisation of Medical Services.	

WORLD WAR I

Subject Matter	Code N°
WAR FILE FOR THE YEAR 1914 - VOLS. I TO III.	C/W/1 - VOLS I to III
WAR FILE FOR THE YEAR 1915, VOLS. I TO III.	C/W2 - VOLS I to III
WAR FILE FOR THE YEAR 1916.	C/W/3
WAR FILE FO THE YEAR 1917.	C/W/4
WAR FILE FOR THE YEAR 1918 to 1919. VOLS. I TO III.	C/W/5 - VOLS I to III
	C/SS/7 VOLS. I & II.
Note :- For Seychelles Labour Corps for service in East Africa see C/SS/7 Vols. I and II. For "Imperial War Graves Commission" - 1921 See C/SS/8	C/SS/8·
WORLD WAR II - 1939 to 1945	
WAR FILE FOR THE YEARS - 1939 to 1940.	C/W/6 - VOL. I
SEYCHELLES DEFENCE REGULATIONS - 1939 to 1945.	C/W/6 - VOL. II
REPORT ON EMERGENCY POLICE FORCE - 1940.	C/W/6 - VOL. III
GARRISON COMPANY OF INDIAN TROOPS STATIONED IN MAHE in 1940.	C/W/6 - VOL. IV
PROVISION IN 1940 OF TWO NAVAL SIX INCH GUNS MANNED BY CEYLON GARRISON ARTILLERY FOR DEFENCE OF VICTORIA.	C/W/6 - VOL. V
WAR FINANCIAL ARRANGEMENTS IN SEYCHELLES - 1939 to 1941.	C/W/6 - VOL. VI
LEGISLATION TO INCREASE CULTIVATION OF FOOD CROPS IN SEYCHELLES 1939 to 1942.	C/W/6 - VOL. VII

Subject Matter	Code N°
SEYCHELLES GIFTS IN AID OF WAR - 1939 to 1942.	C/W/6 - VOL. VIII
ROYAL AIR FORCE. (a) Recruitement of Seychellois. (b) Fatal Air Force crashes in Seychelles.	C/W/6 - VOL. IX
DEFECTION OF FRANCE AND GENERAL DE GAULLE - 1940 to 1941.	C/W/6 - VOL. X
SERVICE BADGES FOR MERCHANT NAVY.	C/W/6 - VOL. XI
SEYCHELLES PIONEER COMPANIES.	C/W/6 - VOL. XII

INDIVIDUAL SUBJECT FILES

Subject Matter	Code Nº
LOAN OF £ 15,000 FOR MAHE ROAD MAKING 1896 to 1903.	C/SS/1
POLITICAL EXILES : ASHANTI - EX-KING PREMPEH & OTHERS 1906 TO 1921. VOLS. I TO V.	C/SS/2. VOLS. I TO V.
POLITICAL EXILES : 1. Ex-SULTAN ABDULLAH OF PERAK. 2 BOER PRISONERS OF WAR AND BOER REBELS. 3. UGANDA DEPORTEES. 4 NYASALAND DEPORTEES. 1887 TO 1937. VOL. VI.	C/SS/2. VOL. VI.
POLITICAL EXILES : 1. INA ALI SHIRREH EX-SULTAN OF WARSAN-GLI (SOMALILAND) 2. SAID KHALID BIN BARGASH. VOL. VII.	C/SS/2. VOL. VII
REPORT OF 1895 CONCERNING EARLY SURVEYS OF LAND CONCESSIONS AND CORRESPONDENCE OF 1903 RELATING TO ABANDONMENT OF "PAS GEOMETRIQUES".	C/SS/3
MANUSCRIPT OF REPORT ON MR. DUPONT'S MISSION TO CEYLON AND THE EAST IN MAY 1903.	C/SS/4
REPORT ON VISIT TO OUTLYING ISLANDS AND HISTORY OF SEYCHELLES BY MR. A. TONNET. 1905.	C/SS/5
PETITION SUBMITTED BY MAMODE HADEE IN 1913 RESPECTING GUARDIANSHIP OF A MINOR WHICH MADE LEGAL HISTORY AND LED TO AMENDMENT OF THE LAW RELATING TO GUARDIANSHIP OF MINORS AND FAMILY COUNCILS. 1913 TO 1916.	C/SS/6
SEYCHELLES LABOUR CORPS FOR SERVICE IN EAST AFRICAN CAMPAIGN. 1916 TO 1918. VOLS. I TO II.	C/SS/7. VOLS. I TO II.
IMPERIAL WAR GRAVES COMMISSION - 1921.	C/SS/8.
PROTECTION OF CARET OR HAWKSBILL TURTLE. 1924 to 1929.	C/SS/9
REPORT OF MR. G.G. AUCHINLECK CONCERNING REORGANISATION OF AGRICULTURE AND SUBSEQUENT MATTERS. 1921 TO 1924.	C/SS/10
MR. STOCKDALE'S REPORT ON THE COLONY'S AGRICULTURE - MATTERS ARISING OUT OF 1931 TO 1936. VOLS. I TO V.	C/SS/11. VOLS. I TO V.

Subject Matter	Code Nº
DEVELOPMENT OF COMMERCIAL FISHERY IN SEYCHELLES WATERS. 1921 TO 1934. VOLS I TO III.	C/SS/12. VOLS. I TO III.
TREASURE TROVE OF ASTOVE ISLAND.1911.	C/SS/13
WHALING INDUSTRY IN SEYCHELLES WATERS.	C/SS/14
ATTEMPTS TO CONTROL PREPARATION AND CONSUMPTION OF BACCA. 1912 TO 1930. AND 1937 - 1942. VOLS. I TO II.	C/SS/15 - VOLS. I TO II
MELITTOMA INSULARE EARLY ATTEMPTS TO ERADICATE. 1922 TO 1940.	C/SS/16
SCALE DISEASES AFFECTING THE COCO-NUT PLANTATIONS OF SEYCHELLES. 1930 TO 1941.	C/SS/17
CAPUCIN LIGHTHOUSE - 1931 TO 1935.	C/SS/18
CORRESPONDENCE ARISING OUT OF A MEMORIAL FROM THE PLANTERS ASSOCIATION ASKING FOR PANIC MEASURES TO MEET FALL IN EXPORT PRICES - 1931.	C/SS/19
PURCHASE OF AUXILIARY KETCH "FLORENCE" - 1919.	C/SS/20
MYSTERIOUS DISAPPEARANCE OF REVD. FATHER THEOPHILE AND THE DISCOVERY OF HIS DEAD BODY IN THE VICINETY OF LA MISERE 1925	C/SS/21
REORGANISATION OF FIRE PRECAUTIONS FOR VICTORIA - 1922 to 1927.	C/SS/22
RAPID INCREASE IN IMPORTATIONS OF MOTOR-VEHICLES AND INTRO-DUCTION OF AN ORDINANCE TO REGULATE THEIR USE. 1927 to 1929.	C/SS/23
RESIGNATION OF UNOFFICIAL MEMBERS MESSRS. W.F. STEPHENS, C. NAGEON DE L'ESTANG AND M. LEMARCHAND FROM THE LEGISLATIVE COUNCIL : STEPS TAKEN TO REPLACE THEM : THE SECRETARY OF STATE'S REGRET FOR THEIR LAMENTABLE ACTION AND REJECTION OF THEIR PLEA FOR CHANGES IN THE CONSTITUTION OF THE COLONY. 1928.	C/SS/24
PREVALENCE OF JUVENILE CRIME IN THE COLONY. 1930.	C/SS/25

Subject Matter	Code N°
UNSUCCESSFUL ATTEMPT TO INTRODUCE A SILK INDUSTRY INTO SEYCHELLES AS A COTTAGE INDUSTRY. 1934 to 1941.	C/SS/26
CIRCULAR LETTERS RECEIVED FROM THE SECRETARY OF STATE FOR THE COLONIES. 1933 to 1940 - VOLS. I TO VI.	C/SS/27 - VOLS. I to VI
MAJOR W.R. JAMES : HIS PROSPECTUS OF THE SEYCHELLES DEVELOPMENT CO. LTD. HIS DISAPPEARANCE WITH SOME TEN THOUSAND RUPEES FRAUDULENTLY COLLECTED IN MAHE : HIS BIGA-MOUS MARRIAGE TO A SEYCHELLES LADY. ENDING IN A WELL-EARNED SENTENCE OF THREE YEARS PENAL SERVITUDE IN DARTMOOR PRISON. 1927.	C/SS/28
TRAFFIC IN WOMEN FROM SEYCHELLES TO BOMBAY - 1930 to 1937.	C/SS/29
MR. R.S. DE VERE'S APPOINTMENT AS ACTING CHIEF JUSTICE AND HIS ATTEMPT TO ASSUME THE ADMINISTRATION. 1928.	C/SS/30
(i) APPLICATIONS FOR THE RELEASE OF PRISONERS ON MEDICAL GROUNDS. (ii) REVISION OF LONG-SENTENCE CONVICTIONS. 1897 to 1936.	C/SS/31
CAMPAIGN FOR THE ERADICATION OF HOOKWORM (ANKYLOSTOMIASIS) 1924-1926.	C/SS/32
WIRELESS TELEPHONE SERVICE FOR SEYCHELLES 1929 to 1934.	C/SS/33
PROPOSED DISESTABLISHMENT OF ANGLICAN AND ROMAN CHURCHES OF SEYCHELLES 1906 to 1907.	C/SS/34
CONTRACT FOR CONSTRUCTION OF SUBMARINE CABLE FROM EAST COAST OF AFRICA TO SEYCHELLES AND LICENCES FOR CABLE LANDING ISSUED TO THE EASTERN TELEGRAPH COMPANY AND TO CABLE AND WIRELESS LTD. 1893 to 1940.	C/SS/35
EDUCATION POLICY IN SEYCHELLES. 1841 to 1938. VOLS. I TO V.	C/SS/36 - VOLS I TO V.
PROPOSALS SUBMITTED BY MR. STEPHENS AND TWO OTHER UNOFFICIAL MEMBERS OF LEGCO FOR THE REORGANISATION OF THE MEDICAL DEPARTMENT. 1926 to 1928.	C/SS/37
PROPOSALS FOR GOVERNMENT REORGANISATION BY MESSRS. BEAMISH AND STEPHENS. 1931.	C/SS/38

Subject Matter	Code N°
CONSTITUTIONAL CHANGES. 1873 to 1931. VOLS. I TO II. 1939 TO 1944. VOL. III.	C/SS/39. VOL.I & II VOL. III.
INTERNATIONAL LABOUR CONFERENCE OF 1920. 1921 to 1939. VOLS. I TO II.	C/SS/40. VOLS. I & II
THE COLONIAL ADMINISTRATIVE SERVICE - SCHEME FOR UNIFICATION OF 1932 to 1938 AND REVISED INSTRUCTIONS FOR COLONIAL AUDIT DEPT. 1952.	C/SS/41
LEVY ON OFFICIAL SALARIES IMPOSED DURING FINANCIAL EMERGENCY OF 1931 ONWARDS BUT SUCH LEVIES HELD UNJUSTIFIED TO MEET FINANCIAL STRINGENCIES CAUSED BY WAR IN 1940. 1931 to 1940.	C/SS/42
POPULATION CENSUSES - 1901 to 1931, VOLS. I and II.	C/SS/43 - VOLS. I & II.
SEYCHELLES POLICE FORCE. INEFFICIENCY OF IN 1926 and 1932. VOL. I.	C/SS/44 - VOL. I.
PETITION FROM MEMBERS OF THE SEYCHELLES BAR TO ALLOW OF AN APPEAL AS OF RIGHT TO THE APPELLATE COURT OF MAURITIUS IN ANY CASE OF PUBLIC INTEREST. 1929 to 1933.	C/SS/45
APPOINTMENT OF MR. T. REID AS FINANCIAL COMMISSIONER TO INVESTIGATE THE COLONY'S FINANCIAL POSITION AND ACTION TAKEN TO IMPLEMENT MR. REID'S RECOMMENDATIONS. 1933 to 1934.	C/SS/46
IMPERIAL DEFENCE. 1889 to 1938. VOLS. I TO III.	C/SS/47. VOLS. I to III.
CEREMONIAL. 1879 to 1931. VOLS. I TO V.	C/SS/48. VOLS. I TO V.
SEYCHELLES FLAG AND PUBLIC SEAL. 1900 to 1923.	C/SS/49.
FOREIGN CONSULAR REPRESENTATIVES IN BRITISH COLONIES 1900 TO 1947.	C/SS/50
ROMAN CATHOLIC BISHOPS OF VICTORIA. 1896 to 1916.	C/SS/51
ESTABLISHMENT OF A NAVAL COALING STATION AT MAHE AND PROPOSAL TO RAISE A LOCAL MILITARY TO STRENGTHEN SEYCHELLES POSITION VIS A VIS FRENCH IN MADAGASCAR. - 1887 to 1904.	C/SS/52

Subject Matter	Code Nº
UNPUBLISHED DOCUMENTS AND MAPS CONCERNING SEYCHELLES ISLANDS PRIOR TO 1810 COLLECTED BY MON. A.A. FAUVEL. 1906 TO 1909.	C/SS/53.
TWO PROPOSALS. (1) TO IMPOSE CONTROL OVER CASUAL LABOUR AND ALLEGED VAGRANCY, AND (2) TO DETER PRAEDIAL LARCENGY AND OTHER OFFENCES BY FLOGGING AND STRICTER PRISON DISCIPLI-NE, (3) ATTITUDE OF PLANTERS TO LABOUR. 1897 and 1938.	C/SS/54
LIBERATED AFRICANS BROUGHT TO SEYCHELLES BY SHIPS OF BRITISH NAVY. 1867 to 1901.	C/SS/55
CELEBRATIONS HELD IN SEYCHELLES TO MARK THE CONCLUSION OF THE FIRST WORLD WAR. 1919.	C/SS/56
TEACHING OF ELEMENTARY HYGIENE IN COLONIAL SCHOOLS. 1903 to 1916.	C/SS/57
ESTABLISHMENT OF BOTANIC STATION IN SEYCHELLES. 1893 to 1903.	C/SS/58
OTTAWA CONFERENCE. 1932 to 1938, VOLS I AND II.	C/SS/59 - VOL. I & II.
BUILDING OF NEW HOSPITAL IN VICTORIA. 1922 to 1925.	C/SS/60.
ESTABLISHMENT OF A PAPER CURRENCY FOR SEYCHELLES IN 1928 AND TWO PROVISIONAL LOCALLY PRINTED ISSUES IN 1914 AND 1919 1898 to 1934.	C/SS/61
SEYCHELLES POSTAL SERVICES. VOLS. I TO IV. 1895 to 1953.	C/SS/62. VOLS. I TO IV.
STEAM-SHIP COMMUNICATIONS WITH SEYCHELLES. 1893 to 1920. VOLS. I AND II.	C/SS/63. VOLS. I & II.
GUANO DEPOSITS IN THE SEYCHELLES - 1895 to 1910.	C/SS/64.
LIGHTING OF VICTORIA BY ELECTRICITY. 1911 to 1926.	C/SS/65
EXHIBITIONS. 1901 to 1938.	C/SS/66

Subject Matter	Code N°
DENIS ISLAND LIGHTHOUSE. 1901 to 1908.	C/SS/67
AIR COMMUNICATIONS WITH THE SEYCHELLES ISLANDS. 1939.	C/SS/68
AGALEGA ISLAND. 1904.	C/SS/69
COLONIAL DEVELOPMENT ACT OF 1929.	C/SS/70
SELECTION OF PETITIONS FROM THE PUBLIC OF SEYCHELLES. 1873 to 1934. VOLS. I TO IV.	C/SS/71. VOLS. I TO IV.
COLONIAL RESEARCH COMMITTEE. 1921.	C/SS/72
ALDABRA GROUP. 1889 to 1943.	C/SS/73
OUTLYING ISLANDS. 1890 to 1936 AND 1944. VOLS.I TO II.	C/SS/74. VOLS. I TO II.
CURIEUSE ISLAND. 1896 to 1934.	C.SS/75
FELICITE ISLAND. 1901 to 1934.	C/SS/76
WAR TROPHIES PRESENTED TO SEYCHELLES. 1929.	C/SS/77
ANNUAL AND DECENNIAL INDICES OF CIVIL STATUS REGISTERS. 1902 to 1920.	C/SS/78
ARCHIVES. 189 to 1955.	C/SS/79
PARA RUBBER, 1903 to 1912.	C/SS/80
GOVERNORSHIP.(a) REMUNERATION OF OFFICERS ADMINISTERING THE GOVERNMENT IN THE ABSENCE OF GOVERNORS. (b) MILITARY STATUS OF GOVERNOR.	C/SS/81
ESTABLISHMENT OF A CORONER'S COURT IN THE COLONY - 1938.	C/SS/82
ESSENTIAL OIL INDUSTRY. REPORT BY MR. E.W. BOVILL - 1931 to 1940.	C/SS/83

Subject Matter	Code N°
ABDICATION OF H.M. KING EDWARD THE EIGHT - 1936.	C/SS/84.
TAXPAYERS AND LANDOWNERS ASSOCIATION. FORMED IN 1939 TO REPLACE DEFUNCT PLANTER'S ASSOCIATION.	C/SS/85
ASTOVE ISLAND LAYING OF MOORINGS - 1934 to 1936.	C/SS/86
TOURIST INDUSTRY KEEN PUBLIC INTEREST IN TOURISM IN 1935 AND 1938 IN FIVE PARTS - VOL. I - 1935 TO 1938.	C/SS/87 - VOL. I.
LOSS OF LAUNCH "MARY JANE" IN INDIAN OCEAN - 1953.	C/SS/88.
SEYCHELLES NATIONAL SHOW - 1966.	C/SS/89

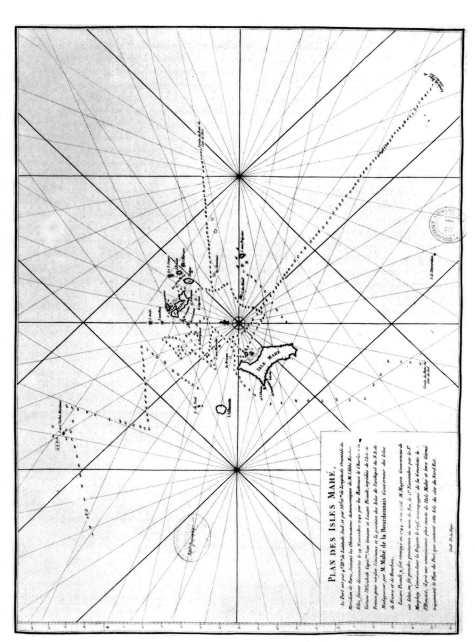

Iles Mahé (2e moitié XVIIIe) (Cli. B.N. C. 82844).

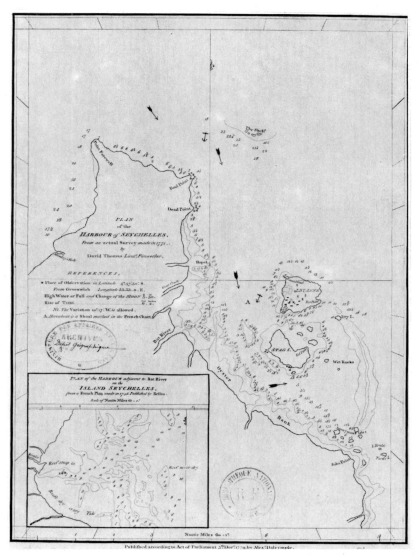

Plan du port – Carte anglaise par Dalrymple 1779 (Cli. B.N. C. 96509).

PUBLICATIONS IMPRIMEES DU GOUVERNEMENT

DES SEYCHELLES

- CLASS D -

PRINTED PUBLICATIONS OF THE GOVERNMENT OF SEYCHELLES

- CLASS D -

Since this class consists entirely of printed publications, researchers can have access to any of them and may quote from them without special permission.

On the whole, gaps in the various headings (see list below) are not serious.

Some explanation concerning "Blue Books" and Colonial Reports is necessary.

Prior to 1938 it was the practice to submit annually a "Blue Book" of the Colony's statistics together with a Covering Report by the Governor. These reports therefore, must be read with their appropriate Blue Books. Covering Reports for 1885 to 1893, and 1908 to 1938 (except 1930, 1932, and 1937) are missing.

No Blue Books or Covering Reports were prepared for 1939 to 1945, but a short review of this war period was included in the Colony's Report for 1945 and Colonial Annual Reports only were prepared. Moreover from 1949 these Annual Colonial Reports were replaced by Biennial Reports.

PRINTED PUBLICATIONS OF THE GOVERNMENT OF SEYCHELLES

INDEX TO CLASS D

Subject	Code N°
BLUE BOOKS	D/1
CENSUS REPORTS (Population & Agriculture)	D/2
COLONIAL REPORTS	D/3
GOVERNMENT GAZETTES	D/4
GOVERNMENT BULLETINS	D/5
REUTER'S TELEGRAMS AND ADVERTISER	D/6
SEYCHELLES BULLETINS	D/7
LAWS, ORDINANCES, PROCLAMATIONS & REGULATIONS, AND STATUTORY REPRINTS.	D/8 to D/10
PROCEEDINGS OF LEGCO, RULES AND ORDERS	D/11
SPECIAL REPORTS	D/12
(TRADE REPORTS) - (Vide Dept : Annual Reports) (VITAL STATISTICS)	
OTHERS MISCELLANEOUS PUBLICATIONS	D/13
DEPARTMENTAL ANNUAL REPORTS	D/14 to D/40 D/42 to D/51
REGULATIONS AND PROCEEDING OF BOARD OF CIVIL COMMISSIONERS	D/41
SEYCHELLES NATIONAL PROVIDENT FUND	D/52

Subject	Code N°
SEYCHELLES REUTER'S TELEGRAMS	D/53
(PUBLIC ACCOUNT COMMITTEE D/54)	
COUNCIL OF MINISTERS	D/55
OFFICIAL GAZETTE	D/58
NATIONS	D/59
STATISTICAL ABSTRACT AND BULLETINS	D/60
DECREES	D/61
BULLETIN DU GOUVERNEMENT DES SEYCHELLES	D/62
BUDGET SPEECHES OR ADDRESSES	D/63
PRESIDENT RENE'S SPEECHES OR ADDRESSES	D/64

BLUE BOOKS - CLASS D/1

BLUE BOOKS.

1872 to 1891	D/1
1896	D/1.1
1899	D/1.2
1900	D/1.3
1901	D/1.4
1902	D/1.5
1903	D/1.6
1904	D/1.7
1905	D/1.8
1906	D/1.9
1907	D/1.10

Subject	Code N°
1908	D/1.11
1909	D/1.12
1910	D/1.13
1911	D/1.14
1912	D/1.15
1913	D/1.16
1914	D/1.17
1915	D/1.18
1916	D/1.19
1917	D/1.20
1918	D/1.21
1919	D/1.22
1920	D/1.23
1921	D/1.24
1922	D/1.25
1923	D/1.26
1924	D/1.27
1925	D/1.28
1926	D/1.29
1927	D/1.30
1928	D/1.31
1929	D/1.32
1930	D/1.33
1931	D/1.34
1932	D/1.35
1933	D/1.36
1934	D/1.37
1935	D/1.38
1936	D/1.39
1937	D/1.40
1938	D/1.41
1939	D/1.42

1880 - 1885

(Note : - Copies missing for 1892 to 1895 and 1897 and 1898,
    but for section on Trade Reports 1894 vide Trade
    Reports D/31)

Subject	Code N°
CENSUS REPORTS - CLASS D/2	
Population Census 1807. (See Group A French Period). A/4.	
- do - 1891, 1901, 1911, 1921, 1931 and 1947 (bound in one volume)	D/2
- do - 1960	D/2.1
Agricultural Census 1960	D/2.2
Code of Census Procedure 1959	D/2.3
(Note :- For International Classification of Occupations and Census Methodology vide Secretariat Library No. HMSO - 30 ; UNO (A) - 10 and 11 ; ILO - 34 and 35.	
Population Census 1971 Enumerators Handbook	D/2.4
Population Census 1971 Draft Final Report	D/2.5
Census 1977 Summary of Results	D/2.6
Census Report. 1977. April, 1978.	D/2.7
COLONIAL REPORTS - CLASS D/3	
COLONIAL REPORTS.	
Annual Reports 1881 to 1884	D/3
-do- 1894 to 1902	D/3.1
-do- 1901 to 1907	D/3.2
-do- 1913, 1915, 1919, 1922 to 1929.	D/3.3
-do- 1930 to 1934, 1936 to 1937	D/3.4

Note :- There were no reports from 1939 to 1945, but a short review of the war period is included in report for 1946

Subject	Code N°
Annual Reports 1946 to 1960	D/3.5
-do- 1961 and 1962	D/3.6
-do- 1963 and 1964	D/3.7
-do- 1965 and 1966	D/3.8
-do- 1967 and 1968	D/3.9
-do- 1935	D/3.10

GOVERNMENT GAZETTES - CLASS D/4

Subject	Code N°
1879	D/4
1880	D/4.1
1881	D/4.2
1882	D/4.3
1883	D/4.4
1884	D/4.5
1885	D/4.6
1886	D/4.7
1887	D/4.8
1889 - 1890	D/4.9
1891 - 1892	D/4.10
1893	D/4.11
1894	D/4.12
1895 - 1896	D/4.13
1897	D/4.14
1898	D/4.15
1899	D/4.16
1900	D/4.17
1901	D/4.18
1902	D/4.19
1903	D/4.20
1904	D/4.21
1905	D/4.22
1906	D/4.23

Subject	Code N°
1907	D/4.24
1908	D/4.25
1909	D/4.26
1910	D/4.27
1911	D/4.28
1912	D/4.29
1913	D/4.30
1914	D/4.31
1915	D/4.32
1916	D/4.33
1917	D/4.34
1918	D/4.35
1919	D/4.36
1920	D/4.37
1921	D/4.38
1922	D/4.39
1923	D/4.40
1924	D/4.41
1925	D/4.42
1926	D/4.43
1927	D/4.44
1928	D/4.45
1929	D/4.46
1930	D.4.47
1931	D.4.48
1932	D.4.49
1933	D.4.50
1934	D.4.51
1935	D.4.52
1936	D.4.53
1937	D.4.54
1938	D.4.55
1939	D.4.56
1940	D.4.57
1941	D.4.58
1942	D.4.59
1943	D.4.60

Subject	Code N°
1944	D/4.61
1945	D/4.62
1946	D/4.63
1947	D/4.64
1948	D/4.65
1949	D/4.66
1950	D/4.67
1951	D/4.68
1952	D/4.69
1953	D/4.70
1954	D/4.71
1955	D/4.72
1956	D/4.73
1957	D/4.74
1958	D/4.75
1959	D/4.76
1960	D/4.77
1961	D/4.78
1962	D/4.79
1963	D/4.80
1964	D/4.81
1890	D/4.82
1892	D/4.83
1896	D/4.84
1965	D/4.85
1966	D/4.86
1967	D/4.87
1968	D/4.88
1969	D/4.89
1970	D/4.90
Copy missing except for the year 1888.	
1971	D/4.91
1972	D/4.92
1973	D/4.93
1974	D/4.94
1975	D/4.95
1976 (January to June)	D/4.96
Official Gazette Vol.1 (June to December) 1976	(see D/58)

Subject	Code N°
GOVERNMENT BULLETINS - CLASS D/5.	
1942	D/5
1943	D/5.1
1944	D/5.2
1945	D/5.3
1946	D/5.4
1947	D/5.5
1948	D/5.6
1949	D/5.7
1950	D/5.8
1951	D/5.9
1952	D/5.10
1953	D/5.11
1954	D/5.12
1955	D/5.13
1956	D/5.14
1957	D/5.15
1958	D/5.16
1959	D/5.17
1960	D/5.18
1961 Vol. I.	D/5.19
REUTER'S TELEGRAMS AND ADVERTISER	
1927	D/6
1929	D/6.1
1930	D/6.2
1931	D/6.3
1932	D/6.4
1933	D/6.5
1939	D/6.6

Subject	Code Nº
SEYCHELLES BULLETINS	
November and December 1961 Vol. II.	D/7
Bound volume for 1962	D/7.1
-do- 1963. Vol. I	D/7.2
-do- 1963. Vol. II	D/7.3
-do- 1964. Vol. I	D/7.4
-do- 1964. Vol. II	D/7.5
-do- 1965. Vol. I	D/7.6
-do- 1965. Vol. II	D/7.7
-do- 1966. Vol. I	D/7.8
-do- 1966. Vol. II	D/7.9
-do- 1967. Vol. I	D/7.10
-do- 1967. Vol. II	D/7.11
-do- 1968. Vol. I	D/7.12
-do- 1968. Vol. II	D/7.13
-do- 1969. Vol. I	D/7.14
-do- 1969. Vol. II	D/7.15
-do- 1970. Vol. I	D/7.16
-do- 1970. Vol. II	D/7.17
-do- 1971. Vol. I	D/7.18
-do- 1971. Vol. II	D/7.19
-do- 1972. Vol. I	D/7.20
-do- 1972. Vol. II	D/7.21
-do- 1973. Vol. I	D/7.22
-do- 1973. Vol. II	D/7.23
-do- 1974. Vol. I	D/7.24
-do- 1974. Vol. II	D/7.25

Subject	Code N°
-do- 1975. Vol. I	D/7.26
-do- 1975. Vol. II	D/7.27
-do- 1976. Vol. I	D/7.28

LAWS. ORDINANCE. PROCLAMATIONS AND REGULATIONS ETC.

CLASS D/8

The Law of Seychelles - 1904.

Vol. I - Mauritius Laws applicable	D/8
Vol. II - Seychelles Local Laws 1872-98	D/8.1
Vol. III - Seychelles Local Laws 1899-1906	D/8.2
Vol. IV - Seychelles Local Laws 1907-1911	D/8.3
Regulations for the Guidances of Public Officers 1902	D/8.4
Seychelles Prison Regulations - 1903	D/8.5
Regulations for the Lunatic Asylum - 1907	D/8.6
Seychelles Penal Code - 1924	D/8.7
Hospital Regulations - 1926	D/8.8
Index to Laws of Seychelles in force at 1st. November - 1930	D/8.9
Digest of Cases, Seychelles - 1870-1933	D/8.10
Local Regulations for Financial Instructions 1933	D/8.11

Laws of Seychelles - 1952.

Vol. I - Chapter 1-71	D/8.12
Vol. II - Chapter 72-117	D/8.13
Vol. III - Chapter 118-224	D/8.14
Vol. IV - Subsidiary Legislation and Index	D/8.15

Subject	Code N°
The Penal Code N° 12 of 1952	D/8.16
The Criminal Procedure Code N° 13 of 1952	D/8.17
Financial Regulations 1960 (Part. I)	D/8.18
(Note :- For Rules for the election of Members, and Standing Rules and Orders of the Legislative Council of Seychelles, see D/11.17 and D/11.18).	
Laws for Co-operative Societies in Seychelles 1960	D/8.19
Defence Regulations and Orders as Amended up to 24 th March, 1944.	D/8.20
Local Regulations of the Seychelles Civil Service 1914.	D/8.21
Rules for the Control of Stores and Furniture and Guidance of Storekeepers 1931.	D/8.22
Standing Order for the Local Boards of Health of Seychelles made by the Administrator under Section 4 (5) of Ordinance N° 31 of 1900.	D/8.23
Subsidiary Legislation 1963	D/8.24
A Collection of the Subsidiary Legislation 1964	D/8.25
-do- 1965	D/8.26
-do- 1966	D/8.27
-do- 1967	D/8.28
-do- 1968	D/8.29
General Orders 1966	D/8.30
Financial Regulations (Part II) undated.	D/8.31
Financial Orders (Part I) Financial Regulations, 1972.	D/8.32
Laws of Seychelles - Revised Edition, December 1971.	
Vol. I - Chapters - 1-41	D/8.33
Vol. II - Chapters - 42-82	D/8.34
Vol. III - Chapters - 83-120	D/8.35

Subject	Code N°
Vol. IV. - Chapters - 121-181	D/8.36
Vol. V - Chapters - 182-195	D/8.37
Vol. VI - Chapters - 196-256	D/8.38
Vol. VII - U.K. Legislation) Chronological Index) General Index)	D/8.39
Financial Instructions. Part. I - January, 1976	D/8.40
Departmental Manuel, 1976	D/8.41
The Seychelles Court of Appeal Reports 1965 to 1976, 1977	D/8.42

STATUTORY REPRINTS OF ORDINANCES - CLASS D/9

Subject	Code N°
The Trade Marks Ordinance, 1956	D/9.16 (a)
The Income Tax Ordinance, 1961	D/9.16 (b)
The Sale of Produce Ordinance, 1962	D/9.16 (c)
Customs Tariff Ordinance, 1963	D/9.16 (d)
Customs and Harbour Dues	D/9.16 (e)
Animals (Diseases and Importation) Ordinance - 1963	D/9.16 (f)
The Patents Ordinance, 1933	D/9.16 (g)
Copra Price Stabilization Ordinance	D/9.16 (h)
Customs Tariff, 1932	D/9.16 (i)
Police Force Ordinance, 1959	D/9.16 (j)
Public Order Ordinance, 1959	D/9.16 (k)
Income Tax Ordinance and Subsidiary Legislation Relating thereto, 1948.	D/9.16 (l)
Immigration Ordinance and Subsidiary Legislation Relating thereto, 1968	D/9.16 (m)
The Control of Rent and Tenancy Agreements Ordinance, (including a reprint of sections 2 and 23 of the Public Health Ordinance, 1959) 1969	D/9.16 (n)

Subject	Code N°
Mortgage and Registration, 1969	D/9.16 (o)
Road Transport, 1969	D/9.16 (p)
Agricultural Loans Board, 1970	D/9.16 (q)
The Land Development (Interim Control) Ordinance and Subsidiary Legislation, 1970	D/9.16 (r)
The Industrial Development. Ordinance, 1970	D/9.16 (s)
Prisons, 1970	D/9.16 (t)
The Road Transport Regulations, 1970	D/9.16 (u)
The Employment of Servants Ordinance Employment Benefits Ordinance, 1970	D/9.16 (v)
Licences, 1970	D/9.16 (w)
Town and Country Planning Ordinance, 1972	D/9.16 (x)
Immovable Property (Transfer Restriction) Ordinance, 1973	D/9.16 (y)
Customs Tariff and Subsidiary Legislation, 1973	D/9.16 (z)
Electricity Supply, 1974	D/9.16 (1)
National Parks and Nature Conservancy, 1974	D/9.16 (2)
Minimum Wages and Conditions of Employment Act, 1973. April, 1977.	D/9.16 (3)
Ordinances. (For 1889-1893 vide D/9.18)	
1894 to 1897	D/9
1898 to 1899	D/9.1
1900 to 1902	D/9.2
1903 to 1908	D/9.3
1909 to 1916	D/9.4
1917 to 1924	D/9.5
1925 to 1933	D/9.6
1934 to 1938	D/9.7
1939	D.9.8

Subject	Code N°
1940 to 1943	D/9.9
1944 to 1947	D/9.10
1948 to 1949	D/9.11
1950 to 1955	D/9.12
1956 to 1961	D/9.13
1962	D/9.14
1963	D/9.15
See D/9.16 (a)	
Ordinances, 1964	D/9.17
-do- 1889 to 1893	D/9.18
-do- 1965	D/9.19
-do- 1966	D/9.20
-do- 1967	D/9.21
-do- 1968	D/9.22
-do- 1969	D/9.23
-do- 1970	D/9.24
-do- 1971	D/9.25
-do- 1972	D/9.26
The Companies Ordinance, 1972	D/9.27
Ordinances, 1973	D/9.28
Ordinances, 1974	D/9.29
-do- 1975	D/9.30
-do- 1975 (Nov. and Dec.) (Original)	D/9.30 (A)
Civil Code of Seychelles Ordinance, 1975	D/9.31
Ordinances and Acts, 1976	D/9.32
- do - (Original)	D/9.32 (A)

Subject	Code N°
Acts, (Feb. to May) 1977	D/9.33
- do - (Original)	D/9.33 (A)
For Presidential Decree from June, 1977 See Under	
DECREES PRESIDENTIAL in D/61.	
PROCLAMATIONS AND REGULATIONS - CLASS D/10.	
1900 to 1902	D/10
1903 to 1912	D/10.1
1913 to 1916	D/10.2
1917 to 1924	D/10.3
1925 to 1931	D/10.4
1932 to 1935	D/10.5
1936 to 1937	D/10.6
1938	D/10.7
1939 to 1940	D/10.8
1941 to 1944	D/10.9
1945 to 1947	
1948	D/10.11
1949	D/10.12
1950	D/10.13
1951 to 1955	D/10.14
1956 to 1960	D/10.15
1961	D/10.16
1962	D/10.17
1963	D/10.18
1964	D/10.19

Subject	Code Nº
1965	D/10.20
1966	D/10.21
1967	D/10.22
1968	D/10.23
1969	D/10.24
1970	D/10.25
1971	D/10.26
1972	D/10.27
1973	D/10.28
1974	D/10.29
1975	D/10.30
1976	D/10.31
1977	D/10.32

PROCEEDING OF LEGCO, RULES AND ORDERS.

(For proceeding of 1889 to 1892 vide D/11.25).

1897 to 1900	D/11
1901 to 1903	D/11.1
1904 to 1908	D/11.2
1909 to 1917	D/11.3
1918 to 1927	D/11.4
1928 to 1936	D/11.5
1937 to 1948	D/11.6
1949 to 1951	D/11.7
1952 to 1954	D/11.8
1955 to 1956	D/11.9
1957 to 1958 (Including Sir John Thorp's Three talks on "Looking Forward")	D/11.10

Subject	Code N°
Jan & July 1959	D/11.11
Proceeding of 1960	D/11.12
-do- 1961	D/11.13
-do - 1962	D/11.14
Addresses to Legco by H.E. the Governor, August, 7 th 1942 to November 16 th 1948.	D/11.15
Standing Rules and Orders of Legco 1924	D/11.16
- do - 1949	D/11.17
Rules for the Elections of Members	D/11.18
Sessional Papers for 1959 to 1960	D/11.19
Summary of Proposed Constitutional Arrangements, 1st. September, 1947	D/11.20
Exchange of Despatches between His Excellency the Governor and the Right Honourable the Secretary of State for the Colonies on the Seychelles Constitution.	D/11.21
Majority Report of the Select Committee of Legislative Council appointed on 7th November, 1960.	D/11.22
Minutes of Legislative Council, 1963	D/11.23
- do - 1964	D/11.24
Proceedings of 1889 to 1892	D/11.25
Minutes of Legco - 1965 & 1966	D/11.26
Minutes of Legco - 1967	D/11.27

Subject	Code Nº
Minutes of the Governing Council	
Minutes of Governing Council - 1968.	D/11.28
Records of the Legislative Assembly.	
Records of the Legislative Assembly held on 31st January and 1st February, 1973.	D/11.29
Report of the Legislative Assembly held on 11 th - July 1972	D/11.30
Record of the Legislative Assembly held on 5 th September, 1973.	D/11.31
Records of the Legislative Assembly held on 11 th December, 1972.	D/11.32
Records of the Legislative Assembly held on 29 th March, 1973.	D/11.33
Records of the Legislative Assembly held on 10th January, 1974. May, 1974.	D/11.34
Records of the Legislative Assembly held on 6th June, 1974. August, 1974.	D/11.35
Records of the Legislative Assembly held on 20 th February, 1975. October, 1975.	D/11.36
Records of the House of Assembly.	
Records of the House of Assembly held on 5 th April, 1976. September, 1976.	D/11.37
Meetings of sessions of the Legislative Assembly 1971 - 1974. (Order papers)	D/11.38
Report on the Budget Session of the Legislative Assembly - 1973	D/11.39

Subject	Code N°
SPECIAL REPORTS (For Report on Crown Land, 1878 vide D/12.49)	
General Survey, Reference Report by S.B. Hobbs, 1900.	D/12
Report on Outer Islands, Dupont, 1907	D/12.1
Report on visit to India, Dupont, 1912	D/12.2
Seychelles Post Office Guide, Touris, 1913	D/12.3
The Turtle Fisheries of the Seychelles Islands - J. Hornelle, 1927.	D/12.4
Report on the Fisheries and Fish Resources of the Seychelles Islands - J. Hornell 1927.	D/12.5
Report of Seychelles Fisheries Committee, on Mr. Hornell's recommendations, 1928.	D/12.6
Report on L'Ankylostomiase, Dr. J. Bradley, 1928.	D/12.7
Report on visit of Governor and Mr. Dupont to Outer Islands, 1929.	D/12.8
Report of Mr. F.A. Stockdale on his visit to Seychelles. Feb - March, 1931.	D/12.9
Enquiry into an outbreack of Bacillary Dysentery, Dr. J. Bradley, 1931.	D/12.10
Investigations into Essential Oil Industry, 1933. By W. Holdsworth-Haines.	D/12.11
Report on Financial Situation of Seychelles, T. Reid, 1933.	D/12.12
Address by Entomologist Mr. Vesey-Fitzgerald to Planters, 1936.	D/12.13

(Note :- For "Report on the Forests of the Granitic Islands
of the Seychelles" by Mr. H.S. Gibson in 1938, see
Class F/3.17).

Subject	Code N°
Report on the Re-organisation of Education by C.B. Smith, 1938.	D/12.14
Educational Re- organisation in the Seychelles by W.W.E. Giles 1945.	D/12.15
Seychelles Ten-year Development Plan, 1947.	D/12.16
Report of Salaries and Conditions in Seychelles public service, Fitzerald, 1948.	D/12.17
Report of the Streamline Committee, 1953.	D/12.18
Report of the Select Committee to Examine Draft Estimates for Development, 1954.	D/12.19
The Biology of Melittomma Insulare (col., Lymexylonidae), and its control in the Seychelles, - E.S. Brown, 1954.	D/12.20
Report of the Committee of Inquiry into Civil Service Salaries, May, 1954.	D/12.21
Report of the Committee of Inquiry into Civil Service Salaries (Supplement) - 1954.	D/12.22
Nethersole Salaries Commission, May, 1954.	D/12.23
Report of the Select Committee to Examine Draft Estimates for Development, 1955.	D/12.24
Health and Morbidity Survey - A.J.W. Spitz, 1956-1957.	D/12.25
Review of Ten Year Development Plan, 1957.	D/12.26
Report on Coconut Industry - F.C. Cooke, 1958.	D/12.27
Report on Financial Administration and Fiscal Policy, - E.R.E. Surridge, 1958.	D/12.28
(For action taken Vide D/13.34).	
Development of Animal Husbandry and Balanced Farming - D.E. Faulkner, 1959.	D/12.29
A Plan for Seychelles, 1959.	D/12.30

Subject	Code N°
Report on Control of Melittomma, - I.W.B. Nye, 1959.	D/12.31
Report on Taxation in the Colony, H.R. Hurd, 1959.	D/12.32
Water Supply of Seychelles, Project Report, Howard Humphreys and Sons, - 1959.	D/12.33
(Waterhouse Report).	
Report on Economy of the Seychelles, J.W.F. Rowe, 1959.	D/12.34
Forestry in the Seychelles, C. Swabey, 1959.	D/12.35
Report on the Tourist Industry, D.O. Mathews, O.B.E., 1959.	D/12.36
Report on Accounting Procedure, G.W. Davies, 1960.	D/12.37
Control of Melittomma, I.W.B. Nye, 1961.	D/12.38
Interim Report on the Guano Resources of The Seychelles, B.H. Baker, 1961.	D/12.39
Seychelles Botanical Survey, By. C. Jeffrey, 1961 to 1962.	D/12.40
A Tuberculosis Case-Finding Programme of Mahe island in Seychelles, 1962.	D/12.41
Report of the Commissioner of Enquiry into the Public Service in Seychelles 1962.	D/12.42
Government Memorandum on Seed Report, 1963.	D/12.43
Government Memorandum on Unestablished Staff 1963.	D/12.44
Government Memorandum on Seed Report : Conversion Tables, 1963.	D/12.45
Geology and Mineral Resources of the Seychelles Archipelago - by B.H. Baker, B. Sc., F.G.S. Geologist, 1963.	D/12.46
Development Plan : Review - 1964 - 1966.	D/12.47
Precis of all information available re : Colony's Archives up to 1962.	D/12.48

Subject	Code N°
Seychelles Report on Crown Land, 1878.	D/12.49
Information transmitted to the Secretary General of the United Nations by Her Majesty's Government in the United Kingdom, in accordance with the provisions of article 73 (e) of the United Nations charter concerning the territory of Seychelles for the year 1963.	D/12.50
Population Growth and Agricultural Policy in the Seychelles - 1964. - By J. Inman and T.A. Phillips.	D/12.51
Economic Study of the Seychelles Islands - 1965 - By D.B. Prell.	D/12.52
Colonial Office - An Economic Survey of the Colonial Territories 1951. Vol. II.including - Seychelles.	D/12.53
Research Work on an Outbreack of Malaria at Assumption and Aldabra Islands in 1930 by K.C. Mathew, M.B., B.S. and J.T. Bradley, M.D.	D/12.54
Report of the Board of Enquiry into the conditions of employment for seamen on local vessels, - 1965.	D/12.55
Dependency and Development in Seychelles - 1963.	D/12.56
An Economic Survey of Seychelles. Aug. 1965. (Barclays Bank D.C.O.)	D/12.57
Security Instructions prepared by the Seychelles Intelligence Committee and Based on the United Kingdom Instructions for Security in Government Departments. N° 23, - 1965.	D/12.58
Recommendations for a retail price index in the Seychelles by W.L. Kendall - 1963.	D/12.59
Development Plan - 1966 to 1969.	D/12.60
Natural Resources and Economic Development Committee 1965.	D/12.61
Social Services Committee Report 1965.	D/12.62
Works and Communications Committee Report 1965.	D/12.63

Subject	Code N°
The Exploitation of Sea Birds in Seychelles by Ridley and Percy, 1958.	D/12.64
"Southern Hemisphere Beach Rock", Seychelles page 42 - 1965.	D/12.65
Development Plan for Mahe 1966 by Crockett, Thomson & Thomson.	D/12.66
Some Aspects of the Development of Tourism & Residential Settlement in Seychelles by D.O. Mathews, 1965.	D/12.67
Marine Sediments and Bottom Communities of the Seychelles by M.S. Lewis and J.D. Taylor - 1966.	D/12.68
Constitutional Report by Sir Colville Deverell in 1966.	D/12.69
Information transmitted to the Secretary General of the United Nations by Her Majesty's Government in the United Kingdom, in accordance with the provisions of article 73 (e) of the United Nations charter concerning the territory of Seychelles for the year 1965.	D/12.70
Salaries Revision 1966 Instructions.	D/12.71
Memorandum Salaries Revision - 1967.	D/12.72
Report on the Public Service of the Colony of Seychelles 1967, by Sir R. Ramage - 1967.	D/12.73
Development Plan - 1964-1966.	D/12.74
British Islands in the Southern Hemisphere 1945-1951.	D/12.75
Report on the Seychelles Tea project by Reginald Child. B. Sc., Ph.D., F.R.I.C. - 1965.	D/12.76
Report on Para Rubber in Seychelles by R. Dupont - 1903.	D/12.77
Report on the Exploitation of Sea Birds Eggs of Seychelles - 1966 by Ridley & Richard Percy	D/12.78
Entomological and Epidemiological Investigations on Bancroftian Filariasis in the Seychelles (Sept. 1968 - Aug. 1969) by Frank L. Lambreeht - 1969.	D/12.79
White paper on Tourism Development in the Seychelles 1970.	D/12.80
Report of the Salaries Commissioner (P.M. Wand-Tetley, O.B.E., M.C.) 1969	D/12.81

Subject	Code N°
Salaries Revision 1969. Instructions.	D/12.82
Report of the Seychelles Constitutional Conference, 1970.	D/12.83
Tourism Tomorrow in Seychelles - 1970 by George A. Boughton.	D/12.84
A Report on a visit to the Outer Islands of Seychelles between October and November 1960, by C.J. Piggott.	D/12.85
Residential Development in the Seychelles - 1970.	D/12.86
Bee-Keeping in Seychelles by R.E.M. Silberrad M.A. - 1970.	D/12.87
Tourism Tomorrow in Seychelles - II - Agriculture and Tourism by S.M. Savy, 1970.	D/12.88
Victoria Reclamation Project 1970.	D/12.89
Land Survey and Land Registration in Seychelles, by A.C. Mc Ewen, 1961.	D/12.90
Commercial Fishing in Seychelles, by R.C. Cole, 1966.	D/12.91
Report on the ground services and facilities required to operate a scheduled air service to the Seychelles, 1959.	D/12.92
PROPOSED AIRPORT FOR THE SEYCHELLES. Report of a joint Ministry of Aviation and Air Ministry Works Directorate Survey Team on the sitting of an Airport	
April - May 1961 - February 1962.	D/12.93
Tourism Tomorrow in Seychelles - III - Marketing of Local Produce by J.G. Kent, 1970.	D/12.94
Cousin Island Report by F. Raymond Fosberg, 1970.	D/12.95
Conservation Policy in the Seychelles, October, 1971.	D/12.96
Award of Arbitration Tribunal appointed for settlement of a trade dispute which exists between the Government of Seychelles and the Government Worker's Union by L.G. Souyave, June, 1972.	D/12.97

Subject	Code N°
Report on two visits to Cousine Island Jan/April 1972, by Chris Feare and David Lloyd.	D/12.98
Preliminary report on a visit to Aride Island Feb/March 1972, by John Procter and Chris Feare.	D/12.99
A New Deal for Agriculture, September, 1972.	D/12.100
Precis of the history of the attempts made to control the preparation and consumption of "Bacca" in the Seychelles, 1912	D/12.101
Conservation in the Seychelles. Report of the Conservation Adviser 1970 - by J. Procter.	D/12.102
Structural Review, Composition of the Service on 1st January 1972 Growth 1900 - 1972, Localisation, Training, Salary, Structure, Manpower, by H.Waller, 1972.	D/12.103
Salary Structure Revision, 1972 Instructions.	D/12.104
Summary of Development Policies 1973 - (an official statement on Development Policy in Seychelles).	D/12.105
Report on the accident in the vicinity of Mahe Seychelles on 11 th December 1973. Piper Cherckee PA28 - 140 VQ - SAB.	D/12.106
Correspondence and reports concerning Antycostomeasis in Seychelles by Dr. J.F. Kendrick - Rockefeller Foundation 1915-1923.	D/12.107
Reports on Hookworn in Seychelles by Dr. C.H. Yeager Rockefeller Foundation 1925	D/12.108
Summary of a Review of Education completed in October, 1973. 1974.	D/12.109
Offshore fishing in the Seychelles. Oceanology International 1975 by C. Ratcliffe.	D/12.110
Draft Syllabus for the use of Teachers English, 1975.	D/12.111
Report on a study of Beef and Dairy Systems as practised in a number of Tropical Countries - July to September, 1974.	D/12.112
The nutrition of the pre-school child in the Seychelles an appraisal in preparation for further studies by Dr. P.T. Fox. December, 1974.	D/12.113

Subject	Code N°
Purse seine trials off Mahe for small pelagic fish 1973 by G. Ratcliffe, Fisheries Adviser.	D/12.114
The sandflies of the Seychelles Islands and their possible control by B.R. Laurence and P.L. Mathias, 1970.	D/12.115
Seychelles Handbook. June 1976.	D/12.116
Socio-Anthropological Survey of the Seychelles. Interim Report. November, 1960. Burton Benedict, Ph. D.	D/12.117
Victoria Reclamation Project. Development of Town Centre 1971.	D/12.118
Draft Planning Code. September, 1969. D.H. Komlosy B.Sc., M.T.P.I., A.R.I.C.S. Planning Adviser.	D/12.119
Summary of Development Policies, 1973. An official statement on Development Policy in Seychelles, April, 1973.	D/12.120
Seychelles Development Plan 1973. Parts I and II : Survey and Proposals. June 1973.	D/12.121
Report on a visit to Uganda, Kenya and the Seychelles 15 - 31 January, 1972. March 1972. George H. Franklin.	D/12.122
Report on Sea Turtles in the Seychelles Area. J. Frazier. September, 1970.	D/12.123
Terminal Report on Sea Turtles in the Seychelles Area. J. Frazier. May, 1973.	D/12.124
The Status of Knowledge on Marine Turtles in the Western Indian Ocean. J. Frazier. November 1974.	D/12.125
Welfare and Social Services Department. An Analysis of Present and Future Work, David W.A. Collett. July, 1970.	D/12.126
Marketing and Co-Operative Division. Progress and Future Development Report. Ian Gibson. December, 1975.	D/12.127
A Review of the Economy, December, 1975.	D/12.128
A Review of the Economy, January, 1976.	D/12.129
A Review of the Economy, June, 1976.	D/12.130

Subject	Code N°
Forestry in the Seychelles Land Resource Report Number 8 PWT Henry. 1976.	D/12.131
Forestry in the Seychelles Appendixes 1-7 Land Resource Report Number 8 PWT Henry. 1976.	D/12.132
Forestry in the Seychelles Appendix 8 Land Resource Report Number 8 PWT Henry. 1976.	D/12.133
Information transmitted to the Secretary-General of the United Nations by Her Majesty's Government in the United Kingdom, in accordance with the provisions of article 73 (e) of the United Nations Charter, concerning the territory of Seychelles for the year 1954.	D/12.34
Report of an Inquiry on the Victoria District Council. November 1969. By. J.R. Todd.	D/12.135
Report on the Coral Reefs of Cousin Island, Seychelles (November 1973) By J.G. Frazier Ophil and N.V.C., Polunin BA.	D/12.136
Guidelines for a Fourth Development Plan on Education 1975-1985. December,1975.	D/12.137
Draft Seychelles Structure Plan 1975.	D/12.138
Seychelles structure Plan 1975.	D/12.139
Vegetable Production in the Republic of Seychelles. 1976. By Cliff S. Adam.	D/12.140
Vogue (Paris) Aux Seychelles. 1976.	D/12.141
Les Seychelles 48e membre de l'OUA (Europe Outremer) N° 559. 1976.	D/12.142
Report on the Employment of Boys Leaving School in 1969. By David W.A. Collect. February, 1971.	D/12.143
Terminal Report on St. Anne Marine National Park. By. K. Buchanan, Warden. October, 1974 - August, 1976.	D/12.144
Seminaire lo Population et Bien-etre la Famille. Février 1976.	D/12.145
Government Salary Scales, 1976. June1, 1976.	D/12.146

Subject	Code N°
National Symposium on Labour and Family Welfare Education. August, 1975.	D/12.147
Review of the Salary Structure and Conditions of Service of the Public Service of Seychelles. By H.P. Ritchie. C.M.G. March, 1977.	D/12.148
First National Development Plan 1977 to 1981. February, 1977.	D/12.149
British Islands in the Southern Hemisphere 1945 - 1951. May, 1951 (Seychelles pp. 19-28).	D/12.150
Looking Forward. (A Series of talks on development in Seychelles, broadcast by Governor Thorp on Radio Seychelles). April, 1959.	D/12.151
A review of peasant land settlement policy in the Seychelles 1939-1975. By David Akroyd. 1977.	D/12.152
National Development Plan 1978-1982. June 5th 1978.	D/12.153
Report on a visit of investigation to Astove, Cosmoledo, Assumption and the Aldabra Group of the Seychelles Islands. By H.P. Thomasset. 1907.	D/12.154
An account of the extent of pollution in the Seychelles. 1978, by L.A. Chong Seng.	D/12.155
Charting Our Course. Report of the Constitutional Commission to President F.A. René and Draft Instructions. 1978.	D/12.156
Tracons Notre Chemin. Rapport de la Commission Constitutionnelle Présenté au Président F.A. René et l'instruction pour la redaction de la Constitution, 1978.	D/12.157
Anou Tras Nou Semen. Rapor Komision Konstitisionel pou Presidan F.A. René. 1978.	D/12.158
Report of National Conference on Employment, Manpower, Incomes and Production, 29th to 30th May, 1978. Septembre 1978.	D/12.159
Conservation of Marine Resources in Seychelles Report on Current Status and Future Management by Rodney V. Salm, IUCN Consultant. August 1978.	D/12.160

Subject	Code N°
Revised Salary Structure and Conditions of Service as from 1st January, 1979. 18th December, 1978.	D/12.161
Un an après la liberation. Juin 1977 - Juin 1978. One year after liberation. June 1977 - June 1978. 1979.	D/12.162

OTHER MISCELLANEOUS PUBLICATIONS - CLASS D/13

Seychelles Police Instruction Book (undated)	D/13
Bulletin du Developpement Agricole, 1923-1934.	D/13.1
Le Vanillier et La Vanille dans le Monde-Guy Lionet, Undated.	D/13.2
Seychelles Jubilee - 1953.	D/13.3
Seychelles Monthly News Summary - 1960-1961	D/13.4
- do - 1962	D/13.5
- do - 1963	D/13.6
- do - 1964	D/13.7
- do - 1965	D/13.8
- do - 1966	D/13.9
- do - 1967	D/13.10
Seychelles Montly Newsletter 1968	D/13.11
- do - 1969	D/13.12 (a)
- do - 1970	D/13.12 (b)
Tourism News and Information. March 1974.	D/13.12 (c)
Lettre Des Seychelles Seychelles Newsletter. Aout 1978.	D/13.12 (d)

Subject	Code N°
Agriculture News Letter - 1961	D/13.12
- do - - 1962	D/13.13
- do - - 1963	D/13.14
- do - - 1964	D/13.15
- do - - 1965	D/13.16
- do - - 1966	D/13.17
- do - - 1967	D/13.18
- do - - 1969	D/13.19
- do - - 1970 (Agrichelles)	D/13.20 (a)
The Seychelles Annual - 1959 to 1963 & 1966	D/13.20 to D/13.25
File of Miscellaneous Printed Programmes for various events.	D/13.30
File of Pamphlets issued by Tourist Dept.	D/13.31
Seychelles Security Instructions - 1940.	D/13.32
The Seychelles Handbook, 1928.	D/13.33
Salaries Revision, 1958, in accordance with Surridge Report (Vide D/12.28)	D/13.34
List of islands which constitute Colony and certain relevant information concerning them.	D/13.35
The British Indian Ocean Territory Order of 1965.	D/13.36
The British Indian Ocean Territory	
Ordinances 1965 - 1976	D/13.36 (A)
Proclamations and Regulations 1965 - 1976	D/13.36 (B)
Gazettes 1965 - 1976.	D/13.36 (C)

Subject	Code N°
Procedure for stores Accounting (undated)	D/13.37
Register of Voters for Seychelles for 1967.	D/13.38
Register of Voters Victoria District Council 1969.	D/13.39
Manuel for the guidance of the Police Force, Seychelles, 1903	D/13.40
The grounds of Government House, Victoria, Mahe.	D/13.41
Standing Orders of the Victoria District Council.	D/13.42
Ready Reckoner for Rates of Wages, 1949.	D/13.43
Standard International Trade Classification, 1972.	D/13.44

FESTIVAL OF SEYCHELLES 1972 - PROGRAMMES OF EVENTS.

1 - Camtole Band Competition	)
2 - Opening Ceremony	)
3 - Pop Festival	)
4 - L'Oeuf à la Coque (Théâtre)	)
5 - Murder in the Cathedral (Theatre)	)
6 - Historical Pageant	) D/13.45
7 - Arts and Crafts Exhibition	)
8 - National Show	)
9 - Miss Seychelles 1973 Contest.	)
10 - Seychelles Football Association	)
11 - Visit of Her Royal Highness The Princess Margaret Countess of Snowdon and the Earl of Snowdon to Seychelles	)

Subject	Code N°
The Seychelles National Provident Fund Employer's Guide (Leaflet 1)	D/13.46
Three years of progress, 1971 - 1974	D/13.47
Register of voters Victoria North, 1975	D/13.48
- do - Victoria South, 1975	D/13.49
- do - North Mahe, 1975	D/13.50
- do - South Mahe, 1975	D/13.51
- do - East Mahe, 1975	D/13.52
- do - West Mahe, 1975	D/13.53
- do - Praslin, 1975	D/13.54
- do - La Digue and Inner Islands, 1975	D/13.55
Your driving test, how to prepare for it, how to pass it 1975	D/13.56
Tide Table, Twilight, Moonrise, Moonset, Sunrise and Sunset forecast for the year 1975	D/13.57
Government unestablished employees basic wage rates, 1974.	D/13.58
Register of Voters 1970 - Victoria North Electoral Area.	D/13.59
Mahe Quay Information Manual 1975	D/13.60
Register of voters Victoria North, 1975	D/13.61
- do - Victoria South, 1975	D/13.62
- do - North Mahe, 1975	D/13.63
- do - South Mahe, 1975	D/13.64
- do - West Mahe, 1975	D/13.65
- do - East Mahe, 1975	D/13.66

Subject	Code N°
Register of voters Praslin, 1975	D/13.67
- do - La Digue and Inner Islands, 1975	D/13.68
Manuel of Government Organisation and Functions. 1977.	D/13.69
Standard International Trade Classification. December, 1971.	D/13.70
Hostess Training Manual. May, 1976.	D/13.71
The Employer's Guide to pay as you earn in Seychelles with Tax Tables. 1975.	D/13.72
The VII General Assembly of the Indian Ocean Tourism Alliance Conference in Seychelles. (ATOI) February, 1974.	D/13.73
Government Salary Scales, 1974. July 1, 1974.	D/13.74
Government Unestablished Employees Basic Wage Rates, 1975. July 1, 1975.	D/13.74 (1)
Government Salary Scales, 1975, July 1, 1975.	D/13.74 (2)
Government Unestablished Employees Basic Wage Rates, 1976. June 1, 1976.	D/13.74 (3)
Government Salary Scales, 1976, June 1, 1976.	D/13.74 (4)
Programme of the Visit of His Royal Highness The Duke of Gloucester Her Majesty's Special Representative and Her Royal Highness The Duchess of Gloucester to Seychelles Independence 1976.	D/13.74 (5)
Visit to Seychelles by His Royal Highness The Duke of Gloucester G.C.V.O. Her Majesty's Special Representative accompanied by Her Royal Highness The Duchess of Gloucester for Seychelles Independence 24th June to 1st July 1976.	D/13.74 (6)
Seychelles Independence Celebrations 27th June to 3rd July 1976. Offical Programme of Events.	D/13.74 (7)
Independence Celebrations. Agricultural Show at La Rosiere. 30th June - 2nd July, 1976.	D/13.74 (8)
Seychelles Highway Code. November 1977.	D/13.74 (9)

Subject	Code N°
The Employer's Guide to pay as you earn in Seychelles with Tax Tables. 1978.	D/13.74 (10)
Tide Table, Forecast for the year 1976. January, 1976.	D/13.74 (11)
Directory of Diplomatic Missions, Consular Posts and International Organisations. 1st May, 1978.	D/13.74 (12)
Seychelles Handbook to the Exhibits at the Imperial Institute W.L. Rind. 1909.	D/13.74 (13)
Notes on Nature Study. (For use by teachers in the schools of the Colony) G.G. Auchinleck. 1922.	D/13.74 (14)
Petit Catéchisme sur les Cocotiers (à l'usage des Planteurs). G.G. Auchinleck. 1922.	D/13.74 (15)
L'Agriculture aux Seychelles. Feuilles des Planteurs (Nos. 1 to 3) G. Auchinleck. 1921-1922.	D/13.74 (16)
L'Agriculture aux Seychelles. Feuilles des Planteurs (Nos. 6,11) G.G. Auchinleck. 1922.	D/13.74 (17)
Timetable of Seychelles Public Transport Corporation. 1968.	D/13.74 (18)
The Tourism (Accommodation and Catering) Development Decree. Minimum Requirements for Hotels, Guest Houses, Self - Catering, Private House, Accommodation and Restaurants. 1968.	D/13.74 (19)
Your career in the Department of Civil Aviation, 1978.	D/13.74 (20)
Acreage of Estates in Mahé, Praslin and La Digue islands for year ended 31st March, 1906.	D/13.74 (21)
Animation et Culture , ... et chante la musique aux Seychelles. 1978.	D/13.74 (22)
Independence Celebration programmes June - July 1976.	D/13.74 (23)
(1) Visit of Her Royal Highness the Princess Margaret Countess of Snowdon and The Earl of Snowdon to Seychelles 1972, and. (2) Programmes for the festival of Seychelles, 1972.	))) D/13.74 (24)))

Subject	Code N°
Schedule of rates of depreciation with general rulings and explanatory notes and the sections of the "Income Tax Assessment Decree, 1978" relative to depreciation allowances. 1978.	D/13.74 (25)
Seychelles Conservation Newsletter - 1972	D/13.75
Agricultural Marketing New - 1973.	D/13.85

PRINTED PUBLICATIONS OF THE GOVERNMENT OF

SEYCHELLES

CLASS - D/14 to D/51

ANNUAL DEPARTMENTAL REPORTS.

Accountant General, (See D/32, see also D/38).	
Agriculture	D/14 (See also D/42)
Annual Civil Statistics and Registry of Deeds (See D/34).	
Architect	D/47 (See also D/30)
Archives	D/45 (See also D/26)
Audit	D/15
Boards of Civil Commissioner	D/41
Civil Service Staff List	D/21
Comptroller and Auditor General	D/16
Co-Operative Development	D/17
Criminal Statistics	D/37 (See also D/48)

Subject	Code Nº
Crown Lands	D/42 (See also D/14)
Curator of Vacant Estates on the Curatelle	D/18
Customs, Trade Reports	D/31
Education	D/19
Electricity	D/49
Estimates of Revenue and Expenditure	D/20
Excise	D/39 (See also D/27)
Harbour	D/35
Income Tax	D/22 (See also D/23)
Inland Revenue	D/23 (See also D/22)
Judicial	(See D/37)
Labour	D/51 (See Also D/24)
Labour and Welfare	D/24 (See also D/51)
Lands and Survey	D/46 (See also D/30)
Local Government-Board	D/36
Mahé Meteorological Station	D/43
Medical	D/25 (See also D/40)
Mortgage, Registration and Archives	D/26 (See also D/34 & D/45).
Nuffield Social Worker	D/44 (See also D/24).
Police	D/27 (See also D/39)
Port and Marine	(See D/35)

Subject	Code N°
Postal	D/28 (See also D/38).
Printing	D/50
Prison	D/29
Probation Service	D/48 (See also D/37)
Public Works	D/30 (See also D/46 & D.47)
Sanitary Inspector	D/40 (See also D/25)
Saving Bank	D/38 (See also D/28 & D/32)
Tourism and Information	D/33
Treasury	D/32 (See also D/38)
Vital Statistics	D/34
Welfare	(See D/24)
Welfare and Social Services	(See D/24)
National Provident Fund	D/52
Seychelles Reuter's Telegrams D/53)	D/53
Public Accounts Committee	D/54
Council of Ministers	D/55
Survey	D/56 (See also D/46)
Lands	D/57 (See also D/46)
Official Gazettes	D/58 (See also D/4)
Nations	D/59 (See also D/7
Statistical Abstract	D/60

Subject	Code N°.
Presidential Decrees	D/61
ACCOUNTANT GENERAL (See Treasury Dept :)	
AGRICULTURE DEPT.	
Annual Reports for 1883, 1884, 1887, 1894, 1904, 1906, 1907, 1910, 1911, 1914, to 1922 and 1924.	D/14
- do - 1925 to 1934	D/14.1
- do - 1935 to 1940	D/14.2
- do - 1941 to 1946	D/14.3
- do - 1947 to 1959	D/14.4
- do - 1960	D/14.5
- do - 1961	D/14.6
- do - 1962	D/14.7
- do - 1963	D/14.8
Special Report on Grand Anse Estates 1949	D/14.9
Annual Report for 1964	D/14.10
- do - 1965	D/14.11
- do - 1966	D/14.12
- do - 1967	D/14.13
- do - 1968	D/14.14
- do - 1969	D/14.15
- do - 1970	D/14.16

Subject	Code N°
- do - 1971	D/14.17
AUDIT DEPT.	
Annual Reports for 1923 to 1925, 1927 to 1929.	D/15
- do - 1930	D/15.1
- do - 1931	D/15.2
Annual Reports for 1934	D/15.3
- do - 1932 to 1933, 1935, 1936, 1938, 1941, 1942 1945 and 1946.	D/15.4
- do - 1947	D/15.5
Report of the Principal Auditor on the Accounts of the V.D.C. for the year ended the 31st December, 1954.	D/15.6
Annual Reports for 1948 to 1959	D/15.7
- do - 1960	D/15.8
- do - 1961	D/15.9
- do - 1962	D/15.10
- do - 1963	D/15.11
- do - 1964	D/15.12
- do - 1965	D/15.13
- do - 1966	D/15.14
- do - 1967	D/15.15
- do - 1968	D/15.16
- do - 1969	D/15.17
- do - 1970	D/15.18

Subject	Code N°
Annual Reports for 1971	D/15.19
- do - 1972	D/15.20
- do - 1973	D/15.21
- do - 1974	D/15.22
- do - 1975	D/15.23
- do - 1976	D/15.24

COMPTROLLER & AUDITOR GENERAL'S REPORTS

CLASS D/16

Annual Reports for 1902 to 1907	D/16

CO-OPERATIVE DEVELOPMENT DEPT. - CLASS D/17

Annual Report 1961	D/17
- do - 1962	D/17.1
- do - 1963	D/17.2
- do - 1964	D/17.3
- do - 1965	D/17.4
- do - 1966	D/17.5
- do - 1967 - 1968	D/17.6
- do - 1971 - 1972	D/17.7
- do - 1973	D/17.8

Subject	Code N°
CURATOR OF VACANT ESTATES ON THE CURATELLE	
CLASS D/18	
Annual Report 1923	D/18
- do - 1927	D/18.1
- do - 1930	D/18.2
- do - 1931 to 1934	D/18.3
- do - 1935	D/18.4
EDUCATION DEPT. - CLASS D/19	
Annual Reports for 1881 to 1899	D/19
- do - 1900 to 1902	D/19.1
- do - 1903, 1904, 1907 and 1915	D/19.2
- do - 1909, 1911 to 1914, 1916 to 1931 and 1935 to 1939	D/19.3
- do - 1932 and 1933	D/19.4
- do - 1940 to 1949	
- do - 1950	D/19.6
- do - 1951 to 1960	D/19.7
Short Report of the Dept. of Education for the year 1962	D/19.8
Annual Report for 1961	D/19.9
General Survey for the period 1961-1964	D/19.10
Short Report for 1965	D/19.11

Subject	Code Nº
Annual Report for 1966	D/19.12
Trinnial Report 1965-1967	D/19.13
Annual Report for 1968	D/19.14
Annual Report for 1969	D/19.15
Annual Report for 1970	D/19.16
Annual Summary for 1971	D/19.17
Annual Summary for 1972	D/19.18
Annual Summary for 1973	D/19.19

ESTIMATES OF REVENUE AND EXPENDITURE - CLASS D/20

(For Estimates for 1872 - 1889 vide D/20.34).

Estimates for 1892 to 1899	D/20
- do - 1901, 1902, 1904, 1906 and 1907	D/20 (a)
- do - 1908 to 1913	D/20.1
- do - 1914 to 1917	D/20.2
- do - 1918 to 1922	D/20.3
- do - 1923 to 1927	D/20.4
- do - 1928 to 1931	D/20.5
- do - 1932 to 1933	D/20.6
- do - 1934	D/20.7
- do - 1935	D/20.8
- do - 1936	D/20.9

Subject	Code N°
Estimates for 1937	D/20.10
- do - 1938	D/20.11
- do - 1939 to 1942	D/20.12
- do - 1943	D/20.13
- do - 1944	D/20.14
- do - 1945 to 1946	D/20.15
- do - 1947	D/20.16
- do - 1948	D/20.17
- do - 1949	D/20.18
- do - 1950	D/20.19
- do - 1951	D/20.20
- do - 1952	D/20.21
- do - 1953	D/20.22
- do - 1953 to 1955	D/20.23
- do - 1956	D/20.24
- do - 1957	D/20.25
- do - 1958 to 1960	D/20.26
- do - 1961	D/20.27
- do - 1962	D/20.28
Praslin and Victoria District Council Estimates for 1952 to 1960	D/20.29
5 years Development Plan Estimates for 1956 to 1961	D/20.30

Subject	Code N°
Estimates for 1963	D/20.31
Victoria District Council Estimates for 1963 and 1964	D/20.32
Estimates for 1964	D/20.33
Estimates for the year 1872 to 1889	D/20.34
- do - 1965	D/20.35
- do - 1966	D/20.36
- do - 1967	D/20.37
- do - 1968	D/20.38
- do - 1969	D/20.39
- do - 1970	D/20.40
- do - 1971	D/20.41
- do - 1972	D/20.42
- do - 1973	D/20.43
- do - 1974	D/20.44
- do - 1975	D/20.45
- do - 1976	D/20.46
- do - 1977	D/20.47
Approved Estimates of Capital Expenditure (U.K. GRANT AIDED PROJECTS) for the year 1977.	D/20.48
Long Term Recurrent Revenue and Expenditure Budgets for the year 1978-1982. (DRAFT)	D/20.49
Approved Estimates of Revenue, Recurrent. Expenditure and Minor Capital Expenditure for the year ending December 31 st., 1978.	D/20.50

Subject	Code Nº
Approved Estimates of Revenue and Recurrent Expenditure for the year ending December 31st, 1979.	D/20.51
Approved Estimates of Capital Expenditure for the year ending December 31st., 1978.	

CIVIL SERVICE STAFF LIST

Lists for 1945 to 1948	D/21
- do - 1949 to 1962	D/21.1
- do - 1963	D/21.2
- do - 1964	D/21.3
- do - 1965	D/21.4
- do - 1966	D/21.5
- do - 1968	D/21.6
- do - 1970	D/21.7
- do - 1971	D/21.8
- do - 1972 (not published)	
- do - 1973	D/21.9
- do - 1974	D/21.10
- do - 1975	D/21.11

INCOME TAX DEPARTMENT

Annual Report for 1960	D/22
- do - 1961	D/22.1
- do - 1962	D/22.2

Subject	Code N°
Instructions to Collectors and Assistant Collectors of Taxes in Relation to the Assessment of Income Tax- 1920.	D/22.3
Annual Report for 1963	D/22.4
- do - 1964	D/22.5
- do - 1965	D/22.6
- do - 1966	D/22.7
- do - 1967	D/22.8
- do - 1968	D/22.9
- do - 1969	D/22.10
- do - 1970	D/22.11
- do - 1971	D/22.12
- do - 1972	D/22.13
- do - 1973 (not published)	
- do - 1974	D/22.14

INLAND REVENUE DEPARTMENT

(Changed to Income Tax Dept. in 1960)

Subject	Code N°
Annual Report 1949	D/23
- do - 1951 to 1953	D/23.1
- do - 1954 to 1955	D/23.2
- do - 1956	D/23.3

Subject	Code N°
LABOUR AND WELFARE DEPARTMENT.	
Annual Report 1955 and 1956	D/24
- do - 1958, 1959 and 1960	D/24.1
- do - 1961 and 1962 (Lean Report)	D/24.2
Triennal Report for 1961, 1962 & 1963	D/24.3
Annual Report 1964	D/24.4
- do - 1965	D/24.5
Triennal Report for 1964, 1965 & 1966	D/24.6
NOW WELFARE DEPARTMENT.	
(See also Labour Department D/51).	
Annual Report 1967	D/24.7
- do - 1968	D/24.8
CHANGED TO WELFARE AND SOCIAL SERVICES DEPARTMENT.	
Annual Report 1969	D/24.9
MEDICAL DEPARTMENT.	
Annual Reports for 1890, 1893, 1894, 1895, 1898, 1899 to 1902.	D/25
- do - 1903, 1904, 1906 to 1916	D/25.1
- do - 1917 to 1931	D/25.2
- do - 1924 and 1925	D/25.3
- do - 1929, 1932 and 1933	D/25.4

Subject	Code N°
Annual Reports for 1934 to 1948	D/25.5
- do - 1949 to 1959	D/25.6
- do - 1960	D/25.7
- do - 1962	D/25.8
- do - 1963	D/25.9
- do - 1964-1967	D/25.10
- do - 1968-1969	D/25.11
- do - 1968-1969 (Appendices)	D/25.11 (a)
MORTGAGE, REGISTRATION & ARCHIVES DEPT.	
Annual Reports for 1889, 1891, 1927 to 1931	D/26
- do - 1932 and 1933	D/26.1
POLICE DEPARTMENT.	
Annual Reports for 1877, 1887, 1889, 1890, 1892, 1893, 1895, and 1898.	D/27
- do - . 1902 to 1904, 1908 to 1912, 1915, 1916 and 1918.	D/27.1
- do - 1923 to 1928	D/27.1 (a)
- do - 1929	
- do - 1930 to 1935 and 1944 to 1947.	D/27.3
- do - 1936 to 1943	D/27.4
- do - 1948 to 1952 & 1954 and 1956	D/27.5

Subject	Code N°
Annual Reports for 1953, 1955, 1957 to 1962.	D/27.6
- do - 1963	D/27.7
- do - 1964	D/27.8
- do - 1965	D/27.9
- do - 1966	D/27.10
- do - 1967	D/27.11
- do - 1968	D/27.12
- do - 1969	D/27.13
- do - 1970	D/27.14
- do - 1971	D/27.15
- do - 1972	D/27.16
- do - 1973 to 1976 not published	
- do - 1977	D/27.17
POSTAL DEPARTMENT.	
Annual Reports for 1894, 1900, 1903, 1906, 1923, 1924 and 1926.	D/28
- do - 1925, 1927 to 1936	D/28.1
- do - 1937 to 1947	D/28.2
- do - 1948 to 1955	D/28.3
- do - 1956 to 1961	D/28.4
- do - 1962	D/28.5
- do - 1963	D/28.6

Subject	Code N°
Annual Reports for 1964	D/28.7
- do - 1965	D/28.8
- do - 1966	D/28.9
- do - 1967	D/28.10
- do - 1968	D/28.11
- do - 1969	D/28.12
- do - 1970	D/28.13
- do - 1971	D/28.14
PRISON DEPARTMENT.	
Annual Reports for 1900 to 1904, 1908, 1910, 1930, 1932 and 1933	D/29
- do - 1923 to 1929, 1931 and 1934.	D/29.1
- do - 1935 to 1944	
- do - 1945	D/29.3
- do - 1946 to 1956	
- do - 1957	D/29.5
- do - 1958	D/29.6
- do - 1959	D/29.7
- do - 1960	D/29.8
- do - 1961	D/29.9
- do - 1962	D/29.10
- do - 1963	D/29.11

Subject	Code N°
Annual Reports for 1964	D/29.12
- do - 1965	D/29.13
- do - 1966-1968	D/29.14
- do - 1969	D/29.15

PUBLIC WORKS DEPARTMENT.

Subject	Code N°
Annual Reports for 1889, 1891, 1893, 1895, 1896, 1902, 1913 and 1916.	D/30
- do - 1917 to 1922	
- do - 1923 to 1933	D/30.2
- do - 1934 to 1948	
- do - 1949	D/30.4
- do - 1950 to 1954	
- do - 1955	D/30.6
- do - 1956	D/30.7
- do - 1957	D/30.8
- do - 1958 to 1960	D/30.9
- do - 1961 to 1962	D/30.10
- do - 1963 to 1964	D/30.11
1965 not published	
- do - 1966	D/30.12

Subject	Code N°
CUSTOMS DEPARTMENT. (Note :- For Trade Reports printed prior to 1929 see Blue Books).	
Trade Reports for 1894 to 1898	D/31
- do - 1913 to 1915, 1918, to 1928.	D/31.1
- do - 1929 to 1935	D/31.2
- do - 1936 to 1940	D/31.3
- do - 1941 to 1944	
- do - 1945	D/31.5
- do - 1946	D/31.6
- do - 1947	
- do - 1948	D/31.8
- do - 1949	
- do - 1950	D/31.10
- do - 1951	D/31.11
- do - 1952	D/31.12
- do - 1953	D/31.13
- do - 1954	
- do - 1955	D/31.15
- do - 1956	D/31.16
- do - 1957	D/31.17
- do - 1958	D/31.18
- do - 1959	D/13.19

Subject	Code N°
Trade Reports for 1960	D/31.20
--do - 1961	D/31.21
- do - 1962	D/31.22
- do - 1963	D/31.23
- do - 1964	D/31.24
- do - 1965	D/31.25
- do - 1966	D/31.26
- do - 1967	D/31.27
- do - 1968	D/31.28
- do - 1970　　(1969 not published)	D/31.29
- do - 1971	D/31.30
- do - 1972	D/31.31
- do - 1973	D/31.32
- do - 1974	D/31.33
- do - 1975	D/31.34
- do - 1976	D/31.35
TREASURY DEPARTMENT.(Note :- See also Accountant General).	
Annual Reports for 1949 to 1952	D/32
- do - 1953 to 1956	D/32.1
- do - 1957	D/32.2
- do - 1958	D/32.3

Subject	Code N°
Annual Reports for 1959	D/32.4
Annual Report of Accountant General 1960	D/32.5
- do - 1961	D/32.6
Instructions for Sub-Accountants and Collectors of Revenue for the Guidance of Officers concerned. - By the Treasurer. (Approved by the Secretary of State in his Confidential despatch of 24 th February, 1922).	D/32.7
Annual Report of Accountant General 1962	D/32.8
- do - 1963	D/32.9
- do - 1941	D/32.10
- do - 1938	D/32.11
- do - 1964	D/32.12
- do - 1965	D/32.13
- do - 1966	D/32.14
- do - 1967	D/32.15
- do - 1968	D/32.16
- do 1969	D/32.17
- do - 1970	D/32.18
- do - 1971	D/32.19
- do - 1972	D/32.20
- do - 1973	D/32.21
- do - 1974	D/32.22
- do - 1975	D/32.23
- do - 1976	D/32.24

Subject	Code N°
TOURISM AND INFORMATION DEPARTMENT.	
Annual Report 1959	D/33
- do - 1960	D/33.1
- do - 1961	D/33.2
- do - 1962	D/33.3
- do - 1963	D/33.4
(For "Some Aspects of the Development of Tourism and Residential Settlement in Seychelles" by D.O. Mathews. 1965. vide D/12.67).	
Report on the Department of Tourism Information and Broadcasting for 1964, 1965 and 1966 up to July.	D/33.5
Annual Report of Tourism 1966.	D/33.6
Information and Broadcasting Dept. 1966-67,	D/33.7
Annual Report of Tourism Information and Broadcasting for the year 1968	D/33.8
VITAL STATISTICS DEPT.	
Annual Civil Statistics Reports for 1889, 1893 to 1897.	D/34
- do - 1899, 1900, 1902 to 1908, 1910 to 1912, 1915 and 1916.	D/34.1
- do - 1923 to 1924	D/34.2
- do - 1955 to 1962	D/34.3
- do - 1963	D/34.4
Annual Civil Statistics and Registry of Deeds report for 1964	D/34.5
- do - 1965	D/34.6
Annual Civil Statistics and Registry of Deeds report for 1966	D/34.7

Subject	Code Nº
Annual Civil Statistics and Registry of Deeds report for 1967	D/34.8
- do - 1968	D/34.9
- do - 1969	D/34.10
- do - 1970	D/34.11

HARBOUR DEPARTMENT (Port and Marine)

Annual Report for 1890, 1893, 1895, 1900, 1903, 1904, 1909, 1913, 1918, 1919, 1923, 1924, 1926, to 1930 and 1932 to 1934.	D/35
Reports for 1936, 1937, & 1938 (See D/35.4)	
Annual Report 1948 (Port, Marine and Lighthouse)	D/35.1
Triennial Report 1958, 1959 and 1960	D/35.2
Annual Reports 1961 and 1962	D/35.3
Annual Reports for 1936, 1937 & 1938	D/35.4
Annual Report for 1935	D.35.5
- do - 1961 to 1963	D/35.6
- do - 1964	D/35.7
- do - 1965-1967	D/35.8

LOCAL GOVERNMENT BOARD.

Annual Reports 1953 and 1954	D/36

CRIMINAL STATISTICS. (Judicial Dept.)

Annual Reports for 1892, 1893, 1901, 1903, 1905, 1906 and 1907	D/37

Subject	Code N°
Annual Reports for 1908 to 1910, 1913 and 1915	D/37.1
- do - 1923, 1925, to 1928	D/37.2
- do - 1929 to 1933	D/37.3
- do - 1961 to 1963	D/37.4
- do - 1964	D/37.5
- do - 1934 to 1941	D/37.6
- do - 1965	D/37.7
- do - 1966	D/37.8
- do - 1967	D/37.9
- do - 1968	D/37.10
- do - 1969	D/37.11
- do - 1970	D/37.12
- do - 1971	D/37.13
- do - 1972	D/37.14
- do - 1973	D/37.15
- do - 1974	D/37.16
- do - 1975	D/37.17
- do - 1976	D/37.18

SAVING BANK.

Annual Reports for 1903, 1915 and 1923	D/38
- do - 1924 to 1933	D/38.1
- do - 1935	D/38.2

Subject	Code N°
EXCISE DEPT.	
Annual Report for 1917, 1918, 1919 and 1924.	D/39
SANITARY INSPECTOR.	
Annual Reports for 1891 and 1894.	D/40
BOARD OF CIVIL COMMISSIONER.	
Annual Reports for 1881 to 1886.	D/41
CROWN LANDS.	
Annual Reports for 1881, 1882, 1883 and 1885.	D/42
MAHE METEOROLOGICAL STATION.	
Annual Reports for 1955-1960.	D/43
NUFFIELD SOCIAL WORKERS.	
First Annual Report of the Nuffield Social Workers for the year beginning 15th Jan. 1961 and ending 15th Janv. 1962.	D/44.
First Annual Report of the Nuffield Social Workers for the year beginning 15th Jan. 1963 and Janv. 1964.	D/44.1
ARCHIVES DEPT.	
Progress Report - 1962 Annual Reports 1964-1966	D/45

Subject	Code N°
Annual Reports 1967	D/45.1
- do - 1968-1969	D/45.2
- do - 1970-1971	D/45.3
- do - 1972-1973	D/45.4
LANDS & SURVEY DEPT.	
Annual Report 1966	D/46
- do - 1967	D/46.1
- do - 1968	D/46.2
- do - 1969	D/46.3
Biennial Report 1970-1971	D/46.4
(Now Lands Department only.)	
ARCHITECT'S DEPT.	
Annual Report for 1966	D/47
PROBATION SERVICE.	
Annual Report 1968	D/48
- do - 1969 (See D/37.11)	
ELECTRICITY DEPARTMENT.	
Annual Report for 1968	D/49
- do - 1969	D/49.1.

Subject	Code N°
Annual Report for 1970	D/49.2
- do - 1971	D/49.3
- do - 1972	D/49.4
- do - 1973	D/49.5
- do - 1974-1976 (not published)	D/49.5
- do - 1977	D/49.6
PRINTING DEPARTMENT.	
Annual Report for 1968	D/50
- do - 1969	D/50.1
- do - 1970	D/50.2
- do - 1971	D/50.3
- do - 1972	D/50.4
- do - 1973	D/50.5
LABOUR DEPARTMENT.	
See Also Labour & Welfare Department (D/24)	
First Biennial Report - Aug. 1967 - Dec. 1968	D/51
Annual Report for the year 1971	D/51.1
- do - 1972	D/51.2
- do - 1973	D/51.3
- do - 1974	D/51.4

Subject	Code N°
NATIONAL PROVIDENT FUND	
Annual Report and Accounts for 1971	D/52
- do - 1972	D/52.1
- do - 1973	D/52.2
- do - 1974	D/52.3
- do - 1975	D/52.4
- do - 1976	D/52.5
- do - 1977	D/52.6
SEYCHELLES REUTER'S TELEGRAMS	
Bound Volume for 1925	D/53
- do - 1926	D/53.1
PUBLIC ACCOUNTS COMMITTEE	
Report of the Public Accounts Committee on the Accounts of Seychelles for the year 1971	D/54
First of the Public Accounts Committee August, 1972	D/54.1
Report of the Public Accounts Committee on the Accounts of Seychelles for the year, 1972.	D/54.2
COUNCIL OF MINISTERS	
Notes on Council of Ministers Procedure, March 1974.	D/55

Subject	Code N°
SURVEY DEPARTMENT	
Annual Reports from 1966-1971 (See under D/46).	
Annual Report for 1972	D/56
- do - 1973	D/56.1
LANDS DEPARTMENT	
(Annual Reports from 1966 to 1971) (See under D/46)	
Annual Report for the year 1973	D/57
- do - 1974	D/57.1
OFFICIAL GAZETTES	(For Government Gazette see D/4)
Vol. I (June to December) 1976	D/58
Vol. II (January to December) 1977	D/58.1
Vol. III 1978	D/58.2
NATIONS	(For Seychelles Bulletins see D/7)
Vol. I (29 June to 31 December) 1976.	D.59
Bound Volume for 1977. Vol. I. (Jan. 4 to June 4)	D/59.1
STATISTICAL ABSTRACT. and BULLETINS.	
Statistical Abstract, 1977	D/60
Statistical Bulletins 1975 - 1978 (Nos. 1-10)	D/60.1

Subject	Code N°
<u>DECREES</u>	
Presidential Decrees, 1977 (June to December)	D/61
- do - (June to December) (original)	D/61 (A)
Presidential Decrees, 1978	D/61.1
" " " (original)	D/61.1 (A)
<u>BULLETIN DU GOUVERNEMENT DES SEYCHELLES</u>	
Janvier, 1947 (3 copies seulement)	D/62
<u>BUDGET SPEECHES OR ADDRESSES</u>	
For the year 1971	D/63
- do - 1975	D/63.1
- do - 1978	D/63.2
- do - 1979	D/63.3
<u>PRESIDENT RENE'S SPEECHES OR ADDRESSES</u>	
Discours prononcé le 29 juin 1977	D/64
African problems must be solved by Africans. (At the OAU Summit Khartoum, Sudan 18-21 July 1978)	D/64.1
Developing and Developed Countries must be partners in Development. (At the Banquet given in his honour by the Lord Mayor of London-- 14 th September, 1978).	D/64.2

ARCHIVES   DE   L'ETAT   CIVIL

_____

- CLASS   E -

C L A S S   - E -

CIVIL STATUS REGISTERS

Two sets of Births, Marriages and Deaths registers are maintained as a measure of protection against possible destruction or damage by fire. The duplicate set, which previously was kept in the Labour and Welfare Department, has now been transferred to the Archives.

The Civil Status Officers has to make frequent searches of his records of the last 50 years or so. Both sets of records are complete from approximately 1900.

For the years 1772 to 1900, however, one nearly complete set only could be brought together. It was therefore decided to place this set in the Archives, and to add to it records between 1772 and 1810 which had recently been transferred from the Mauritius Archives.

The registers in the Archives have been divided into two main periods - 1794 to 1893 and 1894 onwards, the second corresponding with the passing of the Civil Status Ordinance of 1893. Registers prior to 1894 were in so considerable confusion since in many cases single volumes contained mixed entries of births, marriages, divorces and deaths, and there were usually separate volumes for white people and for coloured people. A further complication was that Acts for Praslin and La Digue were included in Central Mahe before 1875 and South Mahe before 1902. It was found necessary therefore, to classify the registers into sub-heads to which the following code numbers were given.

Subject Matter	Code N°
Mixed Registers	E/A
Births Registers	E/B) For whole Colo-
	) ny up to 1894;
Marriages Registers	E/C) for Central and
	) South Mahe up
Deaths Registers	E/D) to 1902 ; and
	) for Central
	) Mahe only
	) thereafter.
PRASLIN DISTRICT (PL)	
Births Registers	E/E
Marriages Registers	E/F)Inclusive of
	)La Digue up to
Deaths Registers	E/G) 1892.
LA DIGUE DISTRICT (LD)	
Births Registers	E/H
Marriages Registers	E/I .
Deaths Registers	E/J
SOUTH MAHE DISTRICT (SM)	
Births Registers	
Marriages Registers	E/L
Deaths Registers	E/M
Marriages (by Ministers of Religious)	E/M.1 (A)
Marriages (in "Articulo Mortis") (Central & North Mahe)	E/M.2
Marriages (in "Articulo Mortis") (South Mahe (SM)	E/M.3
Marriages (- do -) (Praslin) (PL)	E/M.4
Marriages (- do -) (La Digue) (LD)	E/M.5

Subject Matter	Code N°
Divorces (Colony of Seychelles)	E/N.1
Judge's Orders (Central Mahe)	E/N.2
Judge's Orders (Praslin District)	E/N.3
Judge's Orders (La Digue District)	E/N.4
Judge's Orders (South Mahe District)	E/N.5
Births, Index of (Central and North Districts)	E/O.1
Births, Index of (South Mahe District) (SM)	E/O.2
Births, Index of (Praslin and La Digue Districts)	E/O.3
Marriages, Index of (Central and North Districts)	E/O.4
Marriages, Index of (South Mahe District) (SM)	E/O.5
Marriages, Index of (Praslin and La Digue Districts) (PL/LD)	E/O.6
Marriages, Index of (by Ministers of Religions)	E/O.7
Deaths, Index of (Central and North Districts	E/O.8
Deaths, Index of (South Mahe District) (SM)	E/O.9
Deaths, Index of (Praslin and La Digue Districts) (PL/LD)	E/O.10
Acknowledgement of Natural Children	E/P.1

MARRIAGES

There is a further difficulty to this matter of marriages. In addition
to those registered in Civil Status Offices, civil marriages can since
1954 be performed by Ministers of Religions, as also marriages in Articulo
Mortis. As yet only one copy of Acts of Marriages performed by Ministers
have been kept and these, too, are in separate volumes. Thus, in
endeavouring to trace a marriage in any given year one must search 3 instead
of one volume. Efforts are now being made to make second copies of these
registers for the Archives. But it would seem more appropriate that all
Acts of Marriages of whatever type should be placed together in a single
annual volume.

Marriages in Articulo Mortis ! We have them only for 1872 to 1925.

Subject Matter	Code N°
Mixed register for births, marriages and deaths	E/A.1
Mixed registers for WHITE POPULATION.	
Births 1808-1809 and Deaths 1808-1810	E/A.1.1
Marriages and Divorces 1816	E/A.1.2
- do - 1817 and 1818	E/A.1.3
Births and Marriages, June 1817 to Dec. 1819	E/A.1.4
Births, Marriages and Deaths 1820-1824	E/A.1.5
- do - 1825-1829	E/A.1.6
- do - 1830-1837	E/A.1.7
- do - 1938-1840	E/A.1.8
Mixed registers of COLOURED POPULATION	
Births, Marriages, Affranchissements and deaths 1794 to 1809	E/A.1.9
- do - 1808 to 1810	)
- do - 1810 to 1812	)
- do - 1813	) E/A.1.10
- do - 1814	)
- do - 1815	)
- do - 1816 to 1817	)
- do - 10.1.1817 to 18.10.1818	E/A.1.11
- do - 4.7.1817 to 4.12.1819	E/A.1.12
- do - 1820	E/A.1.13
- do - 1821	E/A.1.14
- do - 1822	E/A.1.15
- do - 1823	E/A.1.16
- do - 1824	E/A.1.17

Subject Matter	Code N°
Births, Marriages, Affranchissements and deaths 1825	E/A.1.18
- do - 1826	E/A.1.19
- do - 1827	E/A.1.20
- do - 1828	E/A.1.21
- do - 1829	E/A.1.22

For Births from 1819 to 1840, see Mixed Registers (E/A), Births
from 1841 to 1874 are for the entire Colony ; up to 1902 for
Central and South Mahe. Praslin and La Digue had separated
registers from 1875, and La Digue from 1892.

Births among white population, 1794 to 1817	E/B.1
Births from 1841 to 1843	E/B.1.1
- do - 1844 to October 1848	E/B.1.2
- do - 1848 to April 1853	E/B.1.3
- do - 1853 to May 1855	E/B.1.4
- do - 1856	E/B.1.5
- do - 1857	E/B.1.6
- do - 1858	E/B.1.7
- do - 1859 Vol. I.	E/B.1.8
- do - 1859 Vol. II.	E/B.1.8
- do - 1860 Vol. I.	E/B.1.9
- do - 1860 Vol. II.	E/B.1.9
- do - 1861	E/B.1.10
- do - 1862	E/B.1.11
- do - 1863	E/B.1.12
- do - 1864	E/B.1.13
- do - 1865	E/B.1.14
- do - 1866 Vol. I.	E/B.1.15
- do - 1866 Vol. II.	E/B.1.15

Subject Matter	Code N°
Births from 1841 to 1867	E/B. 1.16
- do - 1868	E/B. 1.17
- do - 1869	E/B. 1.18
- do - 1870 Vol. I.	E/B. 1.19
- do - 1870 Vol. II.	E/B. 1.20
- do - 1871 Vol. I.	E/B. 1.20
- do - 1871 Vol. II.	E/B. 1.20
- do - 1871 Vol. III.	E/B. 1.20
- do - 1871 Vol. IV.	E/B. 1.20
- do - 1872 Vol. I.	E/B. 1.21
- do - 1872 Vol. II.	E/B. 1.21
- do - 1873 Vol. I.	E/B. 1.22
- do - 1873 Vol. II.	E/B. 1.22
- do - 1873 Vol. III.	E/B. 1.22
- do - 1874 Vol. I.	E/B. 1.23
- do - 1874 Vol. II.	E/B. 1.23
- do - 1875	E/B. 1.24
- do - 1876	E/B. 1.25
- do - 1877 Vol. I.	E/B. 1.26
- do - 1877 Vol. II.	E/B. 1.26
- do - 1878	E/B. 1.27
- do - 1879 Vol. I.	E/B. 1.28
- do - 1879 Vol. II.	E/B. 1.28
- do - 1880	E/B. 1.29
- do - 1881	E/B. 1.30
- do - 1882	E/B. 1.31
- do - 1883	E/B. 1.32
- do - 1884 Vol. I.	E/B. 1.33

Subject Matter	Code N°
Births from 1841 to 1884 Vol. II.	E/B. 1.33
- do - 1884 Vol. III.	E/B. 1.33
- do - 1885 Vol. I.	E/B. 1.34
- do - 1885 Vol. II.	E/B. 1.34
- do - 1886 Vol. I.	E/B. 1.35
- do - 1886 Vol. II.	E/B. 1.35
- do - 1887	E/B. 1.36
- do - 1888 Vol. I.	E/B. 1.37
- do - 1888 Vol. II.	E/B. 1.37
- do - 1888 Vol. III.	E/B. 1.37
- do - 1889 Vol. I.	E/B. 1.38
- do - 1889 Vol. II.	E/B. 1.38
- do - 1890 Vol. I.	E/B. 1.39
- do - 1890 Vol. II.	E/B. 1.39
- do - 1891 Vol. I.	E/B. 1.40
- do - 1891 Vol. II.	E/B. 1.40
- do - 1891 Vol. III.	E/B. 1.40
- do - 1891 Vol. IV.	E/B. 1.40
- do - 1892 Vol. I.	E/B. 1.41
- do - 1892 Vol. II.	E/B. 1.41
- do - 1893 Vol. I.	E/B. 1.42
- do - 1893 Vol. II.	E/B. 1.42
- do - 1894	E/B. 1.43
- do - 1895	E/B. 1.44
- do - 1896	E/B. 1.45
- do - 1897	E/B. 1.46
- do - 1898	E/B. 1.47

Subject Matter	Code N°
Births from 1841 to 1899 Vol. I.	E/B. 1.48
- do - 1900	E/B. 1.49
- do - 1901	E/B. 1.50
- do - 1902	E/B. 1.51
- do - 1903	E/B. 1.52
- do - 1904	E/B. 1.53
- do - 1905	E/B. 1.54
- do - 1906	E/B. 1.55
- do - 1907	E/B. 1.56
- do - 1908	E/B. 1.57
- do - 1909	E/B. 1.58
- do - 1910	E/B. 1.59
- do - 1911	E/B. 1.60
- do - 1912	E/B. 1.61
- do - 1913	E/B. 1.62
- do - 1914	E/B. 1.63
- do - 1915	E/B. 1.64
- do - 1916	E/B. 1.65
- do - 1917	E/B. 1.66
- do - 1918 and 1919 Vol. I.	E/B. 1.67
- do - 1919 Vol. II.	E/B. 1.68
- do - 1920	E/B. 1.69
- do - 1921	E/B. 1.70
- do - 1922	E/B. 1.71
- do - 1923	E/B. 1.72
- do - 1924	E/B. 1.73
- do - 1925	E/B. 1.74

Subject Matter	Code N°
Births from 1841 to 1926	E/B. 1.75
- do - 1927	E/B. 1.76
- do - 1928	E/B. 1.77
- do - 1929	E/B. 1.78
- do - 1930	E/B. 1.79
- do - 1931	E/B. 1.80
- do - 1932	E/B. 1.81
- do - 1933	E/B. 1.82
- do - 1934	E/B. 1.83
- do - 1935	E/B. 1.84
- do - 1936	E/B. 1.85
- do - 1937	E/B. 1.86
- do - 1938	E/B. 1.87
- do - 1939	E/B. 1.88
- do - 1940	E/B. 1.89
- do - 1941 and 1942 Vol. I.	E/B. 1.90
- do - 1942 Vol. II	E/B. 1.91
- do - 1943	E/B. 1.92
- do - 1944	E/B. 1.93
- do - 1945	E/B. 1.94
- do - 1946 Vol. I.	E/B. 1.95
- do - 1946 Vol. II and 1947 Vol. I.	E/B. 1.96
- do - 1947 Vol. II and 1948 Vol. I.	E/B. 1.97
- do - 1948 Vols. II and IV.	E/B. 1.97
- do - 1948 Vol. III.	E/B. 1.97
- do - 1949 Vol. I.	E/B. 1.98
- do - 1949 Vol. II.	E/B. 1.98

Subject Matter		Code N°
Births from 1841 to 1950 Vol. I.		E/B. 1.99
- do -	1950 Vol. II.	E/B. 1.99
- do -	1950 Vol. III and 1951 Vol. I.	E/B. 1.100
- do -	1951 Vol. II.	E/B. 1.100
- do -	1951 Vol. III.	E/B. 1.100
- do -	1951 Vol. IV.	E/B. 1.100
- do -	1952 Vol. I.	E/B. 1.101
- do -	1952 Vol. II.	E/B. 1.101
- do -	1953 Vol. I.	E/B. 1.102
- do -	1953 Vol. II.	E/B. 1.102
- do -	1953 Vol. III.	E/B. 1.102
- do -	1954 Vol. I.	E/B. 1.103
- do -	1954 Vol. II.	E/B. 1.103
- do -	1955 Vol. I.	E/B. 1.104
- do -	1955 Vol. II and 1956 Vol. I.	E/B. 1.105
- do -	1956 Vol. II.	E/B. 1.105
- do -	1956 Vol. III.	E/B. 1.105
- do -	1956 Vol. IV and 1957 Vol. I.	E/B. 1.106
- do -	1957 Vol. II.	E/B. 1.106
- do -	1957 Vol. III and 1958 Vol. I.	E/B. 1.107
- do -	1958 Vol. II.	E/B. 1.107
- do -	1958 Vol. III and 1959 Vol. I.	E/B. 1.108
- do -	1959 Vol. II.	E/B. 1.108
- do -	1959 Vol. III.	E/B. 1.108
- do -	1959 Vol. IV and 1960 Vol. I.	E/B. 1.109
- do -	1960 Vol. II.	E/B. 1.109
- do -	1960 Vol. III.	E/B. 1.109

Subject Matter		Code N°
Births from 1841 to	1960 Vol. IV and 1961 Vol. I.	E/B. 1.110
- do -	1961 Vol. II.	E/B. 1.110
- do -	1961 Vol. III.	E/B. 1.110
- do -	1961 Vol. IV and 1962 Vol. I.	E/B. 1.111
- do -	1962 Vol. II	E/B. 1.111
- do -	1962 Vol. III	E/B. 1.111
- do -	1962 Vol. IV	E/B. 1.111
- do -	1962 Vol. V and 1963 Vol. I.	E/B. 1.112
- do -	1963 Vol. II.	E/B. 1.112
- do -	1963 Vol. III.	E/B. 1.112
- do -	1963 Vol. IV and 1964 Vol. I.	E/B. 1.113
- do -	1964 Vol. II	E/B. 1.113
- do -	1964 Vol. III and 1965 Vol. I.	E/B. 1.114
- do -	1965 Vol. II.	E/B. 1.115
- do -	1966 Vol. I.	E/B. 1.116
- do -	1966 Vol. II.	E/B. 1.116
- do -	1967 Vol. I.	E/B. 1.117
- do -	1967 Vol. II.	E/B. 1.117
- do -	1968 Vol. I.	E/B. 1.118
- do -	1968 Vol. II.	E/B. 1.118
- do -	1969 Vol. I.	E/B. 1.119
- do -	1969 Vol. II.	E/B. 1.119
- do -	1970 Vol. I.	E/B. 1.120
- do -	1970 Vol. II.	E/B. 1.120
- do -	1971 Vol. I.	E/B. 1.121
- do -	1971 Vol. II.	E/B. 1.121

Subject Matter	Code N°
Births from 1841 to 1972 Vol. I.	E/B. 1.122
- do - 1972 Vol. II.	E/B. 1.122
- do - 1972 Vol. III. and 1973 Vol. I.	E/B. 1.123
- do - 1973 Vol. II.	E/B. 1.124
- do - 1974 Vol. I.	E/B. 1.125
- do - 1974 Vol. II.	E/B. 1.126
- do - 1975 Vol. I.	E/B. 1.127
- do - 1975 Vol. II.	E/B. 1.128
- do - 1975 Vol. III.	E/B. 1.129
- do - 1976 Vol. I.	E/B. 1.130
- do - 1976 Vol. II.	E/B. 1.131
- do - 1977 Vol. I.	E/B. 1.132
- do - 1977 Vol. II.	E/B. 1.133
- do - 1978 Vol. I.	E/B. 1.134
- do - 1978 Vol. II.	E/B. 1.135

Subject Matter	Code N°
MARRIAGES	
Marriages for 1794 to 1815	E/C.1
- do - 1817 to 1840	E/C.1.1
- do - 1841 to 1849	E/C.1.2
- do - 1849 to 1855	E/C.1.3
- do - 1856	E/C.1.4
- do - 1857 Vol. I	E/C.1.5
- do - 1857 Vol. II	E/C.1.5
- do - 1858	E/C.1.6
- do - 1859	E/C.1.7
- do - 1860	E/C.1.8
- do - 1861 - 1862	E/C.1.9
- do - 1863	E/C.1.10
- do - 1864	E/C.1.11
- do - 1865	E/C.1.12
- do - 1866	E/C.1.13
- do - 1867	E/C.1.14
- do - 1868	E/C.1.15
- do - 1869	E/C.1.16
- do - 1870	E/C.1.17
- do - 1871	E/C.1.18
- do - 1872	E/C.1.19
- do - 1873	E/C.1.20
- do - 1874	E/C.1.21
- do - 1875	E/C.1.22
- do - 1876	E/C.1.23
- do - 1877 Vol. I	E/C.1.24

Subject Matter	Code N°
Marriages for 1877 vol. II.	E/C.1.24
- do - 1878	E/C.1.25
- do - 1879	E/C.1.26
- do - 1880	E/C.1.27
- do - 1881	E/C.1.28
- do - 1882	E/C.1.29
- do - 1883	E/C.1.30
- do - 1884	E/C.1.31
- do - 1885	E/C.1.32
- do - 1886	E/C.1.33
- do - 1887	E/C.1.34
- do - 1888	E/C.1.35
- do - 1889	E/C.1.36
- do - 1890 and 1891 vol. I.	E/C.1.37
- do - 1891 vol. II.	E/C.1.38
- do - 1891 vol. III.	E/C.1.38
- do - 1892 and 1893 Vol. I.	E/C.1.39
- do - 1893 vol. II.	E/C.1.40
- do - 1894	E/C.1.41
- do - 1895	E/C.1.42
- do - 1896	E/C.1.43
- do - 1897	E/C.1.44
- do - 1898	E/C.1.45
- do - 1899	E/C.1.46
- do - 1900	E/C.1.47
- do - 1901	E/C.1.48
- do - 1902	E/C.1.49

Subject Matter	Code N°
Marriages for 1903	E/C.1.50
- do - 1904	E/C.1.51
- do - 1905	E/C.1.52
- do - 1906	E/C.1.53
- do - 1907	E/C.1.54
- do - 1908	E/C.1.55
- do - 1909	E/C.1.56
- do - 1910	E/C.1.57
- do - 1911	E/C.1.58
- do - 1912	E/C.1.59
- do - 1913	E/C.1.60
- do - 1914	E/C.1.61
- do - 1915	E/C.1.62
- do - 1916	E/C.1.63
- do - 1917	E/C.1.64
- do - 1918 and 1919 Vol. I.	E/C.1.65
- do - 1919 Vol. II.	E/C.1.66
- do - 1920	E/C.1.67
- do - 1921	E/C.1.68
- do - 1922	E/C.1.69
- do - 1923	E/C.1.70
- do - 1924 vol. I.	E/C.1.71
- do - 1924 vol. II.	E/C.1.71
- do - 1925 vol. I.	E/C.1.72
- do - 1925 vol. II.	E/C.1.72
- do - 1926 vol. I.	E/C.1.73
- do - 1926 vol. II.	E/C.1.73

Subject Matter	Code N°
Marriages for 1927 vol. I.	E/C.1.74
- do - 1928	E/C.1.75
- do - 1929	E/C.1.76
- do - 1930	E/C.1.77
- do - 1931 vol. I.	E/C.1.78
- do - 1931 vol. II.	E/C.1.78
- do - 1932	E/C.1.79
- do - 1933	E/C.1.80
- do - 1934	E/C.1.81
- do - 1935	E/C.1.82
- do - 1936	E/C.1.83
- do - 1937	E/C.1.84
- do - 1938	E/C.1.85
- do - 1939	E/C.1.86
- do - 1940	E/C.1.87
- do - 1941	E/C.1.88
- do - 1942	E/C.1.89
- do - 1943	E/C.1.90
- do - 1944	E/C.1.91
- do - 1945	E/C.1.92
- do - 1946 vol. I	E/C.1.93
- do - 1946 vol. II and 1947 vol. I.	E/C.1.94
- do - 1947 vol. II and 1948 vol. I.	E/C.1.95
- do - 1948 vol. II.	E/C.1.95
- do - 1949 and 1950 vol. I.	E/C.1.96
- do - 1950 vol. II and 1951 vol. I.	E/C.1.97
- do - 1951 · vol. II	E/C.1.98

Subject Matter	Code N°
Marriages for 1952	E/C.1.99
- do - 1953	E/C.1.100
- do - 1954	E/C.1.101
- do - 1955 and 1956 vol. I.	E/C.1.102
- do - 1956 vol. II and 1957 vol. I.	E/C.1.103
- do - 1957 vol. II, 1958, 1959 and 1960 vol. I.	E/C.1.104
- do - 1960 vol. II and 1961 vol. I.	E/C.1.105
- do - 1961 vol. II, 1962, 1963 and 1964 vol. I.	E/C.1.106
- do - 1964 vol. II and 1965	E/C.1.107
- do - 1966	E/C.1.108
- do - 1967	E/C.1.109
- do - 1968	E/C.1.110
- do - 1969	E/C.1.111
- do - 1970	E/C.1.112
- do - 1971	E/C.1.113
- do - 1972	E/C.1.114
- do - 1973	E/C.1.115
- do - 1974	E/C.1.116
- do - 1975	E/C.1.117
- do - 1976	E/C.1.118
- do - 1977	E/C.1.119
- do - 1978	E/C.1.120

DEATHS

Deaths from 1815 to 1837	E/D.1
- do - 1841 to 1847	E/D.1.1

Subject Matter	Code N°
Deaths from 1848 to 1854 vol. I.	E/D.1.2
- do - 1854 vol. II to 1855	E/D.1.3
Deaths for 1856	E/D.1.4
- do - 1857	E/D.1.5
- do - 1858	E/D.1.6
- do - 1859 vol. I.	E/D.1.7
- do - 1859 vol. II.	E/D.1.7
- do - 1860	E/D.1.8
- do - 1861	E/D.1.9
- do - 1862	E/D.1.10
- do - 1863	E/D.1.11
- do - 1864	E/D.1.12
- do - 1865	E/D.1.13
- do - 1866	E/D.1.14
- do - 1867	E/D.1.15
- do - 1868	E/D.1.16
- do - 1869	E/D.1.17
- do - 1870	E/D.1.18
- do - 1871	E/D.1.19
- do - 1872 vol. I.	E/D.1.20
- do - 1872 vol. II.	E/D.1.20
- do - 1873	E/D.1.21
- do - 1874	E/D.1.22
- do - 1875	E/D.1.23
- do - 1876	E/D.1.24
- do - 1877	E/D.1.25
- do - 1878	E/D.1.26

Subject Matter	Code N°
Deaths for 1879	E/D.1.27
- do - 1880	E/D.1.28
- do - 1881	E/D.1.29
- do - 1882	E/D.1.30
- do - 1883	E/D.1.31
- do - 1884	E/D.1.32
- do - 1885 vol. I.	E/D.1.33
- do - 1885 vol. II.	E/D.1.33
- do - 1886	E/D.1.34
- do - 1887	E/D.1.35
- do - 1888	E/D.1.36
- do - 1889 vol. I.	E/D.1.37
- do - 1889 vol. II.	E/D.1.37
- do - 1890	E/D.1.38
- do - 1891	E/D.1.39
- do - 1892	E/D.1.40
- do - 1893	E/D.1.41
- do - 1894	E/D.1.42
- do - 1895	E/D.1.43
- do - 1896	E/D.1.44
- do - 1897	E/D.1.45
- do - 1898 vol. I.	E/D.1.46
- do - 1898 vol. II.	E/D.1.46
- do - 1899	E/D.1.47
- do - 1900	E/D.1.48
- do - 1901	E/D.1.49
- do - 1902	E/D.1.50

Subject Matter	Code N°
Deaths for 1903	E/D.1.51
- do - 1904	E/D.1.52
- do - 1905	E/D.1.53
- do - 1906	E/D.1.54
- do - 1907	E/D.1.55
- do - 1908	E/D.1.56
- do - 1909	E/D.1.57
- do - 1910	E/D.1.58
- do - 1911	E/D.1.59
- do - 1912	E/D.1.60
- do - 1913	E/D.1.61
- do - 1914	E/D.1.62
- do - 1915	E/D.1.63
- do - 1916	E/D.1.64
- do - 1917 and 1918 vol. I.	E/D.1.65
- do - 1918 vol. II and 1919 vol. I.	E/D.1.66
- do - 1919 vol. II.	E/D.1.67
- do - 1920	E/D.1.68
- do - 1921	E/D.1.69
- do - 1922	E/D.1.70
- do - 1923	E/D.1.71
- do - 1924	E/D.1.72
- do - 1925	E/D.1.73
- do - 1926	E/D.1.74
- do - 1927	E/D.1.75
- do - 1928	E/D.1.76
- do - 1929	E/D.1.77

Subject Matter	Code N°
Deaths for 1930	E/D.1.78
- do - 1931	E/D.1.79
- do - 1932	E/D.1.80
- do - 1933	E/D.1.81
- do - 1934	E/D.1.82
- do - 1935	E/D.1.83
- do - 1936	E/D.1.84
- do - 1937	E/D.1.85
- do - 1938	E/D.1.86
- do - 1939	E/D.1.87
- do - 1940	E/D.1.88
- do - 1941	E/D.1.89
- do - 1942	E/D.1.90
- do - 1943	E/D.1.91
- do - 1944	E/D.1.92
- do - 1945	E/D.1.93
- do - 1946 and 1947 vol. I.	E/D.1.94
- do - 1947 vol. II and 1948 vol. I.	E/D.1.95
- do - 1948 vol. II	E/D.1.96
- do - 1949 and 1950 vol. I.	E/D.1.97
- do - 1950 vol. II and 1951 vol. I.	E/D.1.98
- do - 1951 vol. II	E/D.1.99
- do - 1952 vol. I.	E/D.1.100
- do - 1952 vol. II.	E/D.1.100
- do - 1953	E/D.1.101
- do - 1954	E/D.1.102
- do - 1955 vol. I.	E/D.1.103

Subject Matter	Code N°
Deaths for 1955 Vol. II and 1956 vol. I.	E/D.1.104
- do - 1956 vol. II and 1957 vol. I.	E/D.1.105
- do - 1957 vol. II and 1958 vol. I.	E/D.1.106
- do - 1958 vol. II and 1959 vol. I.	E/D.1.107
- do - 1959 vol. II	E/D.1.107
- do - 1959 vol. III and 1960 vol. I.	E/D.1.108
- do - 1960 vol. II and 1961 vol. I.	E/D.1.109
- do - 1961 vol. II and 1962 vol. I.	E/D.1.110
- do - 1962 vol. II.	E/D.1.110
- do - 1962 vol. III and 1963 vol. I.	E/D.1.111
- do - 1963 vol. II and 1964 vol. I.	E/D.1.112
- do - 1964 **vol. II**	E/D.1.112
- do - 1964 vol. III and 1965 vol. I.	·E/D.1.113
- do - 1965 vol. II.	E/D.1.113
- do - 1965 vol. III	E/D.1.113
- do - 1966	E/D.1.114
- do - ·1967	E/D.1.115
- do - 1968	E/D.1.116
- do - 1969	E/D.1.117
- do - 1970	E/D.1.118
- do - 1971	E/D.1.119
- do - 1972	E/D.1.120
- do - 1973	E/D.1.121
- do - 1974	E/D.1.122
- do - 1975	E/D.1.123
- do - 1976	E/D.1.124
- do - 1977	E/D.1.125

Subject Matter	Code N°
Deaths for 1978	E/D.1.126
PRASLIN DISTRICT (PL) BIRTHS	
Births for 1874	E/E.1
- do - 1875 to 1877	E/E.1.1
- do - 1878	E/E.1.2
- do - 1879 and 1880	E/E.1.3
- do - 1881 and 1882	E/E.1.4
- do - 1883 to 1885	E/E.1.5
- do - 1886 and 1887	E/E.1.6
- do - 1888	E/E.1.7
- do - 1889 and 1890 vol. I.	E/E.1.8
- do - 1890 vol. II to 1893 vol. I.	E/E.1.9
- do - 1893 vol. II	E/E.1.10
- do - 1894	E/E.1.11
- do - 1895	E/E.1.12
- do - 1896	E/E.1.13
- do - 1897 to 1899 vol. I.	E/E.1.14
- do - 1899 vol. II.	E/E.1.15
- do - 1900	E/E.1.16
- do - 1901	E/E.1.17
PRASLIN DISTRICT (PL) MARRIAGES	
Marriages for 1875 to 1879	E/F.1

Subject Matter	Code N°
Marriages for 1880 to 1885	E/F.1.1.
- do - 1886 to 1889	E/F.1.2
- do - 1890 to 1893	E/F.1.3
- do - 1894 vol. I.	E/F.1.4
- do - 1894 vol. II to 1897	E/F.1.5
- do - 1898 and 1899 vol. I.	E/F.1.6
- do - 1899 vol. II	E/F.1.7
- do - 1900	E/F.1.8
- do - 1901	E/F.1.9
- do - 1902	E/F.1.10
- do - 1903	E/F.1.11
- do - 1904	E/F.1.12
- do - 1905	E/F.1.13
- do - 1906	E/F.1.14
- do - 1907	E/F.1.15
- do - 1908	E/F.1.16
- do - 1909	E/F.1.17
- do - 1910	E/F.1.18
- do - 1911	E/F.1.19
- do - 1912	E/F.1.20
- do - 1913	E/F.1.21
- do - 1914	E/F.1.22
- do - 1915	E/F.1.23
- do - 1916	E/F.1.24
- do - 1917	E/F.1.25
- do - 1918	E/F.1.26
- do - 1919	E/F.1.27

Subject Matter	Code N°
Marriages for 1920	E/F.1.28
- do - 1921	E/F.1.29
- do - 1922	E/F.1.30
- do - 1923	E/F.1.31
- do - 1924	E/F.1.32
- do - 1925	E/F.1.33
- do - 1926	E/F.1.34
- do - 1927	E/F.1.35
- do - 1928	E/F.1.36
- do - 1929	E/F.1.37
- do - 1930	E/F.1.38
- do - 1931	E/F.1.39
- do - 1932	E/F.1.40
- do - 1933	E/F.1.41
- do - 1934	E/F.1.42
- do - 1935	E/F.1.43
- do - 1936	E/F.1.44
- do - 1937	E/F.1.45
- do - 1938	E/F.1.46
- do - 1939	E/F.1.47
- do - 1940	E/F.1.48
- do - 1941-1942 vol. I.	E/F.1.49
- do - 1942 vol. II	E/F.1.50

PRASLIN DISTRICT (PL) DEATHS

Deaths for 1874 to 1876	E/G.1.

Subject Matter	Code N°
Deaths for 1877	E/G.1.1
- do - 1878 to 1881	E/G.1.2
- do - 1882 to 1886	E/G.1.3
- do - 1887 to 1889	E/G.1.4
- do - 1890 to 1893	E/G.1.5
- do - 1894 to 1897	E/G.1.6
- do - 1898-1899	E/G.1.7
- do - 1900	E/G.1.8
- do - 1901	E/G.1.9
- do - 1902	E/G.1.10
- do - 1903	E/G.1.11
- do - 1904	E/G.1.12
- do - 1905	E/G.1.13
- do - 1906	E/G.1.14
- do - 1907	E/G.1.15
- do - 1908	E/G.1.16
- do - 1909	E/G.1.17
- do - 1910	E/G.1.18
- do - 1911	E/G.1.19
- do - 1912	E/G.1.20
- do - 1913	E/G.1.21
- do - 1914	E/G.1.22
- do - 1915	E/G.1.23
- do - 1916	E/G.1.24
- do - 1917 vol. I.	E/G.1.25
- do - 1917 vol. II	E/G.1.25
- do - 1918-1919 vol. I	E/G.1.26

Subject Matter	Code N°
Deaths for 1919 vol. II	E/G.1.27
- do - 1919 vol. III	E/G.1.27
- do - 1920	E/G.1.28
- do - 1921	E/G.1.29
- do - 1922	E/G.1.30
- do - 1923	E/G.1.31
- do - 1924	E/G.1.32
- do - 1925	E/G.1.33
- do - 1926	E/G.1.34
- do - 1927	E/G.1.35
- do - 1928	E/G.1.36
- do - 1929	E/G.1.37
- do - 1930	E/G.1.38
- do - 1931	E/G.1.39
- do - 1932	E/G.1.40
- do - 1933	E/G.1.41
- do - 1934	E/G.1.42
- do - 1935	E/G.1.43
- do - 1936	E/G.1.44
- do - 1937	E/G.1.45
- do - 1938	E/G.1.46
- do - 1939	E/G.1.47
- do - 1940	E/G.1.48
- do - 1941	E/G.1.49
- do - 1942	E/G.1.50
- do - 1943	E/G.1.51

Subject Matter	Code N°
Births for 1892	E/H.1
- do - 1893	E/H.1.1
- do - 1897-1898	E/H.1.2
LA DIGUE DISTRICT (LD) MARRIAGES	
Marriages for 1893	E/I.1
- do -	
- do - 1900	E/I.1.2
- do - 1901	E/I.1.3
- do - 1902	E/I.1.4
- do - 1903	E/I.1.5
- do - 1904	E/I.1.6
- do - 1905	E/I.1.7
- do - 1906	E/I.1.8
- do - 1907	E/I.1.9
- do - 1908	E/I.1.10
- do - 1909	E/I.1.11
- do - 1910	E/I.1.12
- do - 1911	E/I.1.13
- do - 1912	E/I.1.14
- do - 1913	E/I.1.15
- do - 1914	E/I.1.16
- do - 1915	E/I.1.17
- do - 1916	E/I.1.18
- do - 1917	E/I.1.19
- do - 1918	E/I.1.20

Subject Matter	Code N°
Marriages for 1919	E/I.1.21
- do - 1920	E/I.1.22
- do - 1921	E/I.1.23
- do - 1922	E/I.1.24
- do - 1923	E/I.1.25
- do - 1924	E/I.1.26
- do - 1925	E/I.1.27
- do - 1926	E/I.1.28
- do - 1927	E/I.1.29
- do - 1928	E/I.1.30
- do - 1929	E/I.1.31
- do - 1930	E/I.1.32
- do - 1931	E/I.1.33
- do - 1932	E/I.1.34
- do - 1933	E/I.1.35
- do - 1934	E/I.1.36
- do - 1935	E/I.1.37
- do - 1936	E/I.1.38
- do - 1937	E/I.1.39
- do - 1938	E/I.1.40
- do - 1939	E/I.1.41
- do - 1940	E/I.1.42
- do - 1941	E/I.1.43
- do - 1942	E/I.1.44

Subject Matter	Code N°
<u>LA DIGUE DISTRICT (LD) DEATHS</u>	
Deaths for 1892	E/J.1
- do -	
- do - 1900	E/J.1.2
- do - 1901	E/J.1.3
- do - 1902	E/J.1.4
- do - 1903	E/J.1.5
- do - 1904	E/J.1.6
- do - 1905	E/J.1.7
- do - 1906	E/J.1.8
- do - 1907	E/J.1.9
- do - 1908	E/J.1.10
- do - 1909	E/J.1.11
- do - 1910	E/J.1.12
- do - 1911	E/J.1.13
- do - 1912	E/J.1.14
- do - 1913	E/J.1.15
- do - 1914	E/J.1.16
- do - 1915	E/J.1.17
- do - 1916	E/J.1.18
- do - 1917	E/J.1.19
- do - 1918	E/J.1.20
- do - 1919	E/J.1.21
- do - 1920	E/J.1.22
- do - 1921	E/J.1.23
- do - 1922	E/J.1.24

Subject Matter	Code N°
Deaths for 1923	E/J.1.25
- do - 1924	E/J.1.26
- do - 1925	E/J.1.27
- do - 1926	E/J.1.28
- do - 1927	E/J.1.29
- do - 1928	E/J.1.30
- do - 1929	E/J.1.31
- do - 1930	E/J.1.32
- do - 1931	E/J.1.33
- do - 1932	E/J.1.34
- do - 1933	E/J.1.35
- do - 1934	E/J.1.36
- do - 1935	E/J.1.37
- do - 1936	E/J.1.38
- do - 1937	E/J.1.39
- do - 1938	E/J.1.40
- do - 1939	E/J.1.41
- do - 1940	E/J.1.42
- do - 1941	E/J.1.43
- do - 1942	E/J.1.44

SOUTH MAHE DISTRICT (SM) MARRIAGES

Note : Registers of marriages for South Mahe District from 1903 to 1908 and 1937, destroyed by white ants at Anse Royale.

Marriages for 1902	E/L.1
- do - 1909	E/L.1.1

Subject Matter	Code N°
Marriages for 1910	E/L.1.2
- do - 1911	E/L.1.3
- do - 1912	E/L.1.4
- do - 1913	E/L.1.5
- do - 1914	E/L.1.6
- do - 1915	E/L.1.7
- do - 1916	E/L.1.8
- do - 1917	E/L.1.9
- do - 1918	E/L.1.10
- do - 1919	E/L.1.11
- do - 1920	E/L.1.12
- do - 1921	E/L.1.13
- do - 1922	E/L.1.14
- do - 1923	E/L.1.15
- do - 1924	E/L.1.16
- do - 1925	E/L.1.17
- do - 1926	E/L.1.18
- do - 1927	E/L.1.19
- do - 1928	E/L.1.20
- do - 1929	E/L.1.21
- do - 1930	E/L.1.22
- do - 1931	E/L.1.23
- do - 1932	E/L.1.24
- do - 1933	E/L.1.25
- do - 1934	E/L.1.26
- do - 1935	E/L.1.27

Subject Matter	Code N°
Marriages for 1936	E/L.1.28
- do - 1937	E/L.1.29
- do - 1938	E/L.1.30
- do - 1939	E/L.1.31
- do - 1940	E/L.1.32
- do - 1941	E/L.1.33
- do - 1942	E/L.1.34
- do - 1943	E/L.1.35
- do - 1944	E/L.1.36
- do - 1945	E/L.1.37
SOUTH MAHE DISTRICT (SM) DEATHS	
Deaths for 1902	E/M.1
- do - 1903	E/M.1.1
- do - 1904	E/M.1.2
- do - 1905	E/M.1.3
- do - 1906	E/M.1.4
- do - 1907	E/M.1.5
- do - 1908	E/M.1.6
- do - 1909	E/M.1.7
- do - 1910	E/M.1.8
- do - 1911	E/M.1.9
- do - 1912	E/M.1.10
- do - 1913	E/M.1.11
- do - 1914	E/M.1.12
- do - 1915	E/M.1.13

Subject Matter	Code N°
Deaths for 1916	E/M.1.14
- do - 1917	E/M.1.15
- do - 1918	E/M.1.16
- do - 1919	E/M.1.17
- do - 1920	E/M.1.18
- do - 1921	E/M.1.19
- do - 1922	E/M.1.20
- do - 1923	E/M.1.21
- do - 1924	E/M.1.22
- do - 1925	E/M.1.23
- do - 1926	E/M.1.24
- do - 1927	E/M.1.25
- do - 1928	E/M.1.26
- do - 1929	E/M.1.27
- do - 1930	E/M.1.28
- do - 1931	E/M.1.29
- do - 1932	E/M.1.30
- do - 1933	E/M.1.31
- do - 1934	E/M.1.32
- do - 1935	E/M.1.33
- do - 1936	E/M.1.34
- do - 1937	E/M.1.35
- do - 1938	E/M.1.36
- do - 1939	E/M.1.37
- do - 1940	E/M.1.38
- do - 1941	E/M.1.39
- do - 1942	E/M.1.40

Subject Matter	Code N°
Deaths for 1943	E/M.1.41
- do - 1944	E/M.1.42
- do - 1945	E/M.1.43
ACT OF MARRIAGES BY MINISTERS OF RELIGION	
Marriages for 1954	E/M.1 (A)
- do - 1955	E/M.1.1 (A)
- do - 1956	E/M.1.2 (A)
- do - 1957	E/M.1.3 (A)
- do - 1958	E/M.1.4 (A)
- do - 1959	E/M.1.5 (A)
- do - 1960	E/M.1.6 (A)
- do - 1961	E/M.1.7 (A)
- do - 1962	E/M.1.8 (A)
- do - 1963	E/M.1.9 (A)
- do - 1964	E/M.1.10 (A)
- do - 1965	E/M.1.11 (A)
- do - 1966	E/M.1.12 (A)
- do - 1967 - 1970	E/M.1.13 (A)
CENTRAL & NORTH -- ACT OF MARRIAGES IN "ARTICULO MORTIS"	
Marriages for 1872 to 1925	E/M.2
SOUTH MAHE - ACTS OF MARRIAGES IN "ARTICULO MORTIS" (SM)	
Marriages for 1903 to 1925	E/M.3

Subject Matter	Code Nº
PRASLIN - ACTS OF MARRIAGES IN "ARTICULO MORTIS" (PL)	
Marriages for 1879 to 1893	E/M.4
- do - 1879 to 1887	E/M.4.1
- do - 1889 to 1897	E/M.4.1
- do - 1894 to 1895 and 1897	E/M.4.2
- do - 1900	E/M.4.3
- do - 1903	E/M.4.4
- do - 1900 to 1925	E/M.4.5
LA DIGUE - ACTS OF MARRIAGES IN "ARTICULO MORTIS" (LD)	
Marriages for 1902	E/M.5
- do - 1900 to 1945	E/M.5.1
COLONY OF SEYCHELLES - DIVORCES	
Divorces for 1883 to 1892	E/N.1
- do - 1896 to 1945	E/N.1.1
CENTRAL MAHE-JUDGE'S ORDERS	
Judge's Orders 1872 to 1903	E/N.2
- do - 1904 to 1945	E/N.2.1
- do - 1946 to 1950	E/N.2.2
- do - 1951 to 1957	E/N.2.3
- do - 1957 to 1965	E/N.2.4
- do - 1965 to 1970	E/N.2.5
PRASLIN DISTRICT-JUDGE'S ORDERS	
Judge's Orders for 1895 to 1930	E/N.3

Subject Matter	Code N°
LA DIGUE DISTRICT-JUDGE'S ORDERS	
Judge's Orders for 1900 to 1908	E/N.4
SOUTH MAHE DISTRICT-JUDGE'S ORDERS	
Judge's Orders for 1903 to 1935	E/N.5
INDEX OF BIRTHS FOR CENTRAL AND NORTH DISTRICTS	
(For the whole Colony of Seychelles from 1790 to 1882).	
Index of Births for 1790 to 1793)	
- do - 1794 to 1810)	E/O.1
- do - 1794 to 1855	E/O.1.1
- do - 1856 to 1872	E/O.1.2
- do - 1873 to 1882	E/O.1.3
- do - 1883 to 1892)	
- do - 1893 to 1902)	E/O.1.4
- do - 1903 to 1912	E/O.1.5
- do - 1913 to 1922	E/O.1.6
- do - 1923 to 1932	E/O.1.7
- do - 1933 to 1940	E/O.1.8
- do - 1941 to 1950	E/O.1.9
- do - 1951 to 1955	E/O.1.10
- do - 1956 to 1960	E/O.1.11
- do - 1961 to 1965	E/O.1.12
- do - 1966 to 1970	E/O.1.13
- do - 1971 to 1975	E/O.1.14

Subject Matter	Code Nº
INDEX OF BIRTHS SOUTH MAHE DISTRICT (SM)	
Index of Births for 1902 to 1912	E/O.2
- do - 1913 to 1922	E/O.2.1
- do - 1923 to 1932	E/O.2.2
- do - 1933 to 1940	E/O.2.3
- do - 1941 to 1950	E/O.2.4
- do - 1951 to 1960	E/O.2.5
- do - 1961 to 1965	E/O.2.6
INDEX OF BIRTHS PRASLIN AND LA DIGUE DISTRICTS (PL/LD)	
Index of Births for 1874 to 1893	E/O.3
- do - 1894 to 1912	E/O.3.1
- do - 1913 to 1922	E/O.3.2
- do - 1923 to 1932	E/O.3.3
- do - 1933 to 1950	E/O.3.4
- do - 1951 to 1960	E/O.3.5
- do - 1961 to 1965	E/O.3.6
INDEX OF MARRIAGES FOR CENTRAL AND NORTH DISTRICTS	
Index of Marriages for 1892 to 1902	E/O.4
- do - 1903 to 1912	E/O.4.1
- do - 1913 to 1922	E/O.4.2
- do - 1923 to 1932	E/O.4.3
- do - 1933 to 1950	E/O.4.4
- do - 1951 to 1960	E/O.4.5
- do - 1961 to 1965	E/O.4.6

Subject Matter	Code N°
Index of Marriages for 1794 to 1872	E/O.4.7
- do -　　　　1872 to 1891	E/O.4.8
INDEX OF MARRIAGES SOUTH MAHE DISTRICT (SM)	
Index of Marriages for 1902 to 1932	E/O.5
- do -　　　　1933 to 1965	E/O.5.1
INDEX OF MARRIAGES PRASLIN AND LA DIGUE DISTRICTS (PL/LD)	
Index of Marriages for 1894 to 1912	E/O.6
- do -　　　　1913 to 1922	E/O.6.1
- do -　　　　1923 to 1965	E/O.6.2
- do -　　　　1875 to 1892	E/O.6.3
INDEX OF MARRIAGES BY MINISTERS OF RELIGIONS	
Index of Marriages for 1954 to 1965	E/O.7
- do -　　　　1966 to 1970	E/O.7.1
INDEX OF DEATHS CENTRAL AND NORTH DISTRICTS	
(For the whole Colony of Seychelles from 1794 to 1882)	
Index of Deaths for 1794 to 1855	E/O.8
- do -　　　　1856 to 1862	E/O.8.1
- do -　　　　1863 to 1872	E/O.8.2
- do -　　　　1873 to 1882	E/O.8.3
- do -　　　　1883 to 1892	E/O.8.4
- do -　　　　1893 to 1902	E/O.8.5
- do -　　　　1903 to 1912	E/O.8.6
- do -　　　　1913 to 1922	E/O.8.7

Subject Matter	Code N°
Index of Deaths for 1923 to 1932	E/O.8.8
- do - 1933 to 1940	E/O.8.9
- do - 1941 to 1950	E/O.8.10
- do - 1951 to 1960	E/O.8.11
- do - 1961 to 1965	E/O.8.12
INDEX OF DEATHS SOUTH MAHE DISTRICT (SM)	
Index of Deaths for 1902 to 1912)	
)	E/O.9
- do - 1913 to 1922)	
- do - 1923 to 1932	E/O.9.1
- do - 1933 to 1960	E/O.9.2
INDEX OF DEATHS PRASLIN AND LA DIGUE DISTRICTS (PL/LD)	
Index of Deaths for 1913 to 1922	E/O.10
- do - 1923 to 1923	E/O.10.1
- do - 1933 to 1965	E/O.10.2
ACKNOWLEDGEMENT OF NATURAL CHILDREN	
Acknowledgement of N.C. from 1896 to 1921	E/P.1

PUBLICATIONS ET OUVRAGES DIVERS RELATIFS A L'HISTOIRE

ET A L'HISTOIRE NATURELLE DES SEYCHELLES

- CLASS F -

UNOFFICIAL AND MISCELLANEOUS PUBLICATIONS RELATING

TO SEYCHELLES

- CLASS F -

As there was an obvious advantage for Researchers and others to have
all these books in one place, and not, as before, in three places
(Archives, Carnegie Library and the office of the Director of Agriculture)
the Trustees of the Carnegie Library agreed to transfer their Research
Section on permanent loan to the Archives. The books transferred,
however, still remain the property of the Carnegie Library.

A glance at the Seychelles Bibliography reveals how serious are the gaps
in this collection at present. Unfortunately, most of the missing books
are now out of print, and the prices demanded for secondhand copies are
high.

Title	Author	Code N°
UNOFFICIAL PUBLICATIONS, HISTORICAL AND GENERAL, ON LOAN FROM CARNEGIE LIBRARY		F/1
UNOFFICIAL PUBLICATIONS, HISTORICAL AND GENERAL, THE PROPERTY OF THE GOVERNMENT ARCHIVES		F/2
UNOFFICIAL PUBLICATIONS, NATURAL HISTORY ON LOAN FROM CARNEGIE LIBRARY		F/3
UNOFFICIAL PUBLICATIONS, NATURAL HISTORY, THE PROPERTY OF THE GOVERNMENT ARCHIVES		F/4

Title	Author	Code N°
Ile de Sardaigne	De Gregorg	F/1
Voyage Round the World. Vol. II	Balcher	F/1.1
Three Voyages of a Naturalist	Nicoll	F/1.2
Islands in a Forgotten Sea	Bulpin	F/1.3
La Grande Riviere de Port-Louis	Froberville	F/1.4
Recollections of Seven years. Residence at Mauritius	Anonymous	F/1.5
An Account of the Island of Mauritius		F/1.6
The Shoals of Capricorn	O manney	F/1.7
England's Colonial Empire. Vol. I. Mauritius and Its Dependences	Pridham	F/1.8
Voyage dans les quatre Principales Iles des Mers d'Afrique. Vol. I	Bory de St. Vincent	F/1.9
Voyage dans les quatre Principales Iles des Mers d'Afrique. Vol. II	Bory de St. Vincent	F/1.10
Voyage dans les quatre Principales Iles des Mers d'Afrique. Vol. III	Bory de St. Vincent	F/1.11
Madagascar before the Conquest	Sibree	F/1.12
Historical Geography of the British Colonies Vol. I.	Lucas	F/1.13
Historical Geography of the British Colonies Vol. II.	Lucas	F/1.14

Title	Author	Code N°
Historical Geography of the British Colonies Vol. III.	Lucas	F/1.15
Historical Geography of the British Colonies (Second Edition) - Vol. I.	Lucas	F/1.16
History of Mauritius	Grant	F/1.17
Voyages Round the World etc...	Holman	F/1.18
Transferred to F/4.18 and F/4.19		
The Colonial Police	Jeffries	F/1.21
The Journal of Mrs. Fenton	Lawrence	F/1.22
The Life and Services of Captain Philip Beaver	Smyth	F/1.23
Madagascar, its History and People	Little	F/1.24
Three visits to Madagascar	Ellis	F/1.25
Some account of the state of Slavery at Mauritius	Telfair	F/1.26
Les Jours Héroïques	Charoux	F/1.27
Voyage à l'Ile de France	Un Officier du Roi	F/1.28
A Voyage Round the World	Holman	F/1.29
Adventures of Robert Drury on Madagascar	Himself	F/1.30
War, Waves and Wanderings. Vol. I.	Francis	F/1.31

Title	Author	Code N°
War, Waves and Wanderings. Vol. II.	Francis	F/1.32
Les Vers à Soie Sauvages de Madagascar	Grangeon	F/1.33
Reves et Chansons	Charoux	F/1.34
Un Project de Republique à l'Ile d'Eden	Quesne	F/1.35
Unpublished documents on the History of the Seychelles Islands	Fauvel	F/1.36
Makarios in Exile	Le Geyt	F/1.37
L'Ile de La Réunion	Maillard	F/1.38
Recollections of a Happy Life. Vol. I.	North	F/1.39
Recollections of a Happy Life. Vol. II	North	F/1.40
Account of Conquest of Mauritius	An Officer	F/1.41
Geographie illustree de l'Ile Maurice et Histoire de l'Ile Maurice	Edwardes	F/1.42
Mauritius and Madagascar	Ryan	F/1.43
The History of Mauritius	Edwardes	F/1.44
The Downfall of Prempeh	B-Powell	F/1.45
The Drama of Madagascar	Howe	F/1.46
Fifty years in Madagascar	Sibee	F/1.47
Island of the Swan	Malim	F/1.48

Title	Author	Code N°
Seychelles Postage Stamps and Postal History	Farmer	F/1.49
Beyond the Reefs	Travis	F/1.50
Shark for Sale	Travis	F/1.51
Aventures d'un Cycliste à travers Madagascar	Duquenois	F/1.52
La Poursuite du "Kaipan"	Monfreid	F/1.53
Aventures d'une Parisienne dans l'Océan Indien.	Muller	F/1.54
Limuria. The Lesser Dependencies of Mauritius	Scott	F/1.55
Madagascar Revisited	Ellis	F/1.56
Madagascar et ses Richesses	Locamus	F/1.57
Fort Jesus and the Portuguese in Mombasa	Boxer & Azevedo	F/1.58
Le Patois Creole	Baissac	F/1.59
Notre épopée Missionnaire Madagascar	Lhande	F/1.60
Two Campaigns Madagascar and Ashantee	Burleigh	F/1.61
South Indian Pilot (fith Edition, 1934)		F/1.62
Voyage aux Iles Mascareignes	Jadin	F/1.63
Paul et Virginie	De Saint-Pierre	F/1.64
Histoire de Madagascar	Deschamps	F/1.65

Title	Author	Code N°
British Contributions to Portuguese and Brazilian studies	Atkinson	F/1.66
Les Tortues de Terre gigantesques des Mascareignes	Sauzier	F/1.67
Danger My Ally	Hedges	F/1.68
Cruise in the "Gorgon"	Cope	F/1.69
Narrative voyages to explore the shores of Africa. Vol. I.	Robinson	F/1.70
Le Bon Grain sur les Iles	Michelet	F/1.71
Guide de l'immigrant Madagascar. Vol. I.		F/1.72
Guide de l'immigrant Madagascar. Vol. II.		F/1.73
Guide de l'immigrant Madagascar. Vol. III.		F/1.74
Cent Années de Rivalité Coloniale	Darcy	F/1.75
Voyage aux Indes Orientales. Vol. I	Tombe	F/1.76
Voyage aux Indes Orientales. Vol. II.	Tombe	F/1.77
Voyage aux Indes Orientales. Vol. III (Collection de Planches et Cartes).	Tombe	F/1.78
A Historical Geography of the British Colonies Vo. V. Canada. Part. I.	Lucas	F/1.79
Mazzotint	Mackenzie	F/1.80
Madagascar, Comores Terres Australes	Deschamps	F/1.81

Title	Author	Code N°
Théses présentées à la Faculté de Sciences de Paris	Cotte	F/1.82
The Life of Philibert Commerson	Elliot	F/1.83
Mahe de la Bourdonnais et la Compagnie des Indes	Herpin	F/1.84
Six years in Seychelles	Estridge	F/1.85
Madagascar, Comores, Réunion, Ile Maurice.	(Hachette)	F/1.86
Considerations Geologiques sur les Iles Oceaniques	Tchihatchef	F/1.87
Ile de France	Saint Elme Le Duc	F/1.88
Slave - catching in the Indian Ocean	Colomb	F/1.89
Indians in a plural Society	Benedict	F/1.90
Bulletin Economique de Madagascar		F/1.91
Le Cerneen		F/1.92
Report on a Visit of investigation, in the Outlying Islands	Dupont	F/1.93
The Garden of Eden	Gordon	F/1.94
Silver Jubilee of King George V		F/1.95
Maps for guide de L'Immigrant à Madagascar		F/1.96
Voyage dans les quatre principales Iles des Mers d'Afrique	Bory de St. Vincent	F/1.97

Title	Author	Code N°
Maritime Discoveries	Clarke	F/1.98
A Voyage to Madagascar and the East Indies	Rochon	F/1.99
Madagascar in War Time	Knight	F/1.100
UNOFFICIAL PUBLICATIONS, HISTORICAL AND GENERAL, THE PROPERTY OF THE GOVERNMENT ARCHIVES.		
Silver Jubilee of King George V		F/2
Story of Seychelles	Webb	F/2.1
Seychelles Postage Stamps & Postal History	Farmer	F/2.2
Bibliography of Mauritius	Toussaint	F/2.3
Bibliographie de l'Archipel des Iles Seychelles	Fauvel	F/2.4
British Commonwealth Postage Stamp Catalogue	Gibbons	F/2.5
The History of Seychelles. Vol. I	Bradley	F/2.6
The History of Seychelles. Vol. II	Bradley	F/2.7
Van Roem Tot Selfmoord	Nienaber	F/2.8
Know your Own Country	Bradshaw	F/2.9
Une Grappe de Cocos Seychellois	Wynburne	F/2.10
La Cuisine Seychelloise	Man-Cham	F/2.11

Title	Author	Code N°
The Colonial Coinages of British Africa	Parsons	F/2.12
Journal of the Seychelles Society.		F/2.13
Historical Miscellanea concerning Seychelles	Webb. & Mc Gaw	F/2.14
Rules and By Laws of Various societies and Associations		F/2.15
From the Tropics to the North Sea	Barkly	F/2.16
The Explorers Club. Vol. XLII. n° I. March, 1964.	Larson	F/2.17
Mauritius and the Spice Trade. The Odyssey of Pierre Poivre - 1958	Ly-Tio-Fane	F/2.18
The Coronation of Their Majesties King George VI & Queen Elisabeth		F/2.19
The Seychelles from a "Traveller's View - a poem by R.M. Blomfield - 1870	Blomfield	F/2.20
Resume of World History from 1953 and 1965		F/2.21
Commonwealth Banking Systems by W.F. Crick - 1965	Crick	F/2.22
People of the Seychelles 1966	Benedict	F/2.23
Social Service Quaterly, 1963	Benedict	F/2.24
Colonies of Mauritius and it dependencies and of the Seychelles - 1965 by Maurice Tyak	Tyak	F/2.25
Loin du Pont d'Avignon by Yvonne Rameau - 1952	Rameau	F/2.26

Title	Author	Code N°
Seychelles Verses by Margaret Le Geyt - 1966	Le Geyt	F/2.27
The Queen's Beasts - 1953		F/2.28
La Bigorne, Caporal de France par Pierre Nord - 1957	Nord	F/2.29
The Duke of Edinburgh's World Tour - 1956-1957		F/2.30
The Opening of the new Chamber of the House of Commons - 1956		F/2.31
Bristol Seychelles Expedition - 1964-1965		F/2.32
Zodiac - 1967		F/2.33
Grammaire Française à l'usage des Ecoliers des Seychelles - Volumes I and II - 1967		F/2.34
Les Iles Seychelles - P. Louis Dayer, Capucin - 1966	Dayer	F/2.35
Terre Malgache - 1968		F/2.36
Forgotten Eden - 1968	Thomas	F/2.37
La Cuisine Seychelloise - 2nd Edition - 1968	Man-Cham	F/2.38
Where the Clocks Chime Twice	Waugh	F/2.39
Journey to an Island	Wilde	F/2.40
Brothers of the Sea	Sherman	F/2.41
A Longing for Quails	Bates	F/2.42

Title	Author	Code N°
Le Petit Prince des Iles Seychelles	Zuber	F/2.43
History of the Indian Ocean	Toussaint	F/2.44
La Route des Iles (Road to the Islands)	Toussaint	F/2.45
Isles of Torment	Doull	F/2.46
The Treasure Island Readers (Introductory and Books One to Six)		F/2.47
The Treasure Island Readers (Third and Fourth Supplementaries Books)		F/2.48
Studies in Portuguese and Creole	Walkhoff	F/2.49
Instructions to Naval Officers, etc..., Slave Trade. Vol. I.		F/2.50
Water supply scheme 1969		F/2.51
New Commonwealth (Focus on Seychelles)		F/2.52
Le "Marie-Jeanne" sur l'Ocean Indien	P. Angelin	F/2.53
Social Organization. Essays presented to Raymond Firth	Freedman	F/2.54
Segas of Seychelles by Mickey and the Buccaneers	Mickey/Buccaneers	F/2.55
Des Oceans pour voir des hommes	Mermod	F/2.56
Norwegian Yearbook of Maritime History (in Norwegian)	Petterson	F/2.57
Camera au poing	Zuber	F/2.58

Title	Author	Code N°
Songs of Seychelles	Mickey/Buccaneers	F/2.59
Paille en Queue. Poemes	Antoine Abel	F/2.60
A Short History of Seychelles	Lionnet	F/2.61
Say it in Creole	Pomeroy	F/2.62
Pidgin and Creole Languages	Hall	F/2.63
Frères en marche		F/2.64
Postage Stamp Catalogue		
British Commonwealth	Gibbons	F/2.65
"Landmark" of Seychelles Football	SFA	F/2.66
Les Mascareignes	D'Unienville	F/2.67
A Comparative Study of Creole French Dialects	Goodman	F/2.68
H.M.S. "Owen" 1960-1962 (Seychelles pages 9, 49-51, 63 & 65)		F/2.69
An Economic Survey, Seychelles, 1965		F/2.70
Seychelles Society		
Constitution and By-Laws, 1960		F/2.71
R.S.P.C.A. Seychelles Branch,		F/2.72
A guide to Seychelles Creole (Revised edition	Townshend	F/2.73

Title	Author	Code N°
Reflections of a Seychellois on the commissioner's report. June, 1958		F/2.74
A Century of Service		
A brief history of Cable and Wireless Ltd. 1868 - 1968. Feb. 1970	Baglehole	F/2.75
The Eastern Associated Telegraph Companies		
Map of Cable System. May 1922		F/2.76
Studiekamraten, 1970. Sprak pa Seychellerna	Sjogren	F/2.77
Aldabra Alone	Beamish	F/2.78
Seychelles îles d'amour, islands of love 1971	Belling	F/2.79
Sea of Zanj, 1969	Lane	F/2.80
A Hero for Leanda, 1970	Garve	F/2.81
Sea and Islands, 1970	Innes	F/2.82
Spillror av en Kontinent, 1971	Sjögren	F/2.83
Forgotten Islands of the Indian Ocean A Cruising Expedition to the Seychelles Amirantes, Farquhar, Aldabra and Comoro Islands, 1970		F/2.84
Cahier du Centre Universitaire de la Réunion, 1971		F/2.85
Constitution of the Established Civil Servants Union 1972		F/2.86

Title	Author	Code N°
Sociétés et Compagnies de Commerce en Orient et dans l'Océan Indien, 1970	Mollat	F/2.87
Souvenir Album of the Royal Visit to the Seychelles by Her Majesty Queen Elisabeth II and H.R.H. Prince Philip 20th March, 1972		F/2.88
Postage Stamps / Photogravure		F/2.89
Histoire Generale de l'Afrique Noire Tome I : Des origines à 1800. 1970	Deschamps	F/2.90
Histoire Generale de l'Afrique Noire Tome II : De 1800 à nos jours. 1971	Deschamps	F/2.91
Seychelles Ultima Speranza Della Condizione Umana, 1971	Mancini	F/2.92
Pirates et Corsaires dans l'Océan Indien, 1971	Filliot	F/2.93
Bulletin de Madagascar, 1972 (Essai sur les îles Seychelles. I. L'archipel, par M.J. Moine)	Moine	F/2.94
Bulletin de Madagascar, 1972. (Essai sur les îles Seychelles. II. La Découverte, par M.J. Moine)	Moine	F/2.95
Histoire de la Réunion, 1966	Scherer	F/2.96
The spread of Printings Mauritius, Réunion, Madagascar and the Seychelles, 1969	Toussaint	F/2.97
Underwater Seychelles, 1972	Venter	F/2.98
New Horizons, S.P.U.P. Policy Statement, 1972		F/2.99

Title	Author	Code N°
Black Night of Quiloa, 1971	Mugot	F/2.100
Histoire des îles Mascareignes, 1972	Toussaint	F/2.101
Cahiers du Centre Universitaire de la Réunion, Juin 1972		F/2.102
Livingstone River - The story of the Zambezi Expedition 1858-1864	Martelli	F/2.103
Population Growth in the Seychelles, 1972		F/2.104
Festival of Seychelles Souvenir Programme, 1972	Roberts	F/2.105
Island Home, 1971	Veevers-Carter	F/2.106
A short History of Seychelles (2nd Edition) 1972	Lionnet	F/2.107
Year Book & Guide to East Africa, 1961	Gordon-Brown	F/2.108
The Seychelles, 1972	Lionnet	F/2.109
Reflections and Echoes from Seychelles, 1972	Mancham	F/2.110
Standard Bank Review, 1972. Seychelles preserving their special attractions while making them more accessible	Martin	F/2.111
Education in Seychelles at the turn of the century ; The work of Sir E.B. Sweet-Escott, 1899-1904, 1972	Stone	F/2.112
L'Eglise et l'éducation aux Seychelles. "Freres en Marche" N° 3, 1972. (Rev. Missionnaire des Capucins)		F/2.113

Title	Author	Code N°
Seychelles Islands of the Sun (English, French and German), 1972	Fischbeck	F/2.114
Paroles de courage. Suisse-Seychelles. "Freres en Marche" n° 5, 1972 (Rev. Missionnaire des Capucins)		F/2.115
Enthronement of George, Lord Bishop of Seychelles on April 3rd, 1973		F/2.116
Islands in a Forgotten Sea - 2nd Edition - 1969	Bulpin	F/2.117
Holiday in Seychelles, 1972	Alexander	F/2.118
Histoire de l'Ile Maurice, 1971	Toussaint	F/2.119
The Stamps and Postal History of Seychelles	Harris	F/2.120
Seychelles - The Territory in Retrospect from Antiquity to Modern Times	Harris	F/2.121
The Boat, 1973	Sherman	F/2.122
Atoll Research Bulletin, 1973	Peters & Lionnet	F/2.123
Alcoholism in Seychelles, 1973	U.C.S.	F/2.124
Les Seychelles, éditions delroisse, 1973		F/2.125
Seychelles : A Visitors' Guide, 1973	Miller	F/2.126
Problems of Education in Seychelles, 1974	U.C.S.	F/2.127
Under the Indian Ocean, 1973	Venter	F/2.128
Dauphin, mon ami, 1972	Sherman	F/2.129

Title	Author	Code N°
A Guide to the Social and Recreational Services of Seychelles, 1972		F/2.130
Survey of Handicapped persons, Seychelles, August, 1973	S.C.F.	F/2.131
Splitter eines Kontinents, 1973	Sjögren	F/2.132
L'Afrique et l'Asie (Les Iles Seychelles), 1972		F/2.133
Coralline United Touring Ltd. in the Seychelles, 1974		F/2.134
The Housing Problem in Seychelles, 1974		F/2.135
Rugby Football Union Kenya Tour 13th - 21st April, 1974		F/2.136
L'Economie 74. Reunion, Maurice, Madagascar, Djibouti, Comores et Seychelles, 1974	Bigaignon	F/2.137
Guide book to the Seychelles, éditions delroisse, 1974	Hoarau	F/2.138
Guide touristique des Seychelles, éditions delroisse, 1974	Hoarau	F/2.139
Touristenfuehrer der Seychelles, éditions delroisse, 1974	Hoarau	F/2.140
La Poste Maritime Française. Tome VI. Les Paquebots de l'Océan Indien, 1967	Salles	F/2.141
L'Air des Seychelles, 1974	Manchan	F/2.142
Levangile Saint Marc. Traduction en Creole Seychelles, 1974		F/2.143

Title	Author	Code N°
Le Lexique du parler Créole de la Réunion, Tome I. 1974	Chaudenson	F/2.144
Le Lexique du parler Créole de la Réunion, Tome II. 1974	Chaudenson	F/2.145
L'Océan Indien au XVIIIe siècle. 1974	Toussaint	F/2.146
Le Folk-Lore de l'Ile Maurice. (Text créole et traduction française). 1967	Baissac	F/2.147
People of the Seychelles. Third edition. 1970	Benedict	F/2.148
Say Bonjour Seychelles. 1975		F/2.149
The Seychelles & Sri Lanka (Formerly Ceylon) 1973	Hill	F/2.150
The Best of David Philoe (Creole songs) 1975		F/2.151
Lettre Pastorale de l'Administrateur Apostolique de Port-Victoria Mgr. Gervais Aeby. Au sujet du problème de la population aux Seychelles et de son devenir. Careme, 1975	Aeby	F/2.152
Les Iles Seychelles - 2e édition. 1974	Dayer (P. Louis)	F/2.153
Actes de la Rencontre Inter-Iles des chefs de Diocèse, 1975.	Margeot, etc...	F/2.154
Pierre Poivre. 1974	Malleret	F/2.155
La Traite des Esclaves vers les Mascareignes aux XVIIIe siècle. 1974	Filliot	F/2.156
The Sinners. 1970	Sherman	F/2.157
L'Afrique noire et l'Océan Indien francophones aujourd'hui, 1973	Bauchar	F/2.158

Title	Author	Code N°
The Living Sea, 1963	Cousteau & Dugan	F/2.159
The Slave Trade of Eastern Africa, 1976	Beachey	F/2.160
Britain and the ending of the Slave Trade, 1975	Miers	F/2.161
A New System of Slavery. (The Export of Indian Labour Overseas 1830-1920), 1974	Tinker	F/2.162
Ti Annan En Foi En Soungoula (Creole Stories from the Seychelles in new proposed Creole orthography) Edited and Translated by Annagret Bollée, 1976	Accouche	F.2.163
Le Creole Français des Seychelles, 1977	Bollée	F/2.164
L'Océan des Perles et du Pétrole. L'Océan Indien, 1975	Blond	F/2.165
Annuaire des Pays de l'Océan Indien. I. 1974	C.E.R.S.O.I.	F/2.166
Voyage en Inde du Comte de Modave 1773-1776	Deloche	F/2.167
Islands of the Indian Ocean. Iles de l'Océan Indien, 1977	Cubitt	F/2.168
L'économie. 75 Réunion, Maurice, Madagascar, Djibouti, Comores, Seychelles, Australie, France, 1975	Bigaignon	F/2.169
Pierre Poivre, 1974	Malleret	F/2.170
Sir William Mac Gregor, 1971	Joyce	F/2.171
Footprints - The Memoirs of Sir Selwyn Selwyn-Clarke, 1975	Sino-American	F/2.172
After You, Robinson Crusoe, 1975	Hastings	F/2.173

Title	Author	Code N°
History of Indians in Mauritius, 1975	Hazareesingh	F/2.174
Les Seychelles, 1975	Nourault	F/2.175
Seychelles (First Edition), 1976	Fayon	F/2.176
Seychelles (Second Edition), 1977	Fayon	F/2.177
Un manuscrit inédit de Pierre Poivre : Les mémoires d'un voyageur, 1968	Malleret	F/2.178
Seychelles Political Castaways, 1976	Lee	F/2.179
Night of the rukh, 1975	Tingay	F/2.180
Uganda and its poeples. King Mwanga	Cunningham	F/2.181
The Bourbon Kings of France, "The Child in the Temple". Louis XVII (1785-1795), 1976	Seward	F/2.182
Trade Directory of Seychelles, 1976		F/2.183
A Telex Directory and Guide to Seychelles, 1977		F/2.184
Parliamentary debates in the House of Commons on Seychelles for the years 1929-1967		F/2.185
Refors in Education in Seychelles. 1899-1904, 1975	Stone	F/2.186
A School for handicapped children in the Seychelles, 1977		F/2.187
Notes on bus tours, glass bottom boat, and general information prepared for TSS guides, 1976	Reeve	F/2.188

Title	Author	Code N°
Women's Corona Society Seychelles Branch Cookery Book, 1976		F/2.189
Victorian Lady Travellers. II. Marianne North 1830-1890 (pp. 54-71), 1965.	Middleton	F/2.190
Journals of the Royal Horticultural Society. Marianne North (pp. 231-240)	Lees - Milne	F/2.191
The Geographical Magazine. Flowers in a Landscape. (pp. 445-462) December 1962	Middleton	F/2.192
Creole Stories from various contributors (Nos.1 to 84). Vol. I.		F/2.193
Creole Stories. (Nos. 1 to 24). Vol. II.	Accouche	F/2.193
The Seychellois : In Search of An Identity - An Analytical Study. 1975	Chang - Him	F/2.194
Flight of the flame, Poems. 1977	Butler-Payette	F/2.195
Mariage et Sacrement de Mariage. 1970. (Mariage et Concubinage aux Seychelles, pp. 43-57 par Gabriel Hoarau)	de Locht	F/2.196
Sept Années aux Seychelles, 1891. (photocopy)	Guerard	F/2.197
Histoire et Description des Iles Seychelles, 1897	Anastas	F/2.198
Bulletins of the Indian Ocean Study Circle (Stamps and Postal History) A to		F/2.199
Catéchèse "Une Eglise où les laïcs tiennent leur place". Session Inter-Iles Juillet - Août - 75, Seychelles.		F/2.200
Lettre Pastorale de Mgr. Felix Paul Evêque de Port Victoria. "Que Ton Règne Vienne". Carême 1976.	Mgr. Paul	F/2.201

Title	Author	Code N°
Lettre Pastorale de Mgr. Felix Paul Evêque de Port Victoria. "Ensemble construisons une Eglise vivante". Carême 1977.	Mgr. Paul	F/2.202
Lettre Pastorale de Mgr. Felix Paul Evêque de Port Victoria. "Marchons vers l'avenir avec confiance". Carême 1978.	Mgr. Paul	F.2.203
Chronique Des Frères De l'Instruction Chrétienne. (Seychelles - Mascareignes. Notre Monde Insulaire, etc... pp. 156-160) 1976.		F/2.204
Chronique Des Frères De L'Instruction Chrétienne. (Seychelles - An I De L'Indépendance - Un peu D'Histoire, pp. 164-171) 1977.		F/2.205
The Indifferent Illusion. 19	Taylon	F/2.206
Frères en marche 2. 1977. (La solidarité un chemin éprouvant, "pp. 22-24")		F/2.207
Frères en marche 3. 1977. (Imprimeurs et missionnaires "Frères Louis Dayer" pp. 24-28)		F/2.208
Vigilat (Seychelles Perle de l'Océan Indien "pp. 2-11".		F/2.209
Vigilat (Seychelles Perle de l'Océan Indien "pp. 8-17").		F/2.210
La Femme Seychelloise et L'Héritage Culturel. Avril, 1976.	Abel	F/2.211
Narrative of voyages of HMS Leven & Barracouta to explore the Shores of Africa, Arabia and Madagascar. (Journal of the Geographical Society, London). 1833.	Wolf	F/2.212
Madagascar, Mauritius and the other East - African Islands (The Seychelles) 1901	Keller	F/2.213

Title	Author	Code N°
Extraits des annonces, affiches et avis divers pour les colonies des Isles de France et de Bourbon. Description des Isles Seychelles et Praslin. 1773.		F/2.214
SMS Konigsberg. A German commerce raider, harried by the Royal Navy, is tracked down to a muddy corner of an East-African backwater.	O'Neill	F/2.215
Histoire de l'Océan Indien. 1955.	Auber	F/2.216
Iles de l'Océan Indien. 1974.	Bianchi/ Schornbock	F/2.217
A Collection of Documents on the Slave trade of Eastern Africa. 1976.	Beachey	F/2.218
Pierre Sonnerat 1748-1814. An account of his Life and work. 1976	Ly-Tio-Fane	F/2.219
Coco Sec. 1977	Abel	F/2.220
Une tortue se rappelle. 1977	Abel	F/2.221
Contes et poèmes des Seychelles. 1977	Abel	F/2.222
Seychelles first invitation pro-am golf tournament. December, 1974		F/2.223
Geography of Seychelles. 1977	Fayon	F/2.224
Atlas for Seychelles. 1977	Fayon & ors	F/2.225
Education in Seychelles : The Government and the Missions 1839-1944. 1977	Stone	F/2.226
Admiral Sir Charles Adam. 1977	Mc. Ateer	F/2.227

Title	Author	Code N°
The Seychelles. An Outline Guide for Expatriate Contract Employeees. (The Royal Commonwealth Society). August 1977	Knights	F/2.228
Ocean Readers. Introductory Book		F/2.229
Ocean Readers. Book 1 "Playing"		F/2.230
Ocean Readers. Book 2 "The Children's Stories"		F/2.231
Ocean Readers. Book 3 "Bamboozle and other stories"		F/2.232
Ocean Readers. Book 3 "More Stories to read"		F/2.233
Ocean Readers. Book 5 "Stories from other countries"		F/2.234
Ocean Readers. Book 6 "Tatles of adventure, Old and New"		F/2.235
Seychelles. 1974. (From the fifteenth edition of Encyclopedia Britannica)	Gustave de Comarmond	F/2.236
Seminaire des Caritas et secours catholique des Iles de l'Océan Indien, 1974		F/2.237
Caritas/Secours Catholique Regional Seminar for the Islands of the Indian Ocean		F/2.238
Les Seychelles. Nouvelle escale Air France, au coeur de l'océan 1er avril, 1974, vol. I.		F/2.239
British airways. Seychelles. 3rd édition/75		F/2.240
Code of Professional Conduct for Members of the Seychelles Society of Auditors and Accountants. 1977		F/2.241

Title	Author	Code N°
Annuaire de l'Eglise Catholique. Tome I. Iles de l'Océan Indien, D.O.M. et T.O.M. (Missions catholiques) 1977. (Seychelles pp. 159-166)	Perraud	F/2.242
Guide des Sources de l'Histoire de l'Afrique. Guide To The Sources of the History of Africa.		
Quellen zur Geschichte Afrikas südlich der Sahara in den Archiven der Bundesrepublik Deutschland. 1970. Vol. I.		F/2.243
Espana Guina des Fuentes para la Historia de Africa Subsahariana. 1971. Vol. 2.		F/2.244
Sources de L'Histoire de l'Afrique au Sud du Sahara dans les Archives et Bibliothèques françaises I - Archives. 1971. Vol. 3.		F/2.245
Sources de l'Histoire de l'Afrique au Sud du Sahara dans les Archives et Bibliothèques françaises II - Bibliothèques. 1976. Vol. 4		F/2.246
Guida delle Fonti per la Storia dell'Africa a Sud del Sahara esistenti in Italia. I. 1973, Vol. 5		F/2.247
Guida delle Fonti per la Storia dell'Africa a Sud del Sahara esistenti in Italia. II. 1974. vol. 6		F/2.248
Scandinavia Sources in Denmark, Norway, and Sweden. 1971. Vol. 8		F/2.249
Volumes 3-4 Index. Sources de l'Histoire de L'Afrique au Sud du Sahara dans les Archives et Bibliothèques françaises I-Archives. II Bibliothèques, 1976		F/2.250
The Language Issue in Seychelles and its Effect Upon Education. December, 1977	Hayman	F/2.251

Title	Author	Code N°
Description of Fregate Island. Wild and Beautiful, 1972.		F.2.252
Seychellen. Tropische Inselwelt im Indischen Ozean, 1978	Guderjahn	F/2.253
Apprenons La Nouvelle Orthographe. Proposition d'une orthographe rationnelle pour le créole des Seychelles avec six contes créoles seychellois, 1978	Bollée/D'Offay	F/2.254
Séminaire Sous Regional Opérationnel d'Alphabétisation Fonctionnelle pour les pays francophone d'Afrique Centrale et de l'Océan Indien. Mahé 10-28 avril, 1978, 1978.		F/2.255
A la Réunion, A l'Ile Maurice, Aux Seychelles. Guides bleus, 1976	Desiles	F/2.256
Ocean Indien Actuel, n° 1 - Decembre 1977		F/2.257
Ocean Indien Actuel N° 6/7 - Mai/Juin 1978		F/2.258
Ocean Indien Actuel, n° 8 - Juillet 1978		F/2.259
Proverbes Des Seychelles, 1978		F/2.260
The Treasure Island Readers. Second Supplementary Book		F/2.261
Rapport de Mgr. Mouard sur la Mission des Seychelles, 1833	Mouard	F/2.262
Oari I monsunen. Resa till seychellerna, 1956. (with general informations on natural history)	Sorlin	F/2.263
Annuaire des Pays de l'Océan Indien. Vol. II. 1975	C.E.R.S.O.I.	F/2.264
Naufrage Aux Seychelles (Roman), 1978	De Villiers	F/2.265

Title	Author	Code N°
Revue Juridique et Politique Indépendance et Coopération. Histoire Constitutionnelle et Politique des Seychelles de 1744 à 1977. (pp. 725-758), 1978.	Mc. Gaw/Garcin	F/2.266

HISTOIRE

Title	Author	Code N°
Cahiers du Centre Universitaire de la Réunion. N°8, décembre, 1976. (L'Océan Indien Occidental avant l'arrivée des Portugais. pp. 5-21)	Le Blevec	F/2.267
Langue Française. 37. Février 1978. Les Parlers Créoles - Presentation	Chaudenson	F/2.268
The Constitution of the Seychelles People's Progressive Front. September, 1978.		F/2.269
Onward to Socialism. SPPF Policy Statement. September, 1978.		F/2.270
Madagascar et la Côte des Somalis - Sainte Marie et les Seychelles. Leur rôle et leur avenir. 1922. L'Archipel des Seychelles : Mahé.	Guilloteaux	F/2.271
Iles Africaines de la mer des Indes. 1848. Rodrigues, Galéga, Les Seychelles, Les Almirantes, etc...	Froberville	F/2.272
Les Voyages du Lieutenant Frappaz dans les mers des Indes, Tananarive, 1939	Frappaz	F/2.273
L'Archipel des Seychelles, 1968		F/2.274
Mauritius and Madagascar (including Seychelles) Journals of an eight years' residence in the Diocese of Mauritius, and of a visit to Madagascar. 1864. By Vincent W. Ryan, D.D. Bishop of Mauritius.	Ryan	F/2.275
The Royal Society Aldabra Newsletters 1969-1978		F./2.276

Title	Author	Code N°
Extr. de : "France - Eurafrique" n° 202, Janv. 1969. "Les Déportés "Terroristes" aux Seychelles et aux Comores (1801-1802)	Cornevin	F/2.277
La grande île Militaire revue des forces armées de M- et dépendances. N° 26, mai 1955. "Mission aux îles Glorieuses et dans les Seychelles Méridionales	Legeais	F/2.278
La Traite des esclaves vers les Mascareignes au XVIIIe siècle, 1974.	Filliot	F/2.279
Early Printing in the Mascarene Islands 1767-1810. 1951	Toussaint	F/2.280
Lettre.Pastorale de Mgr. Félix Paul Evêque de Port Victoria, L'année de L'enfant. Carême 1979.	Mgr. Paul	F/2.281
Annales Maritime et Coloniale. 1843. Rapport adressé à M. le Ministre de la Marine et des Colonies par M. Jehenne, capitaine de corvette, commandant la Prévoyante, au sujet des îles Seychelles, 1841.	Jehenne	F/2.282
Le Tour du Monde. 1894. Voyage aux îles Seychelles, Par M. Charles Alluaud, chargé de Mission Scientifiques.	Alluaud	F/2.283
UNOFFICIAL PUBLICATIONS, NATURAL HISTORY ON LOAN FROM CARNEGIE LIBRARY Histoire Physique Naturelle et Politique de Madagascar. Vol. V	Grandidier	F/3
Histoire Physique Naturelle et Politique de Madagascar. Vol. VI	Grandidier	F/3.1

Title	Author	Code N°
Faunes Ornithologique éteinte de Madagascar	Edwards	F/3.2
Discovery Reports	Wheeler	F/3.3
The Turtle Fisheries of the Seychelles Islands	Hornell	F/3.4
Withdrawn as included in F/4.6		
Discovery Reports. Southern Blue and Fin Whales	Mackintosh and Wheeler	F/3.7
Remains of some Gigantic Land-Tortoises	Gadon	F/3.8
Land Tortoises of Mauritius and Rodriguez		F/3.9
On the Vegetation of Seychelles	Sorlin	F/3.10
Land Birds of the Granitic Islands of Seychelles	Lousteau-Lalanne	F/3.11
Sea and Shore Birds of the Seychelles	Lousteau-Lalanne	F/3.12
List of the Flowering Plants and Ferns of Seychelles	Bailey	F/3.13
Hortus Mauritianus on enumeration des Plantes	Bojer	F/3.14
Fishes of Seychelles	Smith	F/3.15
Genres, Espèces et Races d'Indrisines de Madagascar		F/3.16
Report on Forests of Granitic Islands of Seychelles	Gibson	F/3.17

Title	Author	Code N°
L'Archipel des Seychelles - Ses ressources naturelles, sa faune entomologique et son évolution économique	Dupont	F/3.18
Journal of the Society for Bibliography of Natural History	Bibliography for Seychelles. by A.J. Peters - pp. 238 to 262.	F/3.19
Birds of the Seychelles and other Islands.	Vessey-Fitzerald	F/3.20
Various Botanical Pamphlets		F/3.21
File of Cuttings re : Natural History		F/3.22
inctinal Birds - By the Hon. Walter Rochschild, Ph. D.F.Z.S.	Rochschild	F/3.23

UNOFFICIAL PUBLICATIONS, NATURAL HISTORY, THE PROPERTY OF THE GOVERNMENT ARCHIVES.

Title	Author	Code N°
Bibliography of Scientific Published works bearing Principally on the Natural History of the Seychelles and neighbouring Archipelagos.	Peter and Lionnet	F/4
The Present Status of Certain Rare Land Birds of the Seychelles Islands and Birds of the Seychelles and other islands included within that Colony	V-Fitzerald & Rook	F/4.1
Notes on some of the Seychelles Islands, Indian Ocean	Piggott	F/4.2
Vanilla Cultura as practiced in the Seychelles. 1898.	Galbraith	F/4.3
Popular handbook of Indian Birds	Whistler	F/4.4
A first Guide to South African Birds	Gill	F/4.5

Title	Author	Code N°
Gardiner - Indian Ocean Expédition 1905. Vols. I to VIII	Gardiner	F/4.6
Ichthyological Bulletins by J. L.B. Smith, Janv. 1956 to Oct. 1962	Smith	F/4.7
The Fishes of Aldabra by J.L.B. Smith	Smith	F/4.8
Fishes of the family Carangidae in British East African waters, by F. Williams	Williams	F/4.9
The Genus Lethrinus in the Western Indian Ocean, by J.F.G. Wheeler, D. Sc. 1961	Wheeler	F/4.10
Ichthyology Bulletins of the Fishes of the Indian Ocean by Professor J.L.B. Smith	Smith	F/4.11
The Potential Fish Production of the Seychelles Area and Notes on the Fisheries there by J.F.G. Wheeler. 1946.	Wheeler	F/4.12
Geology and Mineral Resources of the Seychelles Archipelago - By B.H. Baker, B. Sc., F.G.S. Geologist, 1963	Baker	F/4.13
Marckerel-and Tuna-Lole fishes of the Indian Ocean (Scombridae) by B.B. Collette R.H. Gibbs, Jr. - 1963.	Collette	F/4.14
Sea Shells of the World	Abbott	F/4.15
Indo - Pacific Mollusca - Vol. I. - By R. Tucker Abbott	Abbott	F/4.16
Australian Shells - By Joyce Allan, F.R.Z.S.	Allan	F/4.17
Manuel de Conchyliologie by J. Chenu	Chenu	F/4.18
The Sea Shells of Dar-es-Salaam	Spry	F/4.19

Title	Author	Code N°
Lepidopteres des Iles Seychelles et d'Aldabra - by H. Legrand	Legrand	F/4.20
Journal of the Palm Society, Oct. 1965 - article on Coco-de-mer by G. Lionnet	Lionnet	F/4.21
Pamphlets in German on the Birds, Salamandras and Flora of Seychelles - 1966	Honegger	F/4.22
Striking Plants of the Seychelles 1967 - by G. Lionnet	Lionnet	F/4.23
Plants and Man on the Seychelles Coast 1967- by Jonathan D. Sauer	Sauer	F/4.24
Report on the Mauritius - Seychelles Fisheries Survey - 1945-1949	Ommanney	F/4.25
The Morphology of the Fringing Coral Reefs along the East Coast of Mahé Seychelles, 1968	Lewis	F/4.26
The Scallop - Studies of a shell and its influences on humankind		F/4.27
Revision de la famille des Ptilocodidae avec la description d'un nouveau genre et d'une nouvelle espèce	Bouillon	F/4.28
Odanata of the Seychelles and other Indian Ocean island groups based primarily on the Bristol University Expendition of 1964-1965	Blackmann/ Pinhey	F/4.29
Cone Shells of the World	J.A. Marsh & O.H. Rippingale	F/4.30
Soil Survey of Seychelles	C.J. Piggott	F/4.31
British Bee Journal. Janv. 1969 - Article on Bee Keeping in the Seychelles by R.E.M. Silberrad		F/4.32

Title	Author	Code N°
Une Mission Scientifique Belge à l'Archipel des Seychelles	J. Bouillon	F/4.33
Weight-Length relationships for certain Scombroid fishes from the Equatorial Western Indian Ocean	N.R. Merrett	F/4.34
The endemic birds of Seychelles	Gaymer, etc...	F/4.35
Beobachtungen an den Riesenschildkroten (Testudo Gigantea Schweigger) der Inseln im Indischen Ozean	Honegger	F/4.36
Notes on some Indo-Pacific Pontonienae XIII. Propontania Pellucida Gen. Nov., SP. Nov., A new Pontoniid Shrimp from the Amirante Islands	Bruce	F/4.37
The Red Book. Wildlife in danger	Fisher, Simon and Vincent	F/4.38
The Endemic Flora of the Seychelles Islands and its conservation	Swabey	F/4.39
Etude Monographique du Genre Hebiopora de Blanville	Bouillon et Houvenaghet Crevecoeur	F/4.40
Amphibians and Reptiles of the Seychelles	Gaymer	F/4.41
Atoll Research Bulletin. Ecology of Aldabra Atoll, Indian Ocean	Stoddart, etc...	F/4.42
Research Vessel Chain. International Indian Ocean Expedition. March - June 1964. Scientific Program		F/4.43
International Indian Ocean Expedition. R.R.S. "Discovery" Cruise 1. South East Arabian Upwelling Region. Cruise Report. December 1963		F/4.44

Title	Author	Code N°
International Indian Ocean Expedition. R.R.S. Discovery Cruise 2 Report. Geology ahd Geophysics in N.W. Indian Ocean. 1964		F/4.45
International Indian Ocean Expedition. R.R.S. Discovery. Cruise 3 Report. Oceanographic work in the Western Indian, Ocean, 1964		F/4.46
List of the flowering Plants and Ferns of Seychelles. First Edition. February, 1944	Bailey	F/4.47
Bulletin de la Société Entomologique de France :		
(a) Une nouvelle Pyrale des îles Seychelles, 1957	Le Grand	F/4.48
(b) Nouveaux Lepidopteres des îles Seychelles et Cosmoledo, 1958	Le Grand	F/4.48
(c) Note sur la sous-espèce nana ch. Oberthur de Papilio phorbanda Linne des îles Seychelles, 1959	Le Grand	F/4.48
(d) Les Pterophoridae des îles Seychelles, 1962	Bigot	
Records and Descriptions of Exotic Tortricoidea, 1961	Diakonoff	F/4.49
Nouveaux Geometridae d'Aldabra, 1962	Herbulot	F/4.50
The romance of a palm. Coco-de-mer, 1970	Lionnet	F/4.51
List of the Flowering Plants and Ferns of Seychelles, 1971	Bailey	F/4.52
I.C.B.P. Second Report to Subcribers, 1970		F/4.53
L'Origine et la Composition de la Faune Malacologique Terrestre et Fluviatile des Iles Seychelles	Germain	F/4.54

Title	Author	Code N°
Seychelles Botanical Treasure : "The Coco-de-Mer" Palm (Lodoicea maldivica, Pers), 1947	Durocher Yvon	F/4.55
Rendzina Soils of Coastal Flats of the Seychelles, 1952	Lionnet	F/4.56
Plants and Man on the Seychelles Coast : A Study in Historical Biogeography (Manuscript Copy) undated	Sauer	F/4.57
The Origin of Continents and Oceans. Fouth Edition, 1966	Wegener	F/4.58
The Cowries of Seychelles (A colour illustrated Handbook), 1970	Slimming, Jarrett	F/4.59
The Triumph of Jean Nicolas-Géré and His Isle Bourbon Collaborators, 1970	Ly-Tio-Fane	F/4.60
Preliminary Report on the Distribution and Epidemiology of Filariasis in the Seychelles Islands, Indian Ocean, 1971	Lambrecht	F/4.61
Philosophical Transactions of the Royal Society of London. A Discussion on the results of the Royal Society Expedition to Aldabra 1967-1968	Westoll & Stoddart	F/4.62
International Indian Ocean Expedition. Collected reprints (1965-1971) Vols I to VII		F/4.63 to F/4.69
Mosquitoes of the Chagos Archipelago, Indian Ocean, 1971	Lambrecht & Van Someren	F/4.70
The cone shells of Seychelles, 1970	Jarret & Slimming	F/4.71
Rare Shells, 1969	Dance	F/4.72
The Romance of a Palm Coco-de-Mer, 2nd Edition, 1972	Lionnet	F/4.73

Title	Author	Code N°
La vie et la mort des Coraux, 1971	Diole & Cousteau	F/4.74
Bibliography of published work bearing on the Natural History of the Seychelles and neighbouring archipelagoes. The Journal of the Society for the Bibliography of Natural History	Peters	F/4.75
Life on Coral Reefs in the Seychelles, 1972	Vine	F/4.76
Régional Variation in Indian Ocean Coral Reefs	Stoddart & Yonge	F/4.77
I.C.B.P. Third Report on Cousin Island Nature Reserve and other islands, 1971		F/4.78
Etudes de geographie tropicale offertes à Pierre Gourou, 1972	Parsons	F/4.79
The Romance of a Palm "Coco-de-Mer" 3rd Edition, 1973	Lionnet	F/4.80
Biological Conservation Vol. V, n° 2, 1973	Proeter	F/4.81
Info-Nature, Ile de la Réunion, numéro spécial : La Forêt, 1973	Lionnet	F/4.82
International Indian Ocean Expedition. Collected reprints VIII, 1972		F/4.83
International Indian Ocean Expedition. Collected reprints, (Index), 1972		F/4.84
I.C.B.P., Fourth Report on Cousin Island Nature Reserve and other islands, 1972		F/4.85
Pest and Disease Problems in the Seychelles, 1971	Mathias	F/4.86

Title	Author	Code N°
The biology of Leptoconops (Styloconops) Spinosifrons (Carter) (Diptera, Ceratopogonidae) in the Seychelles Islands, with descriptions of the immature stages, 1972	Laurence & Mathias	F/4.87
The coconut Trunk Borer (Melittomma Insulare Fairm. Coleoptera : Lymexylidae) of Seychelles and its associated Microflora, 1972	Mathias	F/4.88
Wildlife Today. The World Conservation Handbook, 1973	Stiwell	F/4.89
Life at the Sea's Frontiers, 1974	Perry	F/4.90
The Endemic Flowering Plants of the Seychelles : an annotated list, 1974	Procter	F/4.91
Annotated bibliography of scientific and technical information compiled from the work and records of the Department of Agriculture, Victoria, Mahé, Seychelles to August, 1972, 1974.	Skidmore	F/4.92
The Birds of Seychelles and the Outlying Islands, 1974	Penny	F/4.93
L'Arche de Noé, 1974	Zuber	F/4.94
The Green turtle and man, 1962	Parsons	F/4.95
The Encyclopédia of Shells. A guide to the World's Shells, 1974	Dance	F/4.96
Muschelm + Schnecken der Weltmeere, 1975	Lindner	F/4.97
A Field Guide to the Coral Reef Fishes of the Indian and West Pacific Oceans, 1977	Carcasson	F/4.98
The Encyclopedia of Aquarium Fish, 1977	Coffey	F/4.99

Title	Author	Code N°
Birds of the Mascarenes and Saint-Brandon, 1976	Staub	F/4.100
Striking Plants of Seychelles, 1976	Lionnet	F/4.101
The Natural History of Seychelles, 1976	High	F/4.102
Cousin Islands Nature Reserve Seychelles. Management Plan 1975 - 9. ICBP, 1976	Diamond	F/4.103
Principes. Journal of the Palm Society. January, 1976. Vol. 20, n° 1 (Inquest of the big seed) (with observations along the way)		F/4.104
Seychelles 1973. Extra Mural Study Tour Report	Gilham/White	F/4.105
The Status Distribution and Diet of the Seychelles Kestrel Falco Araea. (This- Volume XVI, 1974)	Feare etc...	F/4.106
The Utilization of Mangroves by Seychelles Birds. (Ibis - Volume XVI, 1974)	Feare	F/4.107
Marine Demospongiae of Mahe Island in the Seychelles Bank (Indian Ocean, 1973)	Thomas	F/4.108
Hydroids from the Seychelles (Coelenterata), 1973	Millard/Bouillon	F/4.109
Unexpected Visitors to the Seychelles. (Biological Conservation. Volume 6. n° 3, July, 1974)	Feare	F/4.110
Sea Turtles in Seychelles	Frazier	F/4.111
Observation on the Seychelles White-Eye Zosterops Modesta. (The Aux Vol. 92, n° 3, July 25, 1975)	Feare	F/4.112

Title	Author	Code N°
Soldado Virus (Hughes Group) from Ornithodoros (Alectorobius) Capensis (Ixodoidea : Argasidae) Infesting Sooty Tern Colonie in the Seychelles, Indian Ocean. (The American Journal of Tropical Medecine and Hygiene, Vol. 24, n° 6, 1975)	Commerse etc...	F/4.113
Amblyomma Loculosum (Ixodoidea : Ixodidae) : Identity, Marine and Human Hosts, Virus Infection, and Distribution in the Southern Oceans (Annuals of the Entomological Society of America, vol. 69, n° 1, January, 1976)	Hoogstraal, etc...	F/4.114
The Seychelles Islands. An account of the current situation in the field of animal health and production in a small idyllic corner of the world, before the new international airport introduces the tourist and the developers. (Trop. Anim, HLTH, Prod. (1975) 7, 115 - 120)	Frost	F/4.115
The White-throated Rail Dryolimnas cuvieri on Aldabra. 1971. (Phil. Trans. Roy. Soc. Lond. B. 260, 529-548)	Penny/Diamond	F/4.116
The Percy Sladen Trust. Expedition to the Indian Ocean in 1905. Vol. III. (Transations of the Linneau Society), 1909	Gardiner	F/4.117
Beitrage zur Kenntnis der Vegetation und Flora der Seychellen, 1905	Diels	F/4.118
Bulletin d'Information du C.D.D.P. Voyages d'études aux Iles Seychelles, mai 1976	Nougier	F/4.119
Coquillages Exotiques (Espèces Marines), 1970	Arrecgros	F/4.120
The ecology of the sea birds of Aldabra, 1971. (Trans. Roy. Soc. Lond. B.260)	Diamond	F/4.121
Fourth Pan - African Ornithological Congress, 1976		F/4.122
Failure of slope below road on Southern side of St. Louis Flats Victoria and Comments on the		

Title	Author	Code N°
topography, soils and building practices on the island of Mahé, with particular reference to the city of Victoria, 1975	Jennings	F/4.123
Breeding biology and conservation of hawksbill turtles, Eretmochelys Imbricata L., on Cousin Island, Seychelles, 1976	Diamond	F/4.124
Aride Virus, a new ungrouped arbovirus infecting Amblyomma Loculosum ticks from Roseate terns in the Seychelles, 1976	Converse, etc...	F/4.125
The breeding of the Sooty tern Sterna Fuscata in the Seychelles and the effects of experimental removal of its eggs, 1976	Feare	F/4.126
The Herptile. July, 1974. (The Journal of the Reptile and Amphibian Enthusiast)	Delingpole	F/4.127
Desertion and abnormal development in a colony of Sooty terns sterna fuscata infested by virus-infested ticks, 1976	Feare	F/4.128
Post - fledging parental care in crested and Sooty terns, 1975.	Feare	F/4.129
The Pennisula field naturalist. June, 1974.	Wood	F/4.130
Note sur les voyages de Jean-Jacques Dussmier (1792-1883) (Annales de la Société des Sciences Naturelles de la Charente-Maritime. Octobre 1973)	Layssus	F/4.131
Back from the Brink. Success in Wildlife conservation, 1978	Mountfort	F/4.132
An aspect of Medical Entomology and Chemical Control of Leptoconops Spinosifrons in the Seychelles, 1972 & 1978.	Reynolds	F/4.133

Title	Author	Code N°
ANIMALS :		
Vanishing Birds of the Seychelles. Unique inhabitants of a remote island group, 1965.	Newman	F/4.134
Bristol University Seychelles Expedition. Part. I : The islands' endangered species, 1965.	Gaymer	F/4.135
Bristol University Seychelles Expedition. Part. II : Studying the rare birds of Cousin, 1965	Penny	F/4.136
University of Bristol Seychelles Expedition. Part. IV : The Seychelles black paradise flycatcher, 1965	Penny	F/4.137
Bristol University Seychelles Expedition. Part. V : The birds of Aldabra, 1965	Penny	F/4.138
Bristol University Seychelles Expedition. Part. VI : Frigate, home of the magpie robin, 1965.	Dawson	F/4.139
Bristol University Seychelles Expedition. Part. VII : Biological Control. 1965	Blackman	F/4.140
Wildlife Treasures of the Indian Ocean, 1971	Mountfort	F/4.141
Seychelles Amphibians and Reptiles, 1977	Procter	F/4.142
Final Report. Part. 1. Pest status of the crazy ant, Anoplolepis longipes (Jerd)., in the Seychelles, 1978.	Haines	F/4.143
Final Report. Part 2. Colony Structure, Seasonality and food requirements of the crazy ant, Anoplolepis longipes (Jerd). in the Seychelles, 1978.	Haines	F/4.144

Title	Author	Code N°
Final Report. Part. 3. Toxic bait for the control of Anoplolepis longipes (Jerd.), in the Seychelles. I. The basic attractant carrier, its production and weathering properties, 1978.	Haines	F/4.145
Final Report. Part. 4. Toxic bait for the control of Anoplolepis longipes (Jerd.), in the Seychelles II. Effectiveness, specificity and cost of baiting in field applications, 1978.	Haines	F/4.146
Final Report. Part. 5. Toxic bait for the control of Anoplolepis longipes (Jerd.), in the Seychelles. III. Selection of toxicants, 1978.	Haines	F/4.147
Final Report. Part. 6. Residual sprays for the control of Anoplolepis longipes (Jerd.), (Hymenoptera, Formicidae) in the Seychelles, 1978.	Haines	F/4.148
Les oiseaux observés aux Seychelles en 1768 au cours de l'expédition Marion - Dufresne, 1978.	Lionnet	F/4.149
The Romance of a Palm. Coco-De-Mer. Fourth Edition, 1978.	Lionnet	F/4.150
Maladies transmissibles aux îles Seychelles. Epidemiologie - Prophylaxie. Thèse présentée à Lyon pour obtenir le grade de Docteur en Médecine par Martine Garcin - Cibert, mai 1978.	Garcin/Cibert	F/4.151
Un Atoll a Morphologie Enigmatique Farquhar (Seychelles), 1977.	Battistini	F/4.152
The Decline of boody (Sulidae) Populations in the Western Indian Ocean, 1978.	Feare	F/4.153
A guide to Common Reef Fishes of the Western Indian Ocean, 1978.	Bock	F/4.154
Botanic Man, a journey through evolution with David Bellamy, 1978.	Bellamy	F/4.155

Title	Author	Code N°
Geology, Geomorphology and Coastal Dynamics of Mahé, Cerf, Long and Bird Islands, Seychelles, 1978	Nikiforov etc...	F/4.156
Endagered Land Birds, Seychelles. The Seychelles Magpie Robin (Copsychus Sechellarum) 1978.	Watson	F/4.157
Notes on the biology of the Seychelles Bulbul, 1978.	Greig-Smith	F/4.158
Preliminary report on the study of Bird Communities on Silhouette Island. Seychelles, 1979.	Greig-Smith	F/4.159

JOURNAUX ET PERIODIQUES IMPRIMES AUX SEYCHELLES

- CLASS G -

NEWSPAPERS AND JOURNALS PRINTED IN SEYCHELLES

- CLASS G -

The first l'Impartial, which lasted one year, was lithographed, and
one copy, the third issued, still exists. Of the other papers no early
complete copies have been traced till Le Seychellois 1951. The files
of the Clarion were stolen, cut up in squares and sold to shopkeepers
for wrapping customers' purchase. How much more of the social life
of our people could we have gleaned had copies of all these newspapers
been preserved.

Subject Matter	Code Nº
NEWSPAPERS AND JOURNALS PRINTED IN SEYCHELLES	
ACTION,(L') CATHOLIQUE	G/13
BLOW-LAMP (in creole)	G/12
BLUE MOON, THE	G/8
CHALLENGE, THE	G/14
ECHO,(L') DES ILES	G/6
IMPARTIAL (L')	
MONT FLEURI JUNIOR SECONDARY SCHOOL ANNUAL	G/18
NOUVEAU SEYCHELLOIS, LE	G/20
PEOPLE, THE	G/11
REGINA MUNDI CONVENT SCHOOL ANNUAL	G/7
REVEIL, LE	G/2
REVEIL SEYCHELLOIS, LE	G/3
ROTATOR, THE	G/19
SEYCHELLES CATHEDRAL MAGAZINE	G/21
SEYCHELLES CHAMBER OF COMMERCE AND INDUSTRY	G/15
SEYCHELLES CHILDREN'S SOCIETY	G/22
SEYCHELLES CLARION	G/4

Subject Matter	Code N°
SEYCO (SEYCHELLES COLLEGE MAGAZINE)	G/16
SEYCHELLES FOOTBALL ASSOCIATION	G/23
SEYCHELLES WEEKLY	G/10
SEYCHELLOIS, LE	G/5
S.U. CALLING	G/9
VIE-ACTION DES JEUNES TRAVAILLEURS - J.O.C. (in creole)	G/24
YOUNG SCIENTIST, THE	G/17
SEYCHELLES CHILDREN'S SOCIETY NEWSLETTER	G/25
NETBALL NEWS	G/26
SEYCHELLES CULTURE (BULLETIN CULTUREL DES SEYCHELLES)	G/27
L'ACTION DU COMMUNAUTE	G/28
SEYCHELLES BLACK TORTOISES EPOCH	G/29
PARISH MAGAZINE	G/30
SEYCHELLES LIFE	G/31
CABLE AND WIRELESS LIMITED, SEYCHELLES TELEPHONE DIRECTORY	G/32
RANGERS FOOTBALL CLUB	G/33
WEEKEND LIFE	G/34
SEYCHELLES BREWERIES	G/35

Subject Matter	Code N°
LOLLIPOP (IN CREOLE)	G/36
POPCORN (IN CREOLE)	G/37
LOLLIPOPCORN (IN CREOLE)	G/38
L'ECHO DES PALMES	G/39
D.E.A.S. NEWS AND REVIEWS	G/40
ROUND TABLE - PROGRAMME	G/41
DIOCESAN MAGAZINE	G/42
SPORTS MAGAZINE OF THE HAPPY YOUTH CLUB	G/43
THE ISLANDER	G/44
WOMEN'S CORONA SOCIETY - SEYCHELLES BRANCH NEWSLETTER	G/45
THE GOLDEN EAGLE MAGAZINE	G/46
LE PROGRES	G/47

L'IMPARTIAL

Single copy (with cyclostyle enlargement), n° 35 dated 26th May, 1877.	G/1

LE REVEIL

Issues for period 28th April 1899 to 27th April, 1900 and single copy dated 17/8/1912.	G/2

LE REVEIL SEYCHELLOIS

Issues for the years 1924 to 1932	G/3

Subject Matter	Code N°
Issues for the years 1924 to 1921	G/3.1
Issues 22 juin 1935 and 5.12 août 1939	G/3.2
SEYCHELLES CLARION	
Bound volume for 1936	G/4
Bound volume for 1937	G/4.1
Bound volume for 1935, 1937, 1938, 1942, 1947 & 1948	G/4.2
Bound volume for 1935	G/4.3
LE SEYCHELLOIS	
Bound volume for 1958	G/5
- do - 1959	G/5.1
- do - 1960	G/5.2
- do - 1961	G/5.3
- do - 1962	G/5.4
- do - 1963 Vol. I	G/5.5
- do - 1963 Vol. II	G/5.6
- do - 1964 Vol. I	G/5.7
- do - 1964 Vol. II	G/5.8
- do - 1965 Vol. I	G/5.9
- do - 1965 Vol. II	G/5.10
- do - 1966 Vol. I	G/5.11
- do - 1966 Vol. II	G/5.12
- do - 1967 Vol. I	G/5.13
- do - 1967 Vol. II	G/5.14
- do - 1968 Vol. I	G/5.15
- do - 1968 Vol. II	G/5.16

Subject Matter	Code N°
Bound volume for 1969 Vol. I	G/5.17
- do - 1969 Vol. II	G/5.18
- do - 1970 Vol. I	G/5.19
- do - 1970 Vol. II	G/5.20
- do - 1950	G/5.21
- do - 1951	G/5.22
- do - 1952	G/5.23
- do - 1953	G/5.24
- do - 1954	G/5.25
- do - 1955	G/5.26
- do - 1956	G/5.27
- do - 1957	G/5.28
- do - 1971 Vol. I	G/5.29
- do - 1971 Vol. II	G/5.30
LE SEYCHELLOIS	
Bound volume for 1972 Vol. I	G/5.31
- do - 1972 Vol. II	G/5.32
- do - 1973 Vol. I	G/5.33
- do - 1973 Vol. II	G/5.34
- do - 1974 Vol. I	G/5.35
- do - 1974 Vol. II	G/5.36
- do - 1975 Vol. I	G/5.37
- do - 1975 Vol. II	G/5.38
- do - 1976 Vol. I	G/5.39
- do - 1976 Vol. II	G/5.40

Subject Matter	Code N°
Bound Volume for 1977 Vol. I	G/5.41
- do - 1977 Vol. II	G/5.42
- do - 1978	G/5.43
L'ECHO DES ILES	
Bound volume for 1960	G/6
- do - 1961	G/6.1
- do - 1962	G/6.2
- do - 1963	G/6.3
- do - 1964	G/6.4
- do - 1965	G/6.5
- do - 1966	G/6.6
- do - 1967	G/6.7
- do - 1968	G/6.8
- do - 1969	G/6.9
- do - 1970	G/6.10
- do - 1971	G/6.11
- do - 1972	G/6.12
- do - 1973	G/6.13
- do - 1974	G/6.14
- do - 1975	G/6.15
- do - 1976	G/6.16
- do - 1977	G/6.17
- do - 1978	G/6.18
REGINA MUNDI CONVENT SCHOOL ANNUAL	
Copy n° 1, 1957	G/7

Subject Matter	Code N°
Copy n° 2, 1958	G/7.1
- do - 3, 1959	G/7.2
- do - 4, (1861-1961 Centenary Record)	G/7.3
- do - 5, 1962	G/7.4
- do - 6, 1963	G/7.5
- do - 7, 1964	G/7.6
- do - 8, 1965	G/7.7
- do - 9, 1966	G/7.8
- do - 10, 1967	G/7.9
- do - 11, 1968	G/7.10
- do - 12, 1969/1970	G/7.11
- do - 13, 1972	G/7.12
- do - 14, 1972	G/7.13
- do - 15, 1973	G/7.14
- do - 16, 1975	G/7.15
- do - 17, 1976	G/7.16

THE BLUE MOON

Single issue of a Journal the Editor of which was Mr. F. Parsons. 1938	G/8

S.S.U. CALLING

Single copy - 1962	G/9

SEYCHELLES WEEKLY

Bound volume for 1963	G/10
- do - 1964	G/10.1
- do - 1965	G/10.2

Subject Matter	Code N°
Bound volume for 1966	G/10.3
- do - 1967	G/10.4
- do - 1968	G/10.5
- do - 1969	G/10.6
- do - 1970	G/10.7
- do - 1971	G/10.8
- do - 1972	G/10.9
- do - 1973	G/10.10
- do - 1974	G/10.11
- do - 1975	G/10.12
- do - 1976	G/10.13
- do - 1977	G/10.14
THE PEOPLE	
Bound volume for 1964	G/11
- do - 1965	G/11.1
- do - 1966	G/11.2
- do - 1967	G/11.3
- do - 1968	G/11.4
- do - 1969	G/11.5
- do - 1970	G/11.6
- do - 1971	G/11.7
- do - 1972	G/11.8
- do - 1973	G/11.9
New Horizons, S.P.U.P.. Policy Statement, 1972	G/11.10
S.P.U.P. Indian Ocean a Peace Zone, 1974	G/11.11
S.P.U.P. Historic March to Freedom, 1974	G/11.12

Subject Matter	Code N°
S.P.U.P. Majority Wish, Statement issued by the Seychelles People's United Party on 21st January 1974	G/11.13
S.P.U.P. Seychelles General Elections, 1974, Unfair, Unfree, Undemocratic	G/11.14
Bound volume for 1974	G/11.15
Bound volume for 1975	G/11.16
Bound volume for 1976	G/11.17
S.P.U.P. Liberty, Equality, Fraternity. Constitution, 1976.	G/11.18
S.P.U.P. Liberty, Equality, Fraternity, Philosophy of a Struggle. Quotation from Speeches and Statements made by President F.A. René and his Biography. 1977.	G/11.19
Bound volume for 1977	G/11.20
Bound volume for 1978	G/11.21
BLOW-LAMP (in Creole)	
Bound volume for Sept. to Ded, 1964.	G/12
L'ACTION CATHOLIQUE	
Bound volume for the years 1935 - 1937	G/13
THE CHALLENGE	
The Monthly Magazine of the Archdeaconry of Seychelles. Bound volume for the years 1953 and 1954	G/14
SEYCHELLES CHAMBER OF COMMERCE AND INDUSTRY	
N° 1. Vol. I (News Bulletin)	G/15
May, 1970	G/15.1

Subject Matter	Code N°
SEY CO	
Seychelles College Magazine	
Copy n° 1	G/16
Copy n° 2	G/16.1
Bound volume for 1973	G/16.2
Bound volume for 1974 (First Term)	G/16.3
Bound volume for 1976 (1, 2, & 3, Terms)	G/16.4
Annual, 1978	G/16.5
Bound volume for 1977	G/16.6
Bound volume for 1978 (1, 2 & 3 Terms)	G/16.7
THE YOUNG SCIENTIST	
The Magazine of the Young Scientists' Society of Seychelles College.	
Copy n° 1 (March 1968/June 1969) 1969	G/17
Copy n° 2 (Jan/March 1970) 1970	G/17.1
Copy n° 3 (April/October 1970) 1971	G/17.2
Copy n° 4 (December 1970/June 1971) 1971	G/17.3
Copy n° 5 (July/December 1971), 1972	G/17.4
Copy n° 6 (December 1971/May 1972), 1973	G/17.5
MONT FLEURI JUNIOR SECONDARY SCHOOL ANNUAL	
Copy for 1969	G/18
Copy for 1970	G/18.1
Copy for 1971	G/18.2
Copy for 1972	G/18.3

Subject Matter	Code N°
THE ROTATOR	
Copy vol. I. - n° 1, 1969	G/19
Copy vol. II.- n° 2, 1970	G/19.1
SEYCHELLES ROTARY CLUB BULLETIN	
Bound volume for 1973	G/19.2
Bound volume for 1974	G/19.3
LE NOUVEAU SEYCHELLOIS	
Bound volume 1970 (July/Dec.)	G/20
- do - 1971	G/20.1
- do - 1972	G/20.2
- do - 1973	G/20.3
- do - 1974	G/20.4
- do - 1975	G/20.5
- do - 1976	G/20.6
SEYCHELLES CATHEDRAL MAGAZINE	
Single Copy for Nov. 1934	G/21
THE ANGLICAN NEWSLETTER	
Single Copy for March, 1968	G/21.1
SEYCHELLES CHILDREN'S SOCIETY	
Annual Report and Accounts 1970	G/22
- do - 1971	G/22.1
- do - 1972	G/22.2

Subject Matter	Code N°
Annual Report and Accounts 1973	G/22.3
- do - 1974	G/22.4
- do - 1975 (not published)	
- do - 1976	G/22.5
- do - 1977	G/22.6
- do - 1978	G/22.7
SEYCHELLES FOOTBALL ASSOCIATION	
"Landmark of Seychelles Football 1970	G/23
Annual 1971	G/23.1
VIE-ACTION DES JEUNES TRAVAILLEURS J.O.C. -(In Creole)	
Bound volume for 1971	G/24
- do - 1972	G/24.1
- do - 1973	G/24.2
- do - 1973-1974	G/24.3
- do - 1975	G/24.4
- do - 1976	G/24.5
- do - 1977	G/24.6
- do - 1978	G/24.7
SEYCHELLES CHILDREN'S SOCIETY NEWSLETTER	
Bound volume for 1972	G/25
- do - 1973	G/25.1
- do - 1974	G/25.2
- do - 1975	G/25.3

Subject Matter	Code N°
NETBALL NEWS	
Bound volume for 1972	G/26
- do - 1973	G/26.1
- do - 1974	G/26.2
Seychelles Netball Association Handbook, 1975	G/26.3
Bound volume for 1975	G/26.4
SEYCHELLES - CULTURE Bulletin Culturel des Seychelles.	
Bound volume for 1972	G/27
- do - 1973	G/27.1
- do - 1974	G/27.2
- do - 1975	G/27.3
L'ACTION DU COMMUNAUTE	
Bound volume for 1971/1972	G/28
- do - 1973	G/28.1
SEYCHELLES BLACK TORTOISES EPOCH	
Bound volume (for January, February and March), 1972.	G/29
PARISH MAGAZINE	
Bound volume for 1975	G/30
- do - 1976	G/30.1
- do - 1977	G/30.2

Subject Matter	Code N°
SEYCHELLES LIFE	
November 1976 to April 1977	G/31
CABLE AND WIRELESS LIMITED	
SEYCHELLES TELEPHONE DIRECTORY.	
For the year 1961	G/32
- do - 1965	G/32.1
- do - 1967	G/32.2
- do - 1968	G/32.3
- do - 1969	G/32.4
- do - 1970	G/32.5
- do - 1971	G/32.6
- do - 1972	G/32.7
- do - 1973/1974	G/32.8
- do - 1974	G/32.9
- do - 1975	G/32.10
- do - 1977	G/32.11
- do - 1978	G/32.12
RANGERS FOOTBALL CLUB	
G.I.C. Cup Final Ranger v/s Rovers, 1977	G/33
Fashien Competition (RFC) 1977	G/33.1
WEEKEND LIFE	
Bound volume for 1977	G/34
- do - 1978	G/34.1

Subject Matter	Code N°
SEYCHELLES BREWERIES	
Memorandum and Articles of Association 1972	G/35
Annual Report and Accounts 1973	G/35.1
- do - 1974	G/35.2
- do - 1975	G/35.3
- do - 1976	G/35.4
- do - 1977	G/35.5
LOLLILOP (In Creole)	
Bound volume for 1976 & 1977	G/36
Bound volume for 1978	G/36.1
POPCORN (In Creole)	
Bound volume for 1976 & 1977	G/37
Bound volume for 1978	G/37.1
LOLLIPOPCORN (In Creole)	
Single copy (n° 13 of Nov. 1977)	G/38
L'ECHO DES PALMES	
Single Copy for 1975	G/39
D.E.A.S. NEWS AND REVIEWS	
Single Copy for 1975	G/40
- do - 1974	G/40.1
- do - 1975 & 1978	G/40.2

Subject Matter	Code N°
ROUND TABLE - PROGRAMME	
Regatta, 1977	G/41
Regatta, 1978	G/41.1
DIOCESAN MAGAZINE	
June - September 1978	G/42
Advent & Christmas 1978	G/42.1
Whitsunday 14 June 1978	G/42.2
SPORTS MAGAZINE OF THE HAPPY YOUTH CLUB	
n° 1. December, 1974	G/43
THE ISLANDER	
Bound volume for the years 1975 - 1977	G/44
WOMEN'S CORONA SOCIETY - SEYCHELLES BRANCH NEWSLETTER	
Bound volume for 1974	G/45
THE GOLDEN EAGLE MAGAZINE	
Bound volume for 1974	G/46
LE PROGRES	
Single copy for 1948	G/47

CARTES   ET   PLANS

- CLASS   H -

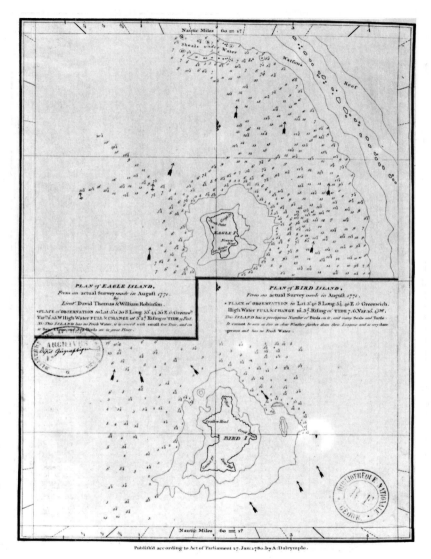

Carte générale archipel – Carte anglaise par Dalrymple 1780 (Cli. B.N. C. 96511).

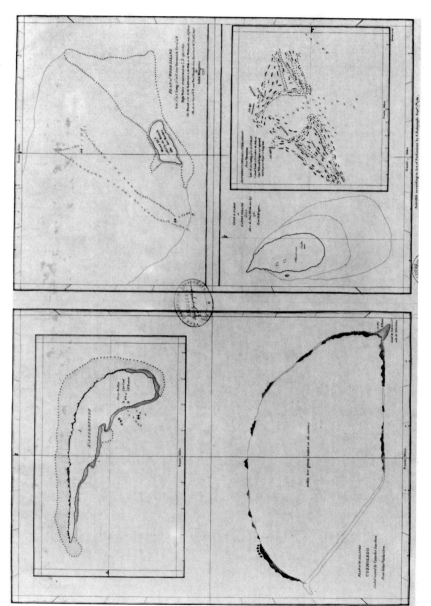

Iles Seychelles par Dalrymple 1782 (Cli. B.N. 96512)

ANCIENT MAPS OF SEYCHELLES ARCHIPELAGO COLLECTED

BY A.A. FAUVEL

CLASS H.

Head	Code N°

ANCIENT MAPS OF SEYCHELLES ARCHIPELAGO COLLECTED

BY A.A. FAUVEL   H/1

MAPS OF MAHE PRIOR TO 1963.

(1) Plan undaded "des Isles Mahe" and said to be based on observations made by L'Abbe Rochon and by Lazare Picault.

(2) Areas surveyed by M. Bataille up to 1787.

(3) Plan Terrier de L'Ile Mahe with details of earliest habitations granted. Prepared by C.J. Hort 1829.

(4) Sketch map of Mahe published by War Office in 1899.

(5) Map of Mahe published by Govt. Seychelles, made in accordance with Ordinance n° 7 of 1898 and based on surveys of H.M.S. Stork in 1890 and plans by S.B. Hobbs.

(6) Sketch map of Mahe published by War Office in 1951.

(7) Mahe, showing districts of electoral areas 1960.

(8) Early plan of Barbaron Estate.

II - TOWNSHIP OF VICTORIA

(1) Plan of L'Etablissement du Roi by Lt. Romanville 1778.

(2) Plan of area under Victoria Town Board (undaded).

(3)   - do -   1951

MISCELLANEOUS ISLANDS

(1) Indian Ocean Islands off north coast of Madagascar. Published by Admiralty in 1897 - Aldabra, Cosmoledo and

Head	Code N°

Farquhar Groups.

(2) Indian Ocean Islands and Reefs between Seychelles and Madagascar. Published by Admiralty in 1883.

(3) Curieuse - enlarged map from plan drawn by Lt. Nash in 1825.

(4) Chart of Islands north east of Madagascar and prepared under orders of Lord Farquhar by Lislet Geoffroy in April 1825.

(5) Cousin and Cousine. Colonial plan of 1904.

(6) Plan of Silhouette - 1939

ADMIRALTY CHARTS   H/4

(1) African East Coast (including Off-lying islands. Compiled from British and Foreign Government Surveys to 1881.

(2) Mahe Island and approaches. H.M. Surveying Ship Stork 1890.

(3) Approaches to Port Victoria. H.M. Surveying Ship Stork 1890.

(4) Seychelles Group with Amirantes and others Outlying Islands. By Capt. Owen 1825.

MAPS CONSTRUCTED. DRAWN AND PHOTOGRAPHED BY DIRECTORATE OF   H/5
OVERSEAS SURVEYS 1963.

Mahe.   Sheets n° 1 to 11

La Digue

Praslin   Sheets n° 1 to 4

ARCHIVES   SOURCES
_____

- CLASS I -

TAPE RECORDINGS AND RECORDS

- CLASS I -

The inclusion of a small collection of sound recordings, both discs
and tapes, is an innovation. Recordings are at times available from
the Information Office and Radio Seychelles of speeches made at
"openings" of one thing or another or of programmes devised by
Seychelles Radio to commemorate a particular occasion.

Cine films should certainly be included when available, since as they
lose topical interest they gain in historical interest.

Head	Code N°
TAPE RECORDINGS AND RECORDS	
Dramatic History of Seychelles. Parts 1.2.3.4 and 5	I/1
Recorded Voices of the late Sir John Thorp and Mr. Maurice Boulle. 4th July, 1961.	I/1.1
Recording of Creole Songs. (Sung by H. Pothin). Theresa. Li Popol. La Ville Quatre Borne. Sega Creole.	I/1.2
Address from the chair delivered in Legislative Council by His Excellency the Governor the Right Honourable the Earl of Oxford and Asquith - Presentation of Budget - 31st May, 1963	I/1.3
Seychelles News. 1st. Copy. Market Street. Sir John Thorp's visit to Praslin and La Digue. Commonwealth Day Celebration of 1960	I/1.4
"The Seychelles" A programme in the series "Others Like us" for B.B.C. West Indies Transmission. Produced by Mervyn Hamilton	I/1.5
Disc of National Anthem of the Federation of Malaya set to the Music of the Seychellois song "Rosalie"	I/1.6
Disc of 4 Creole Songs (Sung by Mickey and the Buccaneers)	I/1.7
Recording of a Creole programme from Praslin	I/1.8
Jacob Marie plays the Bombe	I/1.9
Seychelles, Victoria Duke's visits to Seychelles	I/1.10

TIMBRES ET MONNAIES

- CLASS J -

STAMPS. COINS AND TREASURY NOTES

It was disappointing indeed to find that no copies of the Colony's stamps had
ever been kept for record in the Post Office. The practice was to send two
copies of all new issues to the Governor of the time, and these, quite naturally
perhaps, were considered as for his personal record. As a result the collection
in the Archives commences with the reign of Queen Elizabeth II. Inquires were
made with stamp dealers in England, and the cost of buying a reasonably complete
collection of the Colony's stamps would be in the neighbourhood of £ 2000.
A few Seychellois are know to have fine collections, and the only hope, it seems,
of ever acquiring a collection for the Archives is if some public-spirited
Seychellois bequeathes his collection to the state.

The position as regards the Colony's issues of Coins and Treasury Notes is the
same, but arrangements have now been made for copies of all further issues of
stamps, coins and notes to be supplied to the Archives. It has been possible,
however, to purchase a complete set of Seychelles Coins from 1939, the year of
their introduction to replace Mauritian currency.

Head	Code N°
Seychelles Postage and Revenue Stamps from 1954. Vols. I and II	J/1 & J/1 (a)
Collection of Seychelles Coins, Mint or near mint from 1939 to 31.12.1963.	J/2
Locally printed Treasury Note of 1919	J/3
Specimens of Treasury Notes	J/4
Registered letter stamped envelopes	J/5
Emergency Treasury Notes printed in August 1914. (photocopies)	J/6
Specimens of New Seychelles Currency Notes of 1968	J/7
Set of Seychelles Coins for 1969	J/8
Locally printed Notes of 1919 (presented by Mr. D. Bailey, O.B.E., J.P.)	J/9
Specimens of old currency notes of Rs. 50/-, Rs. 10/- and Rs. 5/- demonetized on 22/7/69.	J/10
Specimens of New Seychelles Coins of 05 cts and 01 cts. issued on 1.2.72.	J/11
British Indian Ocean Territory Postage and Revenue Stamps from 15.1.1968. Volume I.	J/12
British Indian Ocean Territory Postage and Revenue Stamps. Volume II. (Postmarks)	J/13
Seychelles Postage and Revenue Stamps from October, 1971. Volume III.	J/14
Specimen of New Seychelles Coin of Rs. 5/- issued on 1.06.72	J/15

Head	Code N°
Specimens of New Seychelles Coins of Rs. 5/-, Re. 1/-. 50 cts. 25cts. 10 cts. 05 cts. and 04 cts. (issued on 3.07.72).	J/16
One Silver Proof Coin of Rs. 5/- (Issued on 10/8/72)	J/17
Postage and Revenue Stamps Vol. IV (Postmarks)	J/18
Two Silver Proof Coins of Rs. 10/- and Rs. 5/- (Issued on 30/12/74)	J/19
One Silver Proof Coin of Rs. 10/- (Issued on 30/12/74)	J/20
Seychelles Postage and Revenue Stamps from 29th June, 1976 to 10th April, 1978. Volume V.	J/21
Postage Stamps and Postal Stationery of Seychelles from 1890 to Independence Presented to the People of Seychelles by the Indian Ocean Study Circle in September, 1977.	J/22
Set of specimen of New Seychelles Coins issued on 15th December 1976 :- one gold of Rs. 1,000/-, two silver of Rs.10/- and Rs.5/-, threenickel of Rs. 1/-, 50cts and 25cts two aluminium of 05cts and 01ct.	J/23
Set of currency notes issued for the Independence of Seychelles in 1976 :- one of Rs.100/-, one of Rs. 50/-, one of Rs.20/- and one of Rs.10/-	J/24
Set of specimen of New Seychelles Coins issued on 30th May 1978 :- one gold of Rs. 1,500/- two silver of Rs.100/- and Rs.50/-	J/25

SOMMAIRE

P.

CLASS A Documents officiels de l'Administration Française jusqu'en 1810 3

CLASS B Correspondance officielle de l'Administration
Britannique à partir de 1811 15

CLASS C Documents officiels sélectionnés de l'Administration Britannique à partir de 1867 193

CLASS D Publications officielles du Gouvernement des
Seychelles 235

CLASS E Documents d'Etat Civil 303

CLASS F Bibliothèque de publications non-officielles
concernant l'Histoire et l'Histoire naturelle 349

CLASS G Journaux et Revues publiées aux Seychelles 397

CLASS H Cartes et plans 419

CLASS I Bandes magnétiques et disques de gramophone 423

CLASS J Timbre-Poste et Pièces de monnaie 429

Achevé d'imprimer Avril 1981
sur les Presses du G.I.S. Méditerranée
3 et 5 Av. Pasteur 13100 Aix-en-Provence
Dépôt légal Mai 1982
I.S.B.N. 2. 902. 292. 03. 1.